P9-CAD-706

mathematical recreations of lewis carroll

SYMBOLIC LOGIC AND THE GAME OF LOGIC

(both books bound as one)

By Lewis Carroll

Dover Publications, Inc., New York
and Berkeley Enterprises

This new Dover edition first published in 1958 is an unabridged and unaltered republication of the following two books by Lewis Carroll:

Symbolic Logic Part I, Elementary

With a prefatory note by Edmund C. Berkeley
and

The Game of Logic

The material contained in the envelope referred to by Lewis Carroll in the Nota Bene facing the preface to *The Game of Logic* is reproduced on the inside back cover of the Dover edition.

Library of Congress Catalog Card Number: 58-14299

Manufactured in the United States of America

Dover Publications, Inc.
180 Varick Street
New York 14, N. Y.

SYMBOLIC LOGIC

Prefatory Note

Lewis Carroll (C. L. Dodgson) is known and loved by millions as the mathematician author of *Alice in Wonderland* and many other books. Not so well known is the interest that he had in symbolic logic, logical reasoning to be accomplished by the use of symbols efficient in calculating.

This book of his, *Symbolic Logic, Part I: Elementary*, has been out of print and unavailable for many years. It contains a quantity of inimitable and entertaining problems and solutions in symbolic logic, a description of his method of solution using symbolic logic (a method which is now partly out of date), and apparently all that reached printing of the two other parts that he planned to write, *Part II: Advanced* and *Part III: Transcendental*. They were apparently not finished because of his death in 1898.

Lewis Carroll says in the introduction to *Part I: Elementary:* "This is, I believe, the very first attempt that has been made to popularise this fascinating subject." In the last fifty years the applications of symbolic logic have begun to be widely recognized, in the drafting of contracts and rules, in the design and checking of computing and controlling circuits, in the codification of law, in operations research, and other fields of knowledge. It is altogether fitting that Lewis Carroll's fine pioneering effort towards the application of symbolic logic should again go back into print.

EDMUND C. BERKELEY

New York 11, N. Y.
July 1955

A Syllogism worked out.

That story of yours, about your once meeting the sea-serpent, always sets me off yawning;
I never yawn, unless when I'm listening to something totally devoid of interest.

The Premisses, separately.

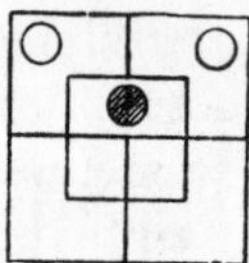

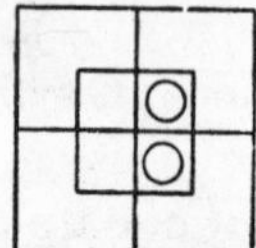

The Premisses, combined.

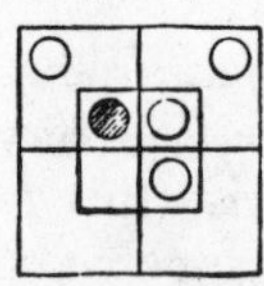

The Conclusion.

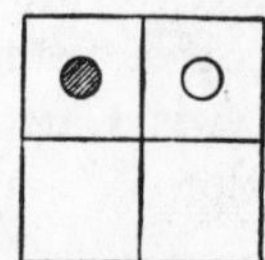

That story of yours, about your once meeting the sea-serpent, is totally devoid of interest.

SYMBOLIC LOGIC

By Lewis Carroll

ADVERTISEMENT.

AN envelope, containing two blank Diagrams (Biliteral and Triliteral) and 9 Counters (4 Red and 5 Grey), may be had, from Messrs. Macmillan, for *3d.*, by post *4d.*

I shall be grateful to any Reader of this book who will point out any mistakes or misprints he may happen to notice in it, or any passage which he thinks is not clearly expressed.

I have a quantity of MS. in hand for Parts II and III, and hope to be able——should life, and health, and opportunity, be granted to me, to publish them in the course of the next few years. Their contents will be as follows:—

PART II. ADVANCED.

Further investigations in the subjects of Part I. Propositions of other forms (such as "Not-all *x* are *y*"). Triliteral and Multiliteral Propositions (such as "All *abc* are *de*"). Hypotheticals. Dilemmas. &c. &c.

PART III. TRANSCENDENTAL.

Analysis of a Proposition into its Elements. Numerical and Geometrical Problems. The Theory of Inference. The Construction of Problems. And many other *Curiosa Logica.*

PREFACE TO FOURTH EDITION.

THE chief alterations, since the First Edition, have been made in the Chapter on 'Classification' (pp. 2, 3) and the Book on 'Propositions' (pp. 10 to 19). The chief additions have been the questions on words and phrases, added to the Examination-Papers at p. 94, and the Notes inserted at pp. 164, 189.

In Book I, Chapter II, I have adopted a new definition of 'Classification', which enables me to regard the whole Universe as a 'Class,' and thus to dispense with the very awkward phrase 'a Set of Things.'

In the Chapter on 'Propositions of Existence' I have adopted a new 'normal form,' in which the Class, whose existence is affirmed or denied, is regarded as the *Predicate*, instead of the *Subject*, of the Proposition, thus evading a very subtle difficulty which besets the other form. These subtle difficulties seem to lie at the root of every Tree of Knowledge, and they are *far* more hopeless to grapple with than any that occur in its higher branches. For example, the difficulties of the Forty-Seventh Proposition of Euclid are mere child's play compared with the mental torture endured in the effort to think out the essential nature of a straight Line. And, in the present work, the difficulties of the "5 Liars" Problem, at p. 188, are "trifles, light as air," compared with the bewildering question "What is a Thing?"

In the Chapter on 'Propositions of Relation' I have inserted a new Section, containing the proof that a Proposition, beginning with "All," is a *Double* Proposition (a fact that is quite independent of the arbitrary rule, laid down in the next Section, that such a Proposition is to be understood as implying the actual *existence* of its Subject). This proof was given, in the earlier editions, incidentally, in the course of the discussion of the Bilateral Diagram: but its *proper* place, in this treatise, is where I have now introduced it.

In the Sorites-Examples, I have made a good many verbal alterations, in order to evade a difficulty, which I fear will have perplexed some of the Readers of the first three Editions. Some of the Premisses were so worded that their Terms were *not* Specieses of the Univ. named in the Dictionary, but of a larger Class, of which the Univ. was only a portion. In all such cases, it was intended that the Reader should perceive that what was asserted of the larger Class was thereby asserted of the Univ., and should ignore, as superfluous, all that it asserted of its *other* portion. Thus, in Ex. 15, the Univ. was stated to be "ducks in this village," and the third Premiss was "Mrs. Bond has no gray ducks," i.e. "No gray ducks are ducks belonging to Mrs. Bond." Here the Terms are *not* Specieses of the Univ., but of the larger Class "ducks," of which the Univ. is only a portion: and it was intended that the Reader should perceive that what is here asserted of "ducks" is thereby asserted of "ducks in this village," and should treat this Premiss as if it were "Mrs. Bond has no gray ducks in this village," and should ignore, as superfluous, what it asserts as to the *other* portion of the Class "ducks," viz. "Mrs. Bond has no gray ducks *out of* this village".

In the Appendix I have given a new version of the Problem of the "Five Liars." My object, in doing so, is to escape the subtle and mysterious difficulties which beset all attempts at regarding a Proposition as being its own Subject, or a Set of Propositions as being Subjects for one another. It is, certainly, a most bewildering and unsatisfactory theory: one cannot help feeling that there is a great lack of *substance* in all this shadowy host——that, as the procession of phantoms glides before us, there is not *one* that we can pounce upon, and say "*Here* is a Proposition that *must* be either true or false!" ——that it is but a Barmecide Feast, to which we have been bidden——and that its prototype is to be found in that mythical island, whose inhabitants "earned a precarious living by taking in each others' washing"! By simply translating "telling 2 Truths" into "taking *both* of 2 condiments (salt and mustard)," "telling 2 Lies" into "taking *neither* of them," and "telling a Truth and a Lie (order not specified)" into "taking only *one* condiment (it is not specified *which*)," I have escaped all those metaphysical puzzles, and have produced a Problem which, when translated into a Set of symbolized Premisses, furnishes the very same *Data* as were furnished by the Problem of the "Five Liars."

The coined words, introduced in previous editions, such as "Eliminands" and "Retinends", perhaps hardly need any apology: they were indispensable to my system: but the new plural, here used for the first time, viz. "Soriteses", will, I fear, be condemned as "bad English", unless I say a word in its defence. We have *three* singular nouns, in English, of plural *form*, "series", "species", and "Sorites": in all three, the awkwardness, of using the same word for both singular and plural, must often have been felt: this has been remedied, in the case of "series" by coining the plural "serieses", which has already found its way into the dictionaries: so I am no rash innovator, but am merely "following suit", in using the new plural "Soriteses".

In conclusion, let me point out that even those, who are obliged to study *Formal* Logic, with a view to being able to answer Examination-Papers in that subject, will find the study of *Symbolic* Logic most helpful for this purpose, in throwing light upon many of the obscurities with which Formal Logic abounds, and in furnishing a delightfully easy method of *testing* the results arrived at by the cumbrous processes which Formal Logic enforces upon its votaries.

This is, I believe, the very first attempt (with the exception of my own little book, *The Game of Logic*, published in 1886, a very incomplete performance) that has been made to *popularise* this fascinating subject. It has cost me *years* of hard work: but if it should prove, as I hope it may, to be of *real* service to the young, and to be taken up, in High Schools and in private families, as a valuable addition to their stock of healthful mental recreations, such a result would more than repay ten times the labour that I have expended on it.

L. C.

29 Bedford Street, Strand.

Christmas, 1896.

INTRODUCTION.

TO LEARNERS.

[N.B. Some remarks, addressed to *Teachers*, will be found in the Appendix, at p. 165.]

THE Learner, who wishes to try the question *fairly*, whether this little book does, or does not, supply the materials for a most interesting mental recreation, is *earnestly* advised to adopt the following Rules:—

(1) Begin at the *beginning*, and do not allow yourself to gratify a mere idle curiosity by dipping into the book, here and there. This would very likely lead to your throwing it aside, with the remark "This is *much* too hard for me!", and thus losing the chance of adding a very *large* item to your stock of mental delights. This Rule (of not *dipping*) is very *desirable* with *other* kinds of books——such as novels, for instance, where you may easily spoil much of the enjoyment you would otherwise get from the story, by dipping into it further on, so that what the author meant to be a pleasant surprise comes to you as a matter of course. Some people, I know, make a practice of looking into Vol. III first, just to see how the story ends: and perhaps it *is* as well just to know that all ends *happily*——that the much-persecuted lovers *do* marry after all, that he is proved to be quite innocent of the murder, that the wicked cousin is completely foiled in his plot and gets the punishment he deserves, and that the rich uncle in India (*Qu.* Why in *India*? *Ans.* Because, somehow, uncles never *can* get rich anywhere else) dies at exactly the right moment——before taking the trouble to read Vol. I.

This, I say, is *just* permissible with a *novel*, where Vol. III has a *meaning*, even for those who have not read the earlier part of the story; but, with a *scientific* book, it is sheer insanity: you will find the latter part *hopelessly* unintelligible, if you read it before reaching it in regular course.

(2) Don't begin any fresh Chapter, or Section, until you are certain that you *thoroughly* understand the whole book *up to that point*, and that you have worked, correctly, most if not all of the examples which have been set. So long as you are conscious that all the land you have passed through is absolutely *conquered*, and that you are leaving no unsolved difficulties *behind* you, which will be sure to turn up again later on, your triumphal progress will be easy and delightful. Otherwise, you will find your state of puzzlement get worse and worse as you proceed, till you give up the whole thing in utter disgust.

(3) When you come to any passage you don't understand, *read it again*: if you *still* don't understand it, *read it again*: if you fail, even after *three* readings, very likely your brain is getting a little tired. In that case, put the book away, and take to other occupations, and next day, when you come to it fresh, you will very likely find that it is *quite* easy.

(4) If possible, find some genial friend, who will read the book along with you, and will talk over the difficulties with you. *Talking* is a wonderful smoother-over of difficulties. When *I* come upon anything——in Logic or in any other hard subject——that entirely puzzles me, I find it a capital plan to talk it over, *aloud*, even when I am all alone. One can explain things so *clearly* to one's self! And then, you know, one is so *patient* with one's self: one *never* gets irritated at one's own stupidity!

If, dear Reader, you will faithfully observe these Rules, and so give my little book a really *fair* trial, I promise you, most confidently, that you will find Symbolic Logic to be one of the most, if not *the* most, fascinating of mental recreations! In this First Part, I have carefully avoided all difficulties which seemed to me to be beyond the grasp of an intelligent child of (say) twelve or fourteen years of age. I have myself taught most of its contents, *vivâ voce*, to *many* children, and have found them take a real intelligent interest in the subject. For those, who succeed in mastering Part I, and who begin, like Oliver, "asking for more," I hope to provide, in Part II, some *tolerably* hard nuts to crack——nuts that will require all the nut-crackers they happen to possess!

Mental recreation is a thing that we all of us need for our mental health; and you may get much healthy enjoyment, no doubt, from Games, such as Back-gammon, Chess, and the new Game "Halma". But, after all, when you have made yourself a first-rate player at any one of these Games, you have nothing real to *show* for it, as a *result!* You enjoyed the Game, and the victory, no doubt, *at the time*: but you have no *result* that you can treasure up and get real *good* out of. And, all the while, you have been leaving unexplored a perfect *mine* of wealth. Once master the machinery of Symbolic Logic, and you have a mental occupation always at hand, of absorbing interest, and one that will be of real *use* to you in *any* subject you may take up. It will give you clearness of thought——the ability to *see your way* through a puzzle——the habit of arranging your ideas in an orderly and get-at-able form——and, more valuable than all, the power to detect *fallacies*, and to tear to pieces the flimsy illogical arguments, which you will so continually encounter in books, in newspapers, in speeches, and even in sermons, and which so easily delude those who have never taken the trouble to master this fascinating Art. *Try it.* That is all I ask of you!

L. C.

29, Bedford Street, Strand.
February 21, 1896.

CONTENTS.

BOOK I.

THINGS AND THEIR ATTRIBUTES.

CHAPTER I.

INTRODUCTORY.

CHAPTER II.

CLASSIFICATION.

CHAPTER III.

DIVISION.

§ 1.

Introductory.

§ 2.

Dichotomy.

CHAPTER IV.

NAMES.

CHAPTER V.

DEFINITIONS.

BOOK II.

PROPOSITIONS.

CHAPTER I.

PROPOSITIONS GENERALLY.

§ 1.

Introductory.

§ 2.

Normal form of a Proposition.

§ 3.

Various kinds of Propositions.

§ 3.

(continued)

CHAPTER II.

PROPOSITIONS OF EXISTENCE.

CHAPTER III.

PROPOSITIONS OF RELATION

§ 1.

Introductory.

§ 2.

Reduction of a Proposition of Relation to Normal form.

§ 3.

A Proposition of Relation, beginning with "All", is a Double Proposition.

---

§ 4.

What is implied, in a Proposition of Relation, as to the Reality of its Terms?

§ 5.

Translation of a Proposition of Relation into one or more Propositions of Existence.

BOOK III.

THE BILITERAL DIAGRAM.

CHAPTER I.

SYMBOLS AND CELLS.

CHAPTER II.

COUNTERS.

CHAPTER III.

REPRESENTATION OF PROPOSITIONS.

§ 1.

Introductory.

§ 2.

Representation of Propositions of Existence.

§ 3.

Representation of Propositions of Relation.

CHAPTER IV.

INTERPRETATION OF BILITERAL DIAGRAM, WHEN MARKED WITH COUNTERS.

BOOK IV.

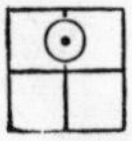

THE TRILITERAL DIAGRAM.

CHAPTER I.

SYMBOLS AND CELLS.

CHAPTER II.

REPRESENTATION OF PROPOSITIONS IN TERMS OF x AND m, OR OF y AND m.

---

§ 1.

Representation of Propositions of Existence in terms of x *and* m, *or of* y *and* m.

---

§ 2.

Representation of Propositions of Relation in terms of x *and* m, *or of* y *and* m.

CHAPTER III.

REPRESENTATION OF TWO PROPOSITIONS OF RELATION, ONE IN TERMS OF x AND m, AND THE OTHER IN TERMS OF y AND m, ON THE SAME DIAGRAM.

CHAPTER IV.

INTERPRETATION, IN TERMS OF x AND y, OF TRILITERAL DIAGRAM, WHEN MARKED WITH COUNTERS OR DIGITS.

BOOK V.

SYLLOGISMS.

CHAPTER I.

INTRODUCTORY.

CHAPTER II.

PROBLEMS IN SYLLOGISMS

---

§ 1.

Introductory.

---

§ 2.

Given a Pair of Propositions of Relation, which contain between them a Pair of codivisional Classes, and which are proposed as Premisses: to ascertain what Conclusion, if any, is consequent from them.

---

§ 3.

Given a Trio of Propositions of Relation, of which every two contain a Pair of codivisional Classes, and which are proposed as a Syllogism: to ascertain whether the proposed Conclusion is consequent from the proposed Premisses, and, if so, whether it is complete.

BOOK VI.
THE METHOD OF SUBSCRIPTS.

CHAPTER I.

INTRODUCTORY.

CHAPTER II.

REPRESENTATION OF PROPOSITIONS OF RELATION.

---

§ 5.

§ 6.

§ 7.

§ 8.

§ 9.

CHAPTER II.

ANSWERS.

CHAPTER III.

SYLLOGISMS.

§ 1.

Representation of Syllogisms.

§ 2.

Formulæ for Syllogisms.

§ 3.

Fallacies.

§ 4.

Method of proceeding with a given Pair of Propositions.

BOOK VII.

SORITESES.

CHAPTER I.

INTRODUCTORY.

CHAPTER II.

PROBLEMS IN SORITESES.

§ 1.

Introductory.

§ 2.

Solution by Method of Separate Syllogisms.

§ 3.

Solution by Method of Underscoring.

BOOK VIII.

EXAMPLES, WITH ANSWERS AND SOLUTION

CHAPTER I.

EXAMPLES.

§ 1.

§ 2.

§ 3.

§ 4.

CHAPTER III.

SOLUTIONS.

§ 1.

Propositions of Relation reduced to normal form.

§ 2.

Method of Diagrams.

§ 3.

Method of Subscripts.

INDEX.

BOOK I.

THINGS AND THEIR ATTRIBUTES.

CHAPTER I.

INTRODUCTORY.

THE Universe contains **'Things.'**

[For example, "I," "London,' "roses," "redness," "old English books," "the letter which I received yesterday."]

Things have **'Attributes.'**

[For example, "large," "red," "old," "which I received yesterday."]

One Thing may have many Attributes; and one Attribute may belong to many Things.

[Thus, the Thing "a rose" may have the Attributes "red," "scented," "full-blown," &c.; and the Attribute "red" may belong to the Things "a rose," "a brick," "a ribbon," &c.]

Any Attribute, or any Set of Attributes, may be called an **'Adjunct.'**

[This word is introduced in order to avoid the constant repetition of the phrase "Attribute or Set of Attributes."

Thus, we may say that a rose has the Attribute "red" (or the Adjunct "red," whichever we prefer); or we may say that it has the Adjunct "red, scented and full-blown."]

CHAPTER II

CLASSIFICATION.

'CLASSIFICATION,' or the formation of Classes, is a Mental Process, in which we imagine that we have put together, in a group, certain Things. Such a group is called a '**Class**.'

This Process may be performed in three different ways, as follows:—

(1) We may imagine that we have put together all Things. The Class so formed (i.e. the Class "Things") contains the whole Universe.

(2) We may think of the Class "Things," and may imagine that we have picked out from it all the Things which possess a certain Adjunct *not* possessed by the whole Class. This Adjunct is said to be '**peculiar**' to the Class so formed. In this case, the Class "Things" is called a '**Genus**' with regard to the Class so formed: the Class, so formed, is called a '**Species**' of the Class "Things": and its peculiar Adjunct is called its '**Differentia**'.

As this Process is entirely *Mental*, we can perform it whether there *is*, or *is not*, an *existing* Thing which possesses that Adjunct. If there *is*, the Class is said to be '**Real**'; if *not*, it is said to be '**Unreal**', or '**Imaginary**.'

[For example, we may imagine that we have picked out, from the Class "Things," all the Things which possess the Adjunct "material, artificial, consisting of houses and streets"; and we may thus form the Real Class "towns." Here we may regard "Things" as a *Genus*, "Towns" as a *Species* of Things, and "material, artificial, consisting of houses and streets" as its *Differentia*.

Again, we may imagine that we have picked out all the Things which possess the Adjunct "weighing a ton, easily lifted by a baby"; and we may thus form the *Imaginary* Class "Things that weigh a ton and are easily lifted by a baby."]

(3) We may think of a certain Class, *not* the Class "Things," and may imagine that we have picked out from it all the Members of it which possess a certain Adjunct *not* possessed by the whole Class. This Adjunct is said to be '**peculiar**' to the smaller Class so formed. In this case, the Class thought of is called a '**Genus**' with regard to the smaller Class picked out from it: the smaller Class is called a '**Species**' of the larger: and its peculiar Adjunct is called its '**Differentia**'.

[For example, we may think of the Class "towns," and imagine that we have picked out from it all the towns which possess the Attribute "lit with gas"; and we may thus form the Real Class "towns lit with gas." Here we may regard "Towns" as a *Genus*, "Towns lit with gas" as a *Species* of Towns, and "lit with gas" as its *Differentia*.

If, in the above example, we were to alter "lit with gas" into "paved with gold," we should get the *Imaginary* Class "towns paved with gold."]

A Class, containing only *one* Member, is called an '**Individual**.'

[For example, the Class "towns having four million inhabitants," which Class contains only *one* Member, viz. "London."]

Hence, any single Thing, which we can name so as to distinguish it from all other Things, may be regarded as a one-Member Class.

[Thus "London" may be regarded as the one-Member Class, picked out from the Class "towns," which has, as its Differentia, "having four million inhabitants."

A Class, containing two or more Members, is sometimes regarded as *one single Thing*. When so regarded, it may possess an Adjunct which is *not* possessed by any Member of it taken separately.

[Thus, the Class "The soldiers of the Tenth Regiment," when regarded as *one single Thing*, may possess the Attribute "formed in square," which is *not* possessed by any Member of it taken separately.]

CHAPTER III.

DIVISION.

---

§ 1.

Introductory.

'DIVISION' is a Mental Process, in which we think of a certain Class of Things, and imagine that we have divided it into two or more smaller Classes.

[Thus, we might think of the Class "books," and imagine that we had divided it into the two smaller Classes "bound books" and "unbound books," or into the three Classes, "books priced at less than a shilling," "shilling-books," "books priced at more than a shilling," or into the twenty-six Classes, "books whose names begin with *A*," "books whose names begin with *B*," &c.]

A Class, that has been obtained by a certain Division, is said to be 'codivisional' with every Class obtained by that Division.

[Thus, the Class "bound books" is codivisional with each of the two Classes, "bound books" and "unbound books."

Similarly, the Battle of Waterloo may be said to have been "contemporary" with every event that happened in 1815.]

Hence a Class, obtained by Division, is codivisional with itself.

[Thus, the Class "bound books" is codivisional with itself.

Similarly, the Battle of Waterloo may be said to have been "contemporary" with itself.]

---

§ 2.

Dichotomy.

If we think of a certain Class, and imagine that we have picked out from it a certain smaller Class, it is evident that the *Remainder* of the large Class does *not* possess the Differentia of that smaller Class. Hence it may be regarded as *another* smaller Class, whose Differentia may be formed, from that of the Class first picked out, by prefixing the word "not"; and we may imagine that we have *divided* the Class first thought of into *two* smaller Classes, whose Differentiæ are *contradictory*. This kind of Division is called '**Dichotomy**'.

[For example, we may divide "books" into the two Classes whose Differentiæ are "old" and "not-old."]

In performing this Process, we may sometimes find that the Attributes we have chosen are used so loosely, in ordinary conversation, that it is not easy to decide *which* of the Things belong to the one Class and *which* to the other. In such a case, it would be necessary to lay down some arbitrary *rule*, as to *where* the one Class should end and the other begin.

[Thus, in dividing "books" into "old" and "not-old," we may say "Let all books printed before A.D. 1801, be regarded as 'old,' and all others as 'not-old'."]

Henceforwards let it be understood that, if a Class of Things be divided into two Classes, whose Differentiæ have contrary meanings, each Differentia is to be regarded as equivalent to the other with the word "not" prefixed.

[Thus, if "books" be divided into "old" and "new," the Attribute "old" is to be regarded as equivalent to "not-new," and the Attribute "new" as equivalent to "not-old."]

After dividing a Class, by the Process of *Dichotomy*, into two smaller Classes, we may sub-divide each of these into two still smaller Classes; and this Process may be repeated over and over again, the number of Classes being doubled at each repetition.

[For example, we may divide "books" into "old" and "new" (i.e. "*not*-old"): we may then sub-divide each of these into "English" and "foreign" (i.e. "*not*-English"), thus getting *four* Classes, viz.

(1) old English;
(2) old foreign;
(3) new English;
(4) new foreign.

If we had begun by dividing into "English" and "foreign," and had then sub-divided into "old" and "new," the four Classes would have been

(1) English old;
(2) English new;
(3) foreign old;
(4) foreign new.

The Reader will easily see that these are the very same four Classes which we had before.]

CHAPTER IV.

NAMES.

THE word "Thing", which conveys the idea of a Thing, *without* any idea of an Adjunct, represents *any* single Thing. Any other word (or phrase), which conveys the idea of a Thing, *with* the idea of an Adjunct represents *any* Thing which possesses that Adjunct; i.e., it represents any Member of the Class to which that Adjunct is *peculiar*.

Such a word (or phrase) is called a '**Name**'; and, if there be an existing Thing which it represents, it is said to be a Name of that Thing.

[For example, the words "Thing," "Treasure," "Town, and the phrases "valuable Thing," "material artificial Thing consisting of houses and streets," "Town lit with gas," "Town paved with gold," "old English Book."]

Just as a Class is said to be *Real*, or *Unreal*, according as there *is*, or *is not*, an existing Thing in it, so also a Name is said to be *Real*, or *Unreal*, according as there *is*, or *is not*, an existing Thing represented by it.

[Thus, "Town lit with gas" is a *Real* Name: "Town paved with gold" is an *Unreal* Name.]

Every Name is either a Substantive only, or else a phrase consisting of a Substantive and one or more Adjectives (or phrases used as Adjectives).

Every Name, except "Thing", may usually be expressed in three different forms:—

(*a*) The Substantive "Thing", and one or more Adjectives (or phrases used as Adjectives) conveying the ideas of the Attributes;

(*b*) A Substantive, conveying the idea of a Thing with the ideas of *some* of the Attributes, and one or more Adjectives (or phrases used as Adjectives) conveying the ideas of the *other* Attributes;

(*c*) A Substantive conveying the idea of a Thing with the ideas of *all* the Attributes.

[Thus, the phrase "material living Thing, belonging to the Animal Kingdom, having two hands and two feet" is a Name expressed in Form (*a*).

If we choose to roll up together the Substantive "Thing" and the Adjectives "material, living, belonging to the Animal Kingdom," so as to make the new Substantive "Animal," we get the phrase "Animal having two hands and two feet," which is a Name (representing the same Thing as before) expressed in Form (*b*).

And, if we choose to roll up the whole phrase into one word, so as to make the new Substantive "Man," we get a Name (still representing the very same Thing) expressed in Form (*c*).]

A Name, whose Substantive is in the *plural* number, may be used to represent either

(1) Members of a Class, *regarded as separate Things*;
or (2) a whole Class, *regarded as one single Thing*.

[Thus, when I say "Some soldiers of the Tenth Regiment are tall," or "The soldiers of the Tenth Regiment are brave," I am using the Name "soldiers of the Tenth Regiment" in the *first* sense; and it is just the same as if I were to point to each of them *separately*, and to say "*This* soldier of the Tenth Regiment is tall," "*That* soldier of the Tenth Regiment is tall," and so on.

But, when I say "The soldiers of the Tenth Regiment are formed in square," I am using the phrase in the *second* sense; and it is just the same as if I were to say "The *Tenth Regiment* is formed in square."]

CHAPTER V.

DEFINITIONS.

It is evident that every Member of a *Species* is *also* a Member of the *Genus* out of which that Species has been picked, and that it possesses the *Differentia* of that Species. Hence it may be represented by a Name consisting of two parts, one being a Name representing any Member of the *Genus*, and the other being the *Differentia* of that Species. Such a Name is called a '**Definition**' of any Member of that Species, and to give it such a Name is to '**define**' it.

[Thus, we may define a "Treasure" as a "valuable Thing." In this case we regard "Things" as the *Genus*, and "valuable" as the *Differentia*.]

The following Examples, of this Process, may be taken as models for working others.

[Note that, in each Definition, the Substantive, representing a Member (or Members) of the *Genus*, is printed in Capitals.]

1. Define "a Treasure."

Ans. "a valuable THING."

2. Define "Treasures."

Ans. "valuable THINGS."

3. Define "a Town."

Ans. "a material artificial THING, consisting of houses and streets."

4. Define "Men."

Ans. "material, living THINGS, belonging to the Animal Kingdom, having two hands and two feet";

or else

"ANIMALS having two hands and two feet."

5. Define "London."

Ans. "the material artificial THING, which consists of houses and streets, and has four million inhabitants";

or else

"the TOWN which has four million inhabitants."

[Note that we here use the article "the" instead of "a", because we happen to know that there is only *one* such Thing.

The Reader can set himself any number of Examples of this Process, by simply choosing the Name of any common Thing (such as "house," "tree," "knife"), making a Definition for it, and then testing his answer by referring to any English Dictionary.]

BOOK II.

PROPOSITIONS.

CHAPTER I.

PROPOSITIONS GENERALLY.

---

§ 1.

Introductory.

NOTE that the word "some" is to be regarded, henceforward, as meaning "one or more."

The word 'Proposition,' as used in ordinary conversation, may be applied to *any* word, or phrase, which conveys any information whatever.

[Thus the words "yes" and "no" are Propositions in the ordinary sense of the word; and so are the phrases "you owe me five farthings" and "I don't!"

Such words as "oh!" or "never!", and such phrases as "fetch me that book!" "which book do you mean?" do not seem, at first sight, to convey any *information;* but they can easily be turned into equivalent forms which do so, viz. "I am surprised," "I will never consent to it," "I order you to fetch me that book," "I want to know which book you mean."]

But a '**Proposition**,' as used in this First Part of "Symbolic Logic," has a peculiar form, which may be called its '**Normal**

form'; and if any Proposition, which we wish to use in an argument, is not in normal form, we must reduce it to such a form, before we can use it.

A '**Proposition**,' when in normal form, asserts, as to certain two Classes, which are called its '**Subject**' and '**Predicate**,' either

(1) that *some* Members of its Subject are Members of its Predicate;
or (2) that *no* Members of its Subject are Members of its Predicate;
or (3) that *all* Members of its Subject are Members of its Predicate.

The Subject and the Predicate of a Proposition are called its '**Terms**.'

Two Propositions, which convey the *same* information, are said to be '**equivalent**'.

[Thus, the two Propositions, "I see John" and "John is seen by me," are equivalent.]

---

§ 2.

Normal form of a Proposition.

A Proposition, in normal form, consists of four parts, viz.—

(1) The word "some," or "no," or "all." (This word, which tells us *how many* Members of the Subject are also Members of the Predicate, is called the '**Sign of Quantity**.')
(2) Name of Subject.
(3) The verb "are" (or "is"). (This is called the '**Copula**.')
(4) Name of Predicate.

---

§ 3.

Various kinds of Propositions.

A Proposition, that begins with "Some", is said to be '**Particular.**' It is also called 'a Proposition **in I**.'

[Note, that it is called 'Particular,' because it refers to a *part* only of the Subject.]

A Proposition, that begins with "No", is said to be '**Universal Negative.**' It is also called 'a Proposition **in E.**'

A Proposition, that begins with "All", is said to be '**Universal Affirmative.**' It is also called 'a Proposition **in A.**'

[Note, that they are called 'Universal', because they refer to the *whole* of the Subject.]

A Proposition, whose Subject is an *Individual*, is to be regarded as *Universal*.

[Let us take, as an example, the Proposition "John is not well". This of course implies that there is an *Individual*, to whom the speaker refers when he mentions "John", and whom the listener *knows* to be referred to. Hence the Class "men referred to by the speaker when he mentions 'John'" is a one-Member Class, and the Proposition is equivalent to "*All* the men, who are referred to by the speaker when he mentions 'John', are not well."]

Propositions are of two kinds, 'Propositions of Existence' and 'Propositions of Relation.'

These shall be discussed separately.

CHAPTER II.

PROPOSITIONS OF EXISTENCE.

A '**Proposition of Existence**', when in normal form, has, for its *Subject*, the Class "existing Things".

Its Sign of Quantity is "Some" or "No".

[Note that, though its Sign of Quantity tells us *how many* existing Things are Members of its Predicate, it does *not* tell us the *exact* number: in fact, it only deals with *two* numbers, which are, in ascending order, "0" and "1 or more."]

It is called "a Proposition of Existence" because its effect is to assert the *Reality* (i.e. the real *existence*), or else the *Imaginariness*, of its Predicate.

[Thus, the Proposition "Some existing Things are honest men" asserts that the Class "honest men" is *Real*.

This is the *normal* form; but it may also be expressed in any one of the following forms:—

(1) "Honest men exist";
(2) "Some honest men exist";
(3) "The Class 'honest men' exists";
(4) "There are honest men";
(5) "There are some honest men".

Similarly, the Proposition "No existing Things are men fifty feet high" asserts that the Class "men 50 feet high" is *Imaginary*.

This is the *normal* form; but it may also be expressed in any one of the following forms:—

(1) "Men 50 feet high do not exist";
(2) "No men 50 feet high exist";
(3) "The Class 'men 50 feet high' does not exist ;
(4) "There are not any men 50 feet high";
(5) "There are no men 50 feet high."]

CHAPTER III.

PROPOSITIONS OF RELATION.

---

§ 1.

Introductory.

A **Proposition of Relation**, of the kind to be here discussed, has, for its Terms, two Specieses of the same Genus, such that each of the two Names conveys the idea of some Attribute *not* conveyed by the other.

[Thus, the Proposition "Some merchants are misers" is of the right kind, since "merchants" and "misers" are Specieses of the same Genus "men"; and since the Name "merchants" conveys the idea of the Attribute "mercantile", and the name "misers" the idea of the Attribute "miserly", each of which ideas is *not* conveyed by the other Name.

But the Proposition "Some dogs are setters" is *not* of the right kind, since, although it is true that "dogs" and "setters" are Specieses of the same Genus "animals", it is *not* true that the Name "dogs" conveys the idea of any Attribute not conveyed by the Name "setters". Such Propositions will be discussed in Part II.]

The Genus, of which the two Terms are Specieses, is called the **'Universe of Discourse,'** or (more briefly) the **'Univ.'**

The Sign of Quantity is "Some" or "No" or "All".

[Note that, though its Sign of Quantity tells us *how many* Members of its Subject are *also* Members of its Predicate, it does not tell us the *exact* number: in fact, it only deals with *three* numbers, which are, in ascending order, "0", "1 or more", "the total number of Members of the Subject".]

It is called "a Proposition of Relation" because its effect is to assert that a certain *relationship* exists between its Terms.

§ 2.

Reduction of a Proposition of Relation to Normal form.

The Rules, for doing this, are as follows :—

(1) Ascertain what is the *Subject* (i.e., ascertain what Class we are *talking about*);

(2) If the verb, governed by the Subject, is *not* the verb "are" (or "is"), substitute for it a phrase beginning with "are" (or "is");

(3) Ascertain what is the *Predicate* (i.e., ascertain what Class it is, which is asserted to contain *some*, or *none*, or *all*, of the Members of the Subject);

(4) If the Name of each Term is *completely expressed* (i.e. if it contains a Substantive), there is no need to determine the 'Univ.'; but, if either Name is *incompletely expressed*, and contains *Attributes* only, it is then necessary to determine a 'Univ.', in order to insert its Name as the Substantive.

(5) Ascertain the *Sign of Quantity*;

(6) Arrange in the following order :—

Sign of Quantity,
Subject,
Copula,
Predicate.

[Let us work a few Examples, to illustrate these Rules.

(1)

"Some apples are not ripe."

(1) The Subject is "apples."
(2) The Verb is "are."
(3) The Predicate is "not-ripe * * * ." (As no Substantive is expressed, and we have not yet settled what the Univ. is to be, we are forced to leave a blank.)
(4) Let Univ. be "fruit."
(5) The Sign of Quantity is "some."
(6) The Proposition now becomes

"Some | apples | are | not-ripe fruit."

(2)

"None of my speculations have brought me as much as 5 per cent."

(1) The Subject is "my speculations."

(2) The Verb is "have brought," for which we substitute the phrase "are * * * that have brought".

(3) The Predicate is "* * * that have brought &c."

(4) Let Univ. be "transactions."

(5) The Sign of Quantity is "none of."

(6) The Proposition now becomes

"None of | my speculations | are | transactions that have brought me as much as 5 per cent."

(3)

"None but the brave deserve the fair."

To begin with, we note that the phrase 'none but the brave" is equivalent to "no *not*-brave."

(1) The Subject has for its *Attribute* "not-brave." But no *Substantive* is supplied. So we express the Subject as "not-brave * * *."

(2) The Verb is "deserve," for which we substitute the phrase "are deserving of".

(3) The Predicate is " * * * deserving of the fair.'

(4) Let Univ. be "persons."

(5) The Sign of Quantity is ' no."

(6) The Proposition now becomes

"No | not-brave persons | are | persons deserving of the fair."

(4)

"A lame puppy would not say "thank you" if you offered to lend it a skipping-rope."

(1) The Subject is evidently "lame puppies," and all the rest of the sentence must somehow be packed into the Predicate.

(2) The Verb is "would not say," &c., for which we may substitute the phrase "are not grateful for."

(3) The Predicate may be expressed as " * * * not grateful for the loan of a skipping-rope."

(4) Let Univ. be "puppies."

(5) The Sign of Quantity is "all."

(6) The Proposition now becomes

"All | lame puppies | are | puppies not gratefu for the loan of a skipping-rope."

(5)

"No one takes in the *Times*, unless he is well-educated."

(1) The Subject is evidently persons who are not well-educated ("no *one*" evidently means "no *person*").

(2) The Verb is "takes in," for which we may substitute the phrase "are persons taking in."

(3) The Predicate is "persons taking in the *Times*."

(4) Let Univ. be "persons."

(5) The Sign of Quantity is "no."

(6) The Proposition now becomes

"No | persons who are not well-educated | are | persons taking in the *Times*."

(6)

"My carriage will meet you at the station."

(1) The Subject is "my carriage." This, being an 'Individual,' is equivalent to the Class "my carriages." (Note that this Class contains only *one* Member.)

(2) The Verb is "will meet", for which we may substitute the phrase "are * * * that will meet."

(3) The Predicate is "* * * that will meet you at the station."

(4) Let Univ. be "things."

(5) The Sign of Quantity is "all."

(6) The Proposition now becomes

"All | my carriages | are | things that will meet you at the station."

(7)

"Happy is the man who does not know what 'toothache' means!"

(1) The Subject is evidently "the man &c." (Note that in this sentence, the *Predicate* comes first.) At first sight, the Subject seems to be an '*Individual*'; but on further consideration, we see that the article "the" does *not* imply that there is only *one* such man. Hence the phrase "the man who" is equivalent to "all men who".

(2) The Verb is "are."

(3) The Predicate is "happy * * *."

(4) Let Univ. be "men."

(5) The Sign of Quantity is "all."

(6) The Proposition now becomes

"All | men who do not know what 'toothache' means | are | happy men."]

(8)

"Some farmers always grumble at the weather, whatever it may be."

(1) The Subject is "farmers."

(2) The Verb is "grumble," for which we substitute the phrase "are * * * who grumble."

(3) The Predicate is " * * * who always grumble &c.

(4) Let Univ. be "persons."

(5) The Sign of Quantity is "some."

(6) The Proposition now becomes

"Some | farmers | are | persons who always grumble at the weather, whatever it may be."

(9)

"No lambs are accustomed to smoke cigars."

(1) The Subject is "lambs."

(2) The Verb is "are."

(3) The Predicate is " * * * accustomed &c."

(4) Let Univ. be "animals."

(5) The Sign of Quantity is "no."

(6) The Proposition now becomes

"No | lambs | are | animals accustomed to smoke cigars."

(10)

"I ca'n't understand examples that are not arranged in regular order, like those I am used to."

(1) The Subject is "examples that," &c.

(2) The Verb is "I ca'n't understand," which we must alter, so as to have "examples," instead of "I," as the nominative case. It may be expressed as "are not understood by me."

(3) The Predicate is " * * * not understood by me."

(4) Let Univ. be "examples."

(5) The Sign of Quantity is "all."

(6) The Proposition now becomes

"All | examples that are not arranged in regular order like those I am used to | are | examples not understood by me."

---

§ 3.

A Proposition of Relation, beginning with "All", is a Double Proposition.

A Proposition of Relation, beginning with "All", asserts (as we already know) that "*All* Members of the Subject are Members of the Predicate". This évidently contains, as a *part* of what it tells us, the smaller Proposition "*Some* Members of the Subject are Members of the Predicate".

[Thus, the Proposition "*All* bankers are rich men" evidently contains the smaller Proposition "*Some* bankers are rich men".]

The question now arises "What is the *rest* of the information which this Proposition gives us?"

In order to answer this question, let us begin with the smaller Proposition, "*Some* Members of the Subject are Members of the Predicate," and suppose that this is *all* we have been told; and let us proceed to inquire what *else* we need to be told, in order to know that "*All* Members of the Subject are Members of the Predicate".

[Thus, we may suppose that the Proposition "*Some* bankers are rich men" is all the information we possess; and we may proceed to inquire what *other* Proposition needs to be added to it, in order to make up the entire Proposition "*All* bankers are rich men".]

Let us also suppose that the 'Univ.' (i.e. the Genus, of which both the Subject and the Predicate are Specieses) has been divided (by the Process of *Dichotomy*) into two smaller Classes, viz.

(1) the Predicate;

(2) the Class whose Differentia is *contradictory* to that of the Predicate.

[Thus, we may suppose that the Genus "men," (of which both "bankers" and "rich men" are Specieses) has been divided into the two smaller Classes, "rich men", "poor men".]

Now we know that *every* Member of the Subject is (as shown at p. 6) a Member of the Univ. Hence *every* Member of the Subject is either in Class (1) or else in Class (2).

[Thus, we know that *every* banker is a Member of the Genus "men". Hence, *every* banker is either in the Class "rich men", or else in the Class "poor men".]

Also we have been told that, in the case we are discussing, *some* Members of the Subject are in Class (1). What *else* do we need to be told, in order to know that *all* of them are there? Evidently we need to be told that *none* of them are in Class (2); i.e. that *none* of them are Members of the Class whose Differentia is *contradictory* to that of the Predicate.

[Thus, we may suppose we have been told that *some* bankers are in the Class "rich men". What *else* do we need to be told, in order to know that *all* of them are there? Evidently we need to be told that *none* of them are in the Class "*poor* men".]

Hence a Proposition of Relation, beginning with "All", is a *Double* Proposition, and is '**equivalent**' to (i.e. gives the same information as) the *two* Propositions

(1) "*Some* Members of the Subject are Members of the Predicate";

(2) "*No* Members of the Subject are Members of the Class whose Differentia is *contradictory* to that of the Predicate".

[Thus, the Proposition "*All* bankers are rich men" is *Double* Proposition, and is equivalent to the *two* Propositions

(1) "*Some* bankers are rich men";

(2) "*No* bankers are *poor* men".]

---

§ 4.

What is implied, in a Proposition of Relation, as to the Reality of its Terms?

Note that the rules, here laid down, are *arbitrary*, and only apply to Part I of my "Symbolic Logic."

A Proposition of Relation, beginning with "Some", is henceforward to be understood as asserting that there are *some existing Things*, which, being Members of the Subject, are also Members of the Predicate; i.e. that *some existing Things* are Members of *both* Terms at once. Hence it is to be understood as implying that *each* Term, taken by itself, is *Real.*

[Thus, the Proposition "Some rich men are invalids" is to be understood as asserting that *some existing Things* are "rich invalids". Hence it implies that *each* of the two Classes, "rich men" and "invalids", taken by itself, is *Real.*]

A Proposition of Relation, beginning with "No", is henceforward to be understood as asserting that there are *no existing Things* which, being Members of the Subject, are also Members of the Predicate; i.e. that *no existing Things* are Members of *both* Terms at once. But this implies nothing as to the *Reality* of either Term taken by itself.

[Thus, the Proposition "No mermaids are milliners" is to be understood as asserting that *no existing Things* are "mermaid-milliners". But this implies nothing as to the *Reality*, or the *Unreality*, of either of the two Classes, "mermaids" and "milliners", taken by itself. In this case as it happens, the Subject is *Imaginary*, and the Predicate *Real.*]

A Proposition of Relation, beginning with "All", contains (see § 3) a similar Proposition beginning with "Some". Hence it is to be understood as implying that *each* Term, taken by itself, is *Real.*

[Thus, the Proposition "All hyænas are savage animals" contains the Proposition "Some hyænas are savage animals". Hence it implies that *each* of the two Classes, "hyænas" and "savage animals". taken by itself, is *Real.*]

---

§ 5.

Translation of a Proposition of Relation into one or more Propositions of Existence.

We have seen that a Proposition of Relation, beginning with "Some," asserts that *some existing Things*, being Members of its Subject, are *also* Members of its Predicate. Hence, it asserts that some existing Things are Members of *both*; i.e. it asserts that some existing Things are Members of the Class of Things which have *all* the Attributes of the Subject and the Predicate.

Hence, to translate it into a Proposition of Existence, we take "existing Things" as the new *Subject*, and Things, which have *all* the Attributes of the Subject and the Predicate, as the new Predicate.

Similarly for a Proposition of Relation beginning with "No".

A Proposition of Relation, beginning with "All", is (as shown in § 3) equivalent to *two* Propositions, one beginning with "Some" and the other with "No", each of which we now know how to translate.

[Let us work a few Examples, to illustrate these Rules.

(1)

"Some apples are not ripe."

Here we arrange thus :—

"Some" . . . . *Sign of Quantity.*
"existing Things" . . . . *Subject.*
"are" . . . . *Copula.*
"not-ripe apples" . . . . *Predicate.*

or thus :—

"Some | existing Things | are | not-ripe apples."

(2)

Some farmers always grumble at the weather, whatever it may be."

Here we arrange thus :—

"Some | existing Things | are | farmers who always grumble at the weather, whatever it may be."

(3)

"No lambs are accustomed to smoke cigars."

Here we arrange thus :—

'No | existing Things | are | lambs accustomed to smoke cigars."

(4)

"None of my speculations have brought me as much as 5 per cent."

Here we arrange thus :—

"No | existing Things | are | speculations of mine, which have brought me as much as 5 per cent."

(5)

"None but the brave deserve the fair."

Here we note, to begin with, that the phrase "none but the brave" is equivalent to "no not-brave men." We then arrange thus :—

"No | existing Things | are | not-brave men deserving of the fair."

(6)

' All bankers are rich men."

This is equivalent to the two Propositions Some bankers are rich men" and "No bankers are poor men."

Here we arrange thus :—

' Some | existing Things | are | rich bankers" ;
and
No | existing Things | are | poor bankers."

[Work Examples § 1, 1—4 (p. 97]

BOOK III.

THE BILITERAL DIAGRAM.

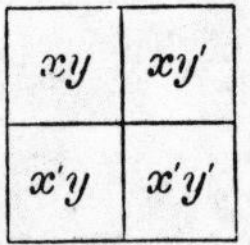

CHAPTER I.

SYMBOLS AND CELLS.

FIRST, let us suppose that the above Diagram is an enclosure assigned to a certain Class of Things, which we have selected as our 'Universe of Discourse,' or, more briefly, as our 'Univ'.

[For example, we might say "Let Univ. be 'books'"; and we might imagine the Diagram to be a large table, assigned to all "books."]

[The Reader is strongly advised, in reading this Chapter, *not* to refer to the above Diagram, but to draw a large one for himself, *without any letters*, and to have it by him while he reads, and keep his finger on that particular *part* of it, about which he is reading.]

Secondly, let us suppose that we have selected a certain Adjunct, which we may call "x," and have divided the large Class, to which we have assigned the whole Diagram, into the two smaller Classes whose Differentiæ are "x" and "not-x" (which we may call "x'"), and that we have assigned the *North* Half of the Diagram to the one (which we may call "the Class of x-Things," or "the x-Class"), and the *South* Half to the other (which we may call "the Class of x'-Things," or "the x'-Class").

[For example, we might say "Let x mean 'old,' so that x' will mean 'new'," and we might suppose that we had divided books into the two Classes whose Differentiæ are "old" and "new," and had assigned the *North* Half of the table to "*old* books" and the *South* Half to "*new* books."

Thirdly, let us suppose that we have selected another Adjunct, which we may call "y", and have subdivided the x-Class into the two Classes whose Differentiæ are "y" and "y'", and that we have assigned the North-*West* Cell to the one (which we may call "the xy-Class"), and the North-*East* Cell to the other (which we may call "the xy'-Class").

[For example, we might say "Let y mean 'English,' so that y' will mean 'foreign'", and we might suppose that we had subdivided "old books" into the two Classes whose Differentiæ are "English" and "foreign", and had assigned the North-*West* Cell to "old *English* books", and the North-*East* Cell to "old *foreign* books."]

Fourthly, let us suppose that we have subdivided the x'-Class in the same manner, and have assigned the South-*West* Cell to the $x'y$-Class, and the South-*East* Cell to the $x'y'$-Class.

[For example, we might suppose that we had subdivided "new books" into the two Classes "new *English* books" and "new *foreign* books", and had assigned the South-*West* Cell to the one, and the South-*East* Cell to the other.]

It is evident that, if we had begun by dividing for y and y', and had then subdivided for x and x', we should have got the *same* four Classes. Hence we see that we have assigned the *West* Half to the y-Class, and the *East* Half to the y'-Class.

[Thus, in the above Example, we should find that we had assigned the *West* Half of the table to "*English* books" and the *East* Half to "*foreign* books."

We have, in fact, assigned the four Quarters of the table to four different Classes of books, as here shown.

old English books	old foreign books
new English books	new foreign books

The Reader should carefully remember that, in such a phrase as "the x-Things," the word "Things" means that particular *kind* of Things, to which the whole Diagram has been assigned.

[Thus, if we say "Let Univ. be 'books'," we mean that we have assigned the whole Diagram to "books." In that case, if we took "x" to mean "old", the phrase "the x-Things" would mean "the old books."]

The Reader should not go on to the next Chapter until he is *quite familiar* with the *blank* Diagram I have advised him to draw.

He ought to be able to name, *instantly*, the *Adjunct* assigned to any Compartment named in the right-hand column of the following Table.

Also he ought to be able to name, *instantly*, the *Compartment* assigned to any Adjunct named in the left-hand column.

To make sure of this, he had better put the book into the hands of some genial friend, while he himself has nothing but the blank Diagram, and get that genial friend to question him on this Table, *dodging* about as much as possible. The Questions and Answers should be something like this :—

TABLE I.

Adjuncts of Classes.	*Compartments, or Cells, assigned to them.*
x	North Half.
x' . . .	South "
y	West "
y' . . .	East "
xy . . .	North-West Cell.
xy' . . .	" East "
$x'y$ . . .	South-West "
$x'y'$ . . .	" East "

Q. "Adjunct for West Half?"
A. "*y*."
Q. "Compartment for xy'?"
A. "North-East Cell."
Q. "Adjunct for South-West Cell?"
A. "$x'y$."
&c., &c.

After a little practice, he will find himself able to do without the blank Diagram, and will be able to see it *mentally* ("in my mind's eye, Horatio!") while answering the questions of his genial friend. When *this* result has been reached, he may safely go on to the next Chapter.

CHAPTER II.

COUNTERS.

Let us agree that a *Red* Counter, placed within a Cell, shall mean "This Cell is *occupied*" (i.e. "There is at least *one* Thing in it").

Let us also agree that a *Red* Counter, placed on the partition between two Cells, shall mean "The Compartment, made up of these two Cells, is *occupied;* but it is not known *whereabouts*, in it, its occupants are." Hence it may be understood to mean "At least *one* of these two Cells is occupied: possibly *both* are."

Our ingenious American cousins have invented a phrase to describe the condition of a man who has not yet made up his mind *which* of two political parties he will join: such a man is said to be "**sitting on the fence.**" This phrase exactly describes the condition of the Red Counter.

Let us also agree that a *Grey* Counter, placed within a Cell, shall mean "This Cell is *empty*" (i.e. "There is *nothing* in it").

[The Reader had better provide himself with 4 Red Counters and 5 Grey ones.]

CHAPTER III.

REPRESENTATION OF PROPOSITIONS.

---

§ 1.

Introductory.

HENCEFORWARDS, in stating such Propositions as "Some x-Things exist" or "No x-Things are y-Things", I shall omit the word "Things", which the Reader can supply for himself, and shall write them as "Some x exist" or "No x are y".

[Note that the word "Things" is here used with a special meaning, as explained at p. 23.]

A Proposition, containing only *one* of the Letters used as Symbols for Attributes, is said to be '**Uniliteral**'.

[For example, "Some x exist", "No y' exist", &c.]

A Proposition, containing *two* Letters, is said to be '**Biliteral**'.

[For example, "Some xy' exist", "No x' are y", &c.]

A Proposition is said to be '**in terms of**' the Letters it contains, whether with or without accents.

[Thus, "Some xy' exist", "No x' are y", &c, are said to be *in terms of* x and y.]

---

§ 2.

Representation of Propositions of Existence.

Let us take, first, the Proposition "Some x exist".

[Note that this Proposition is (as explained at p. 12) equivalent to "Some existing Things are x-Things."]

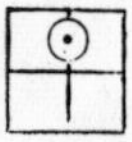

This tells us that there is at least *one* Thing in the North Half; that is, that the North Half is *occupied.* And this we can evidently represent by placing a *Red* Counter (here represented by a *dotted* circle) on the partition which divides the North Half.

[In the "books" example, this Proposition would be "Some old books exist".]

Similarly we may represent the three similar Propositions "Some x' exist", "Some y exist", and "Some y' exist".

[The Reader should make out all these for himself.
In the "books" example, these Propositions would be "Some new books exist", &c.]

Let us take, next, the Proposition "No x exist".

This tells us that there is *nothing* in the North Half; that is, that the North Half is *empty;* that is, that the North-West Cell and the North-East Cell are both of them *empty.* And this we can represent by placing *two Grey* Counters in the North Half, one in each Cell.

[The Reader may perhaps think that it would be enough to place a *Grey* Counter on the partition in the North Half, and that, just as a *Red* Counter, so placed, would mean "This Half is *occupied*", so a *Grey* one would mean "This Half is *empty*".

This, however, would be a mistake. We have seen that a *Red* Counter, so placed, would mean "At least *one* of these two Cells is occupied: possibly *both* are." Hence a *Grey* one would merely mean "At least *one* of these two Cells is empty: possibly *both* are". But what we have to represent is, that both Cells are *certainly* empty: and this can only be done by placing a *Grey* Counter in *each* of them.

In the "books" example, this Proposition would be "No old books exist".]

Similarly we may represent the three similar Propositions "No x' exist", "No y exist", and "No y' exist".

[The Reader should make out all these for himself.
In the "books" example, these three Propositions would be "No new books exist", &c.]

Let us take, next, the Proposition "Some xy exist".

This tells us that there is at least *one* Thing in the North-West Cell; that is, that the North-West Cell is *occupied*. And this we can represent by placing a *Red* Counter in it.

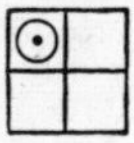

[In the "books" example, this Proposition would be "Some old English books exist".]

Similarly we may represent the three similar Propositions "Some xy' exist", "Some $x'y$ exist", and "Some $x'y'$ exist".

[The Reader should make out all these for himself.
In the "books" example, these three Propositions would be Some old foreign books exist", &c.]

Let us take, next, the Proposition "No xy exist".

This tells us that there is *nothing* in the North-West Cell; that is, that the North-West Cell is *empty*. And this we can represent by placing a *Grey* Counter in it.

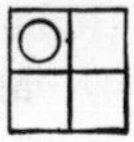

[In the "books" example, this Proposition would be "No old English books exist".]

Similarly we may represent the three similar Propositions "No xy' exist", "No $x'y$ exist", and "No $x'y'$ exist".

[The Reader should make out all these for himself.
In the "books" example, these three Propositions would be "No old foreign books exist", &c.]

We have seen that the Proposition "No x exist" may be represented by placing *two Grey* Counters in the North Half, one in each Cell.

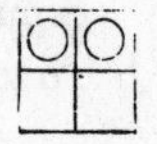

We have also seen that these two *Grey* Counters, taken *separately*, represent the two Propositions "No xy exist" and "No xy' exist".

Hence we see that the Proposition "No x exist" is a *Double* Proposition, and is equivalent to the *two* Propositions "No xy exist" and "No xy' exist".

[In the "books" example, this Proposition would be "No old books exist".

Hence this is a *Double* Proposition, and is equivalent to the *two* Propositions "No old *English* books exist" and "No old *foreign* books exist".

---

§ 3.

Representation of Propositions of Relation.

Let us take, first, the Proposition "Some x are y".

This tells us that at least *one* Thing, in the *North* Half, is also in the *West* Half. Hence it must be in the space *common* to them, that is, in the *North-West Cell.* Hence the North-West Cell is *occupied.* And this we can represent by placing a *Red* Counter in it.

[Note that the *Subject* of the Proposition settles which *Half* we are to use; and that the *Predicate* settles in which *portion* of it we are to place the Red Counter.

In the "books" example. this Proposition would be "Some old books are English".]

Similarly we may represent the three similar Propositions "Some x are y'", "Some x' are y", and "Some x' are y'".

[The Reader should make out all these for himself.

In the "books" example, these three Propositions would be "Some old books are foreign", &c.]

Let us take, next, the Proposition "Some *y* are *x*".

This tells us that at least *one* Thing, in the *West* Half, is also in the *North* Half. Hence it must be in the space *common* to them, that is, in the *North-West Cell.* Hence the North-West Cell is *occupied.* And this we can represent by placing a *Red* Counter in it.

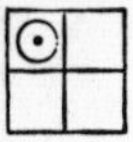

[In the "books" example, this Proposition would be "Some English books are old".]

Similarly we may represent the three similar Propositions "Some *y* are *x′*", "Some *y′* are *x*", and "Some *y′* are *x′*".

[The Reader should make out all these for himself.
In the "books" example, these three Propositions would be "Some English books are new", &c.]

We see that this *one* Diagram has now served to represent no less than *three* Propositions, viz.

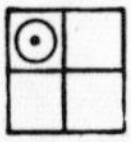

(1) "Some *xy* exist;
(2) Some *x* are *y;*
(3) Some *y* are *x*".

Hence these three Propositions are equivalent.

[In the "books" example, these Propositions would be
(1) "Some old English books exist;
(2) Some old books are English;
(3) Some English books are old".]

The two equivalent Propositions, "Some *x* are *y*" and "Some *y* are *x*", are said to be '**Converse**' to each other; and the Process, of changing one into the other, is called '**Converting**', or '**Conversion**'.

[For example, if we were told to convert the Proposition
"Some apples are not ripe,"
we should first choose our Univ. (say "fruit"), and then complete the Proposition, by supplying the Substantive "fruit" in the Predicate, so that it would be
"Some apples are not-ripe fruit";
and we should then convert it by interchanging its Terms, so hat it would be
"Some not-ripe fruit are apples".]

Similarly we may represent the three similar Trios of equivalent Propositions; the whole Set of *four* Trios being as follows:—

(1) "Some xy exist" = "Some x are y" = "Some y are x".
(2) "Some xy' exist" = "Some x are y'" = "Some y' are x".
(3) "Some $x'y$ exist" = "Some x' are y" = "Some y are x'".
(4) "Some $x'y'$ exist" = "Some x' are y'" = "Some y' are x'".

Let us take, next, the Proposition "No x are y".

This tells us that no Thing, in the *North* Half, is also in the *West* Half. Hence there is *nothing* in the space *common* to them, that is, in the *North-West Cell.* Hence the North-West Cell is *empty.* And this we can represent by placing a *Grey* Counter in it.

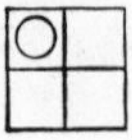

[In the "books" example, this Proposition would be "No old books are English".]

Similarly we may represent the three similar Propositions "No x are y'", and "No x' are y", and "No x' are y'".

[The Reader should make out all these for himself.
In the "books" example, these three Propositions would be "No old books are foreign", &c.]

Let us take, next, the Proposition "No y are x".

This tells us that no Thing, in the *West* Half, is also in the *North* Half. Hence there is *nothing* in the space *common* to them, that is, in the *North-West Cell.* That is, the North-West Cell is *empty.* And this we can represent by placing a *Grey* Counter in it.

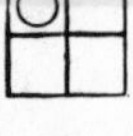

[In the "books" example, this Proposition would be 'No, English books are old".]

Similarly we may represent the three similar Propositions "No y are x'", "No y' are x", and "No y' are x'".

[The Reader should make out all these for himself.
In the "books" example, these three Propositions would be "No English books are new", &c.]

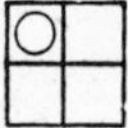

We see that this *one* Diagram has now served to represent no less than *three* Propositions, viz.

(1) "No xy exist;

(2) No x are y;

(3) No y are x."

Hence these three Propositions are equivalent.

[In the "books" example, these Propositions would be
(1) "No old English books exist;
(2) No old books are English;
(3) No English books are old".]

The two equivalent Propositions, "No x are y" and "No y are x", are said to be 'Converse' to each other.

[For example, if we were told to convert the Proposition
"No porcupines are talkative",
we should first choose our Univ. (say "animals"), and then complete the Proposition, by supplying the Substantive "animals" in the Predicate, so that it would be
"No porcupines are talkative animals",
and we should then convert it, by interchanging its Terms, so that it would be
"No talkative animals are porcupines".]

Similarly we may represent the three similar Trios of equivalent Propositions; the whole Set of *four* Trios being as follows:—

(1) "No xy exist" = "No x are y" = "No y are x".

(2) "No xy' exist" = "No x are y'" = "No y' are x".

(3) "No $x'y$ exist" = "No x' are y" = "No y are x'".

(4) "No $x'y'$ exist" = "No x' are y'" = "No y' are x'".

Let us take, next, the Proposition "All x are y".

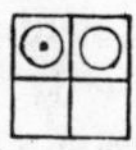

We know (see p. 17) that this is a *Double* Proposition, and equivalent to the *two* Propositions "Some x are y" and "No x are y'", each of which we already know how to represent.

[Note that the *Subject* of the given Proposition settles which *Half* we are to use; and that its *Predicate* settles in which *portion* of that Half we are to place the Red Counter.]

TABLE II.

Some x exist		No x exist	
Some x' exist		No x' exist	
Some y exist		No y exist	
Some y' exist		No y' exist	

Similarly we may represent the seven similar Propositions "All x are y'", "All x' are y", "All x' are y'", "All y are x", "All y are x'", "All y' are x", and "All y' are x'".

Let us take, lastly, the Double Proposition "Some x are y and some are y'", each part of which we already know how to represent.

Similarly we may represent the three similar Propositions, "Some x' are y and some are y'", "Some y are x and some are x'", "Some y' are x and some are x'".

The Reader should now get his genial friend to question him, severely, on these two Tables. The *Inquisitor* should have the Tables before him: but the *Victim* should have nothing but a blank Diagram, and the Counters with which he is to represent the various Propositions named by his friend, e.g. "Some y exist", "No y' are x", "All x are y", &c. &c.

TABLE III.

Some xy exist = Some x are y = Some y are x	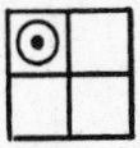	All x are y	
Some xy' exist = Some x are y' = Some y' are x	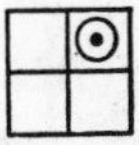	All x are y'	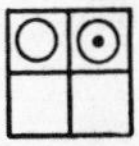
Some $x'y$ exist = Some x' are y = Some y are x'	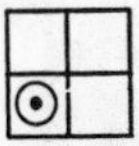	All x' are y	
Some $x'y'$ exist = Some x' are y' = Some y' are x'	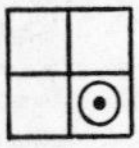	All x' are y'	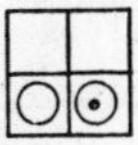
No xy exist = No x are y = No y are x	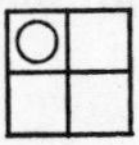	All y are x	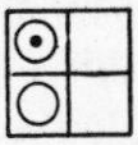
No xy' exist = No x are y' = No y' are x	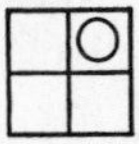	All y are x'	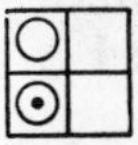
No $x'y$ exist = No x' are y = No y are x'	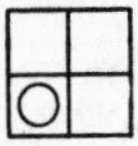	All y' are x	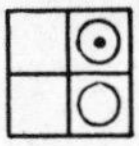
No $x'y'$ exist = No x' are y' = No y' are x'	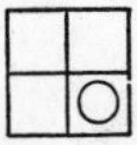	All y' are x'	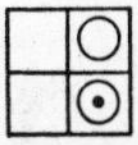
Some x are y, and some are y'		Some y are x, and some are x'	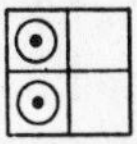
Some x' are y, and some are y'		Some y' are x, and some are x'	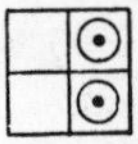

CHAPTER IV.

INTERPRETATION OF BILITERAL DIAGRAM, WHEN MARKED WITH COUNTERS.

THE Diagram is supposed to be set before us, with certain Counters placed upon it; and the problem is to find out what Proposition, or Propositions, the Counters represent.

As the process is simply the reverse of that discussed in the previous Chapter, we can avail ourselves of the results there obtained, as far as they go.

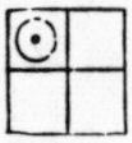

First, let us suppose that we find a *Red* Counter placed in the North-West Cell.

We know that this represents each of the Trio of equivalent Propositions

"Some xy exist" = "Some x are y" = "Some y are x".

Similarly we may interpret a *Red* Counter, when placed in the North-East, or South-West, or South-East Cell.

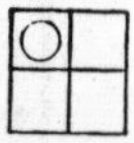

Next, let us suppose that we find a *Grey* Counter placed in the North-West Cell.

We know that this represents each of the Trio of equivalent Propositions

"No xy exist" = "No x are y" = "No y are x".

Similarly we may interpret a *Grey* Counter, when placed in the North-East, or South-West, or South-East Cell.

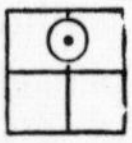

Next, let us suppose that we find a *Red* Counter placed on the partition which divides the North Half.

We know that this represents the Proposition "Some x exist."

Similarly we may interpret a *Red* Counter, when placed on the partition which divides the South, or West, or East Half.

Next, let us suppose that we find *two Red* Counters placed in the North Half, one in each Cell.

We know that this represents the *Double* Proposition "Some x are y and some are y'".

Similarly we may interpret *two Red* Counters, when placed in the South, or West, or East Half.

Next, let us suppose that we find *two Grey* Counters placed in the North Half, one in each Cell.

We know that this represents the Proposition "No x exist".

Similarly we may interpret *two Grey* Counters, when placed in the South, or West, or East Half.

Lastly, let us suppose that we find a *Red* and a *Grey* Counter placed in the North Half, the *Red* in the North-*West* Cell, and the *Grey* in the North-*East* Cell.

We know that this represents the Proposition, "All x are y".

[Note that the *Half*, occupied by the two Counters, settles what is to be the *Subject* of the Proposition, and that the *Cell*, occupied by the *Red* Counter, settles what is to be its *Predicate*.]

Similarly we may interpret a *Red* and a *Grey* Counter, when placed in any one of the seven similar positions

Red in North-East, Grey in North-West;
Red in South-West, Grey in South-East;
Red in South-East, Grey in South-West;
Red in North-West, Grey in South-West;
Red in South-West, Grey in North-West;
Red in North-East, Grey in South-East;
Red in South-East, Grey in North-East,

Once more the genial friend must be appealed to, and requested to examine the Reader on Tables II and III, and to make him not only *represent* Propositions, but also *interpret* Diagrams when marked with Counters.

The Questions and Answers should be like this:—

Q. Represent "No x' are y'."
A. Grey Counter in S.E. Cell.
Q. Interpret Red Counter on E. partition.
A. "Some y' exist."
Q. Represent "All y' are x."
A. Red in N.E. Cell; Grey in S.E.
Q. Interpret Grey Counter in S.W. Cell.
A. "No $x'y$ exist" = "No x' are y" = "No y are x'".

&c., &c.

At first the Examinee will need to have the Board and Counters before him; but he will soon learn to dispense with these, and to answer with his eyes shut, or gazing into vacancy.

[Work Examples § **1**, 5—8 (p. 97).]

BOOK IV.

THE TRILITERAL DIAGRAM.

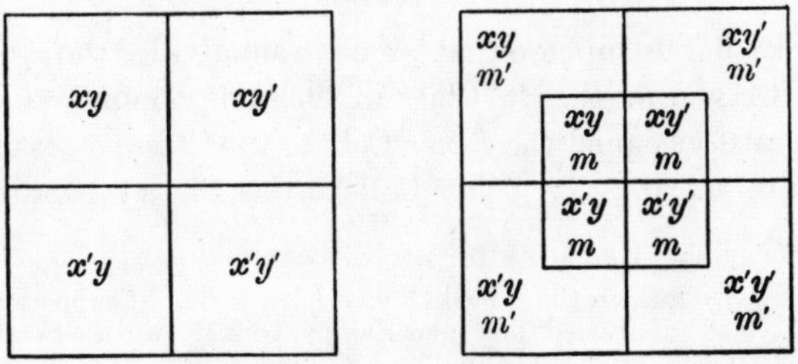

xy	xy'
$x'y$	$x'y'$

xy m'			xy' m'
	xy m	xy' m	
	$x'y$ m	$x'y'$ m	
$x'y$ m'			$x'y'$ m'

CHAPTER I.

SYMBOLS AND CELLS.

First, let us suppose that the above *left*-hand Diagram is the Biliteral Diagram that we have been using in Book III., and that we change it into a *Triliteral* Diagram by drawing an *Inner Square*, so as to divide each of its 4 Cells into 2 portions, thus making 8 Cells altogether. The *right*-hand Diagram shows the result.

[The Reader is strongly advised, in reading this Chapter, *not* to refer to the above Diagrams, but to make a large copy of the right-hand one for himself, *without any letters*, and to have it by him while he reads, and keep his finger on that particular *part* of it, about which he is reading.]

Secondly, let us suppose that we have selected a certain Adjunct, which we may call "m", and have subdivided the xy-Class into the two Classes whose Differentiæ are m and m', and that we have assigned the N.W. *Inner* Cell to the one (which we may call "the Class of xym-Things", or "the xym-Class"), and the N.W. *Outer* Cell to the other (which we may call "the Class of xym'-Things", or "the xym'-Class").

[Thus, in the "books" example, we might say "Let m mean 'bound', so that m' will mean 'unbound'", and we might suppose that we had subdivided the Class "old English books" into the two Classes, "old English bound books" and "old English unbound books", and had assigned the N.W. *Inner* Cell to the one, and the N.W. *Outer* Cell to the other.]

Thirdly, let us suppose that we have subdivided the xy'-Class, the $x'y$-Class, and the $x'y'$-Class in the same manner, and have, in each case, assigned the *Inner* Cell to the Class possessing the Attribute m, and the *Outer* Cell to the Class possessing the Attribute m'.

[Thus, in the "books" example, we might suppose that we had subdivided the "new English books" into the two Classes, "new English bound books" and "new English unbound books", and had assigned the S.W. *Inner* Cell to the one, and the S.W. *Outer* Cell to the other.]

It is evident that we have now assigned the *Inner Square* to the m-Class, and the *Outer Border* to the m'-Class.

[Thus, in the "books" example, we have assigned the *Inner Square* to "bound books" and the *Outer Border* to "unbound books".]

When the Reader has made himself familiar with this Diagram, he ought to be able to find, in a moment, the Compartment assigned to a particular *pair* of Attributes, or the Cell assigned to a particular *trio* of Attributes. The following Rules will help him in doing this:—

(1) Arrange the Attributes in the order x, y, m.

(2) Take the *first* of them and find the Compartment assigned to it.

(3) Then take the *second*, and find what *portion* of that Compartment is assigned to it.

(4) Treat the *third*, if there is one, in the same way.

[For example, suppose we have to find the Compartment assigned to ym. We say to ourselves "y has the *West* Half; and m has the *Inner* portion of that West Half."

Again, suppose we have to find the Cell assigned to $x'ym'$. We say to ourselves "x' has the *South* Half; y has the *West* portion of that South Half, i.e. has the *South-West Quarter*; and m' has the *Outer* portion of that South-West Quarter."]

The Reader should now get his genial friend to question him on the Table given on the next page, in the style of the following specimen-Dialogue.

Q. Adjunct for South Half, Inner Portion?

A. $x'm$.

Q. Compartment for m'?

A. The Outer Border.

Q. Adjunct for North-East Quarter, Outer Portion?

A. $xy'm'$.

Q. Compartment for ym?

A. West Half, Inner Portion.

Q. Adjunct for South Half?

A. x'.

Q. Compartment for $x'y'm$?

A. South-East Quarter, Inner Portion.

&c. &c.

TABLE IV.

Adjunct of Classes.	*Compartments, or Cells, assigned to them.*
x	North Half.
x' . . .	South ,,
y	West ,,
y' . . .	East ,,
m . . .	Inner Square.
m' . . .	Outer Border.
xy . . .	North-West Quarter.
xy' . . .	,, East ,,
$x'y$ . . .	South-West ,,
$x'y'$ . . .	,, East ,,
xm . . .	North Half, Inner Portion.
xm' . . .	,, ,, Outer ,,
$x'm$ . . .	South ,, Inner ,,
$x'm'$ . .	,, ,, Outer ,,
ym . . .	West ,, Inner ,,
ym' . . .	,, ,, Outer ,,
$y'm$ . . .	East ,, Inner ,,
$y'm'$ . .	,, ,, Outer ,,
xym . . .	North-West Quarter, Inner Portion.
xym' . .	,, ,, ,, Outer ,,
$xy'm$ . .	,, East ,, Inner ,,
$xy'm'$ . .	,, ,, ,, Outer ,,
$x'ym$ . .	South-West ,, Inner ,,
$x'ym'$ . .	,, ,, ,, Outer ,,
$x'y'm$ . .	,, East ,, Inner ,,
$x'y'm'$ . .	,, ,, ,, Outer ,,

CHAPTER II.

REPRESENTATION OF PROPOSITIONS IN TERMS OF x AND m, OR OF y AND m.

---

§ 1.

Representation of Propositions of Existence in terms of x *and* m, *or of* y *and* m.

LET us take, first, the Proposition "Some *xm* exist".

> [Note that the *full* meaning of this Proposition is (as explained at p. 12) "Some existing Things are *xm*-Things".]

This tells us that there is at least *one* Thing in the Inner portion of the North Half; that is, that this Compartment is *occupied*. And this we can evidently represent by placing a *Red* Counter on the partition which divides it.

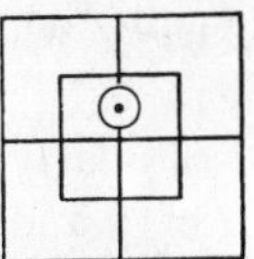

> [In the "books" example, this Proposition would mean "Some old bound books exist" (or "There are some old bound books").]

Similarly we may represent the seven similar Propositions, "Some *xm′* exist", "Some *x′m* exist", "Some *x′m′* exist", "Some *ym* exist", "Some *ym′* exist", "Some *y′m* exist", and "Some *y′m′* exist".

Let us take, next, the Proposition "No *xm* exist".

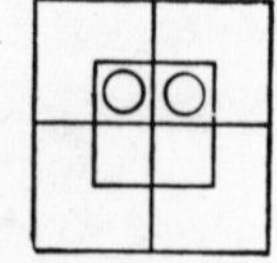

This tells us that there is *nothing* in the Inner portion of the North Half; that is, that this Compartment is *empty*. And this we can represent by placing *two Grey* Counters in it, one in each Cell.

Similarly we may represent the seven similar Propositions, in terms of *x* and *m*, or of *y* and *m*, viz. "No *xm′* exist", "No *x′m* exist", &c.

These sixteen Propositions of Existence are the only ones that we shall have to represent on this Diagram.

---

§ 2.

Representation of Propositions of Relation in terms of x *and* m, *or of* y *and* m.

Let us take, first, the Pair of Converse Propositions

"Some *x* are *m*" = "Some *m* are *x*."

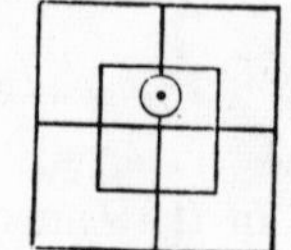

We know that each of these is equivalent to the Proposition of Existence "Some *xm* exist", which we already know how to represent.

Similarly for the seven similar Pairs, in terms of *x* and *m*, or of *y* and *m*.

Let us take, next, the Pair of Converse Propositions

"No *x* are *m*" = "No *m* are *x*."

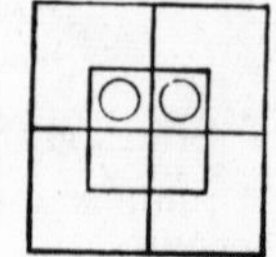

We know that each of these is equivalent to the Proposition of Existence "No *xm* exist", which we already know how to represent.

Similarly for the seven similar Pairs, in terms of *x* and *m*, or of *y* and *m*.

Let us take, next, the Proposition "All *x* are *m*."

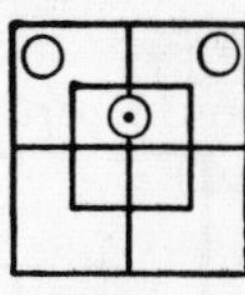

We know (see p. 18) that this is a *Double* Proposition, and equivalent to the *two* Propositions "Some *x* are *m*" and "No *x* are *m′*", each of which we already know how to represent.

Similarly for the fifteen similar Propositions, in terms of *x* and *m*, or of *y* and *m*.

These thirty-two Propositions of Relation are the only ones that we shall have to represent on this Diagram.

The Reader should now get his genial friend to question him on the following four Tables.

The Victim should have nothing before him but a blank Triliteral Diagram, a Red Counter, and 2 Grey ones, with which he is to represent the various Propositions named by the Inquisitor, *e.g.* "No *y′* are *m*", "Some *xm′* exist", &c., &c.

TABLE V.

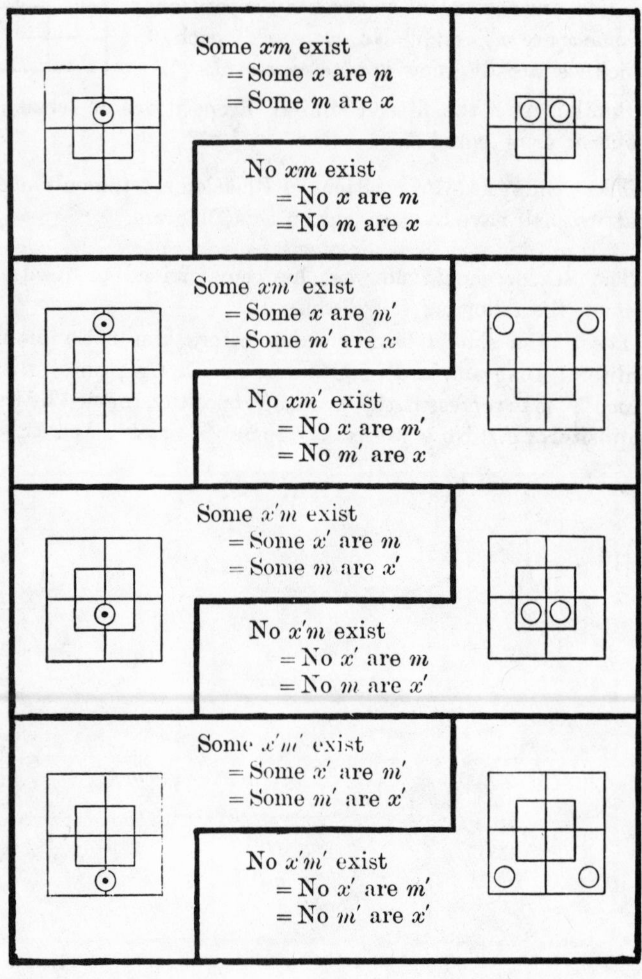
Some xm exist
= Some x are m
= Some m are x
No xm exist
= No x are m
= No m are x
Some xm' exist
= Some x are m'
= Some m' are x
No xm' exist
= No x are m'
= No m' are x
Some $x'm$ exist
= Some x' are m
= Some m are x'
No $x'm$ exist
= No x' are m
= No m are x'
Some $x'm'$ exist
= Some x' are m'
= Some m' are x'
No $x'm'$ exist
= No x' are m'
= No m' are x'

TABLE VI.

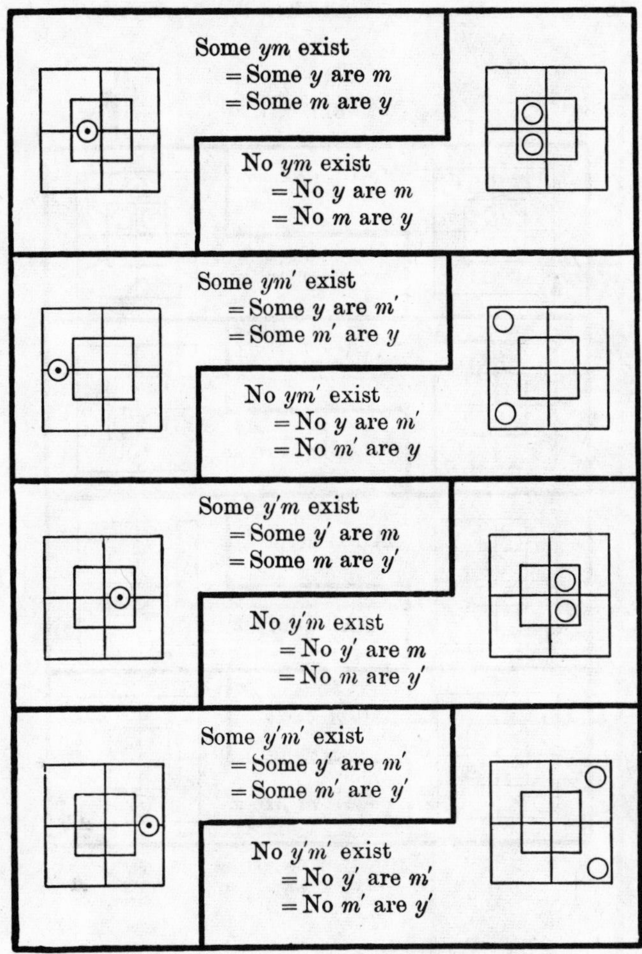
Some *ym* exist
= Some *y* are *m*
= Some *m* are *y*
No *ym* exist
= No *y* are *m*
= No *m* are *y*
Some *ym′* exist
= Some *y* are *m′*
= Some *m′* are *y*
No *ym′* exist
= No *y* are *m′*
= No *m′* are *y*
Some *y′m* exist
= Some *y′* are *m*
= Some *m* are *y′*
No *y′m* exist
= No *y′* are *m*
= No *m* are *y′*
Some *y′m′* exist
= Some *y′* are *m′*
= Some *m′* are *y′*
No *y′m′* exist
= No *y′* are *m′*
= No *m′* are *y′*

TABLE VII.

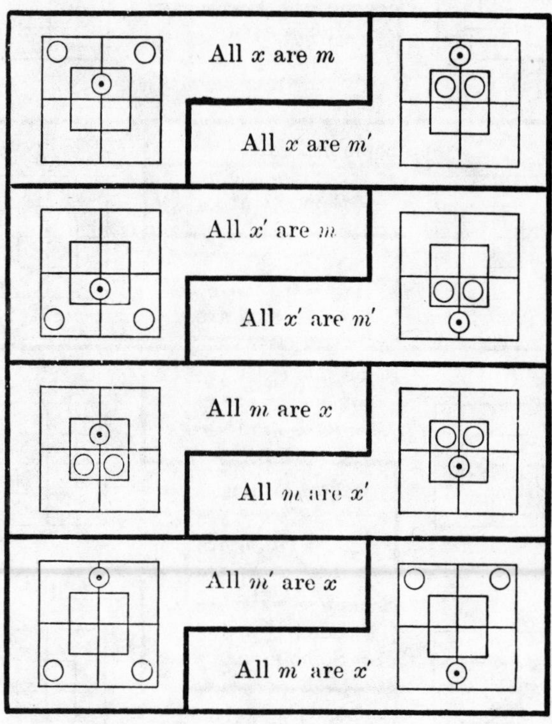
All x are m
All x are m'
All x' are m
All x' are m'
All m are x
All m are x'
All m' are x
All m' are x'

TABLE VIII.

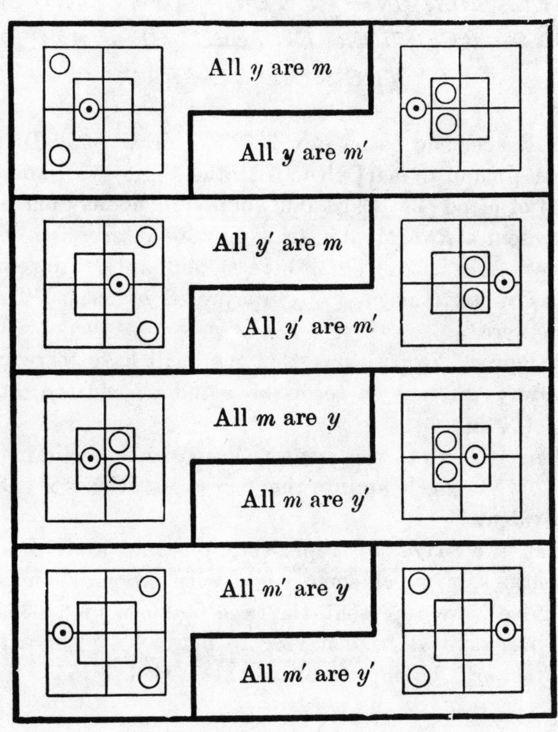
All y are m
All y are m'
All y' are m
All y' are m'
All m are y
All m are y'
All m' are y
All m' are y'

CHAPTER III

REPRESENTATION OF TWO PROPOSITIONS OF RELATION, ONE IN TERMS OF x AND m, AND THE OTHER IN TERMS OF y AND m, ON THE SAME DIAGRAM.

THE Reader had better now begin to draw little Diagrams for himself, and to mark them with the Digits "I" and "O", instead of using the Board and Counters: he may put a "I" to represent a *Red* Counter (this may be interpreted to mean "There is at least *one* Thing here"), and a "O" to represent a *Grey* Counter (this may be interpreted to mean "There is *nothing* here").

The Pair of Propositions, that we shall have to represent, will always be, one in terms of x and m, and the other in terms of y and m.

When we have to represent a Proposition beginning with "All", we break it up into the *two* Propositions to which it is equivalent.

When we have to represent, on the same Diagram, Propositions, of which some begin with "Some" and others with "No", we represent the *negative* ones *first*. This will sometimes save us from having to put a "I" "on a fence" and afterwards having to shift it into a Cell.

[Let us work a few examples.

(1)

"No x are m';
No y' are m".

Let us first represent "No x are m'". This gives us Diagram a.

Then, representing "No y' are m" on the same Diagram, we get Diagram b.

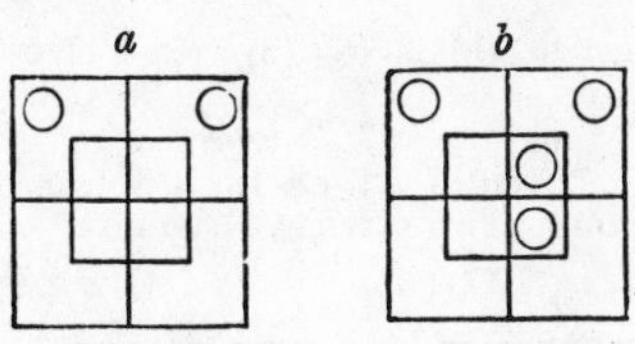

(2)
"Some m are x,
No m are y".

If, neglecting the Rule, we were to begin with "Some m are x", we should get Diagram *a*.

And if we were then to take "No m are y", which tells us that the Inner N.W. Cell is *empty*, we should be obliged to take the "I" off the fence (as it no longer has the choice of *two* Cells), and to put it into the Inner N.E. Cell, as in Diagram *c*.

This trouble may be saved by beginning with "No m are y", as in Diagram *b*.

And *now*, when we take "Some m are x", there is no fence to sit on! The "I" has to go, at once, into the N.E. Cell, as in Diagram *c*.

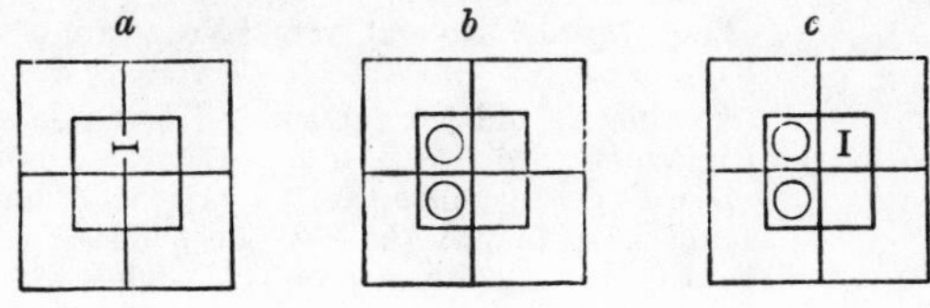

(3)
"No x' are m';
All m are y".

Here we begin by breaking up the Second into the two Propositions to which it is equivalent. Thus we have *three* Propositions to represent, viz.—

(1) "No x' are m';
(2) Some m are y;
(3) No m are y'".

These we will take in the order 1, 3, 2.

First we take No. (1), viz. "No x' are m'". This gives us Diagram *a*.

Adding, to this, No. (3), viz. "No m are y'", we get Diagram b.

This time the "I", representing No. (2), viz. "Some m are y," *has* to sit on the fence, as there is no "O" to order it off! This gives us Diagram c.

a *b* *c*

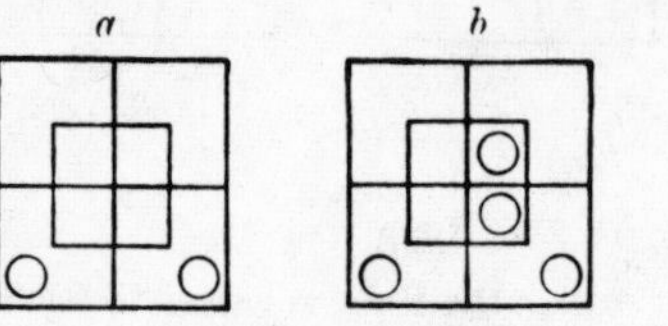

(4)

"All m are x;
All y are m".

Here we break up *both* Propositions, and thus get *four* to represent, viz.—

(1) "Some m are x;
(2) No m are x';
(3) Some y are m;
(4) No y are m'.

These we will take in the order 2, 4, 1, 3.

First we take No. (2), viz. "No m are x'". This gives us Diagram a.

To this we add No. (4), viz. "No y are m'", and thus get Diagram b.

If we were to add to this No. (1), viz. "Some m are x", we should have to put the "I" on a fence: so let us try No. (3) instead, viz. "Some y are m". This gives us Diagram c.

And now there is no need to trouble about No. (1), as it would not add anything to our information to put a "I" on the fence. The Diagram *already* tells us that "Some m are x".]

a *b* *c*

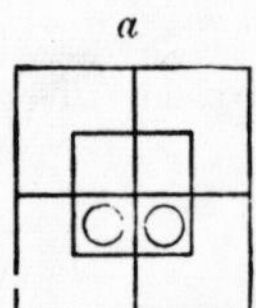

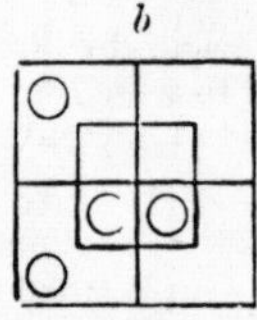

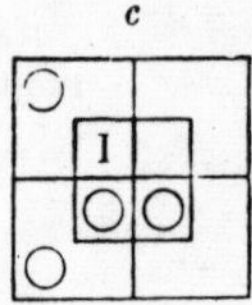

[Work Examples § **1**, 9—12 (p. 97 : § **2**, 1—20 (p. 98)]

CHAPTER IV.

INTERPRETATION, IN TERMS OF x AND y, OF TRILITERAL DIAGRAM, WHEN MARKED WITH COUNTERS OR DIGITS.

THE problem before us is, given a marked Triliteral Diagram, to ascertain *what* Propositions of Relation, in terms of x and y, are represented on it.

The best plan, for a *beginner*, is to draw a *Biliteral* Diagram alongside of it, and to transfer, from the one to the other, all the information he can. He can then read off, from the Biliteral Diagram, the required Propositions. After a little practice, he will be able to dispense with the Biliteral Diagram, and to read off the result from the Triliteral Diagram itself.

To *transfer* the information, observe the following Rules :—

(1) Examine the N.W. Quarter of the Triliteral Diagram.

(2) If it contains a "I", in *either* Cell, it is certainly *occupied*, and you may mark the N.W. Quarter of the Biliteral Diagram with a "I".

(3) If it contains *two* "O"s, one in *each* Cell, it is certainly *empty*, and you may mark the N.W. Quarter of the Biliteral Diagram with a "O".

(4) Deal in the same way with the N.E., the S.W., and the S.E. Quarter.

[Let us take, as examples, the results of the four Examples worked in the previous Chapters.

(1)

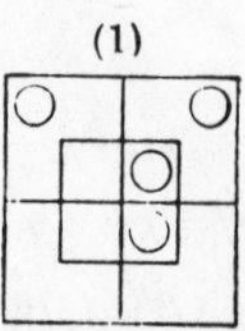

In the N.W. Quarter, only *one* of the two Cells is marked as *empty:* so we do not know whether the N.W. Quarter of the Biliteral Diagram is *occupied* or *empty:* so we cannot mark it.

In the N.E. Quarter, we find *two* "O"s: so *this* Quarter is certainly *empty;* and we mark it so on the Biliteral Diagram.

In the S.W. Quarter, we have no information *at all.*

In the S.E. Quarter, we have not enough to use.

We may read off the result as "No x are y'", or "No y are x," whichever we prefer.

(2)

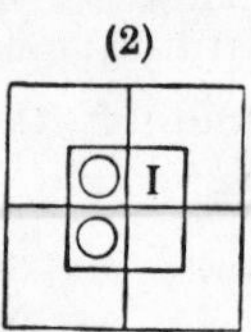

In the N.W. Quarter, we have not enough information to use.

In the N.E. Quarter, we find a "I". This shows us that it is *occupied:* so we may mark the N.E. Quarter on the Biliteral Diagram with a "I".

In the S.W. Quarter, we have not enough information to use.

In the S.E. Quarter, we have none at all.

We may read off the result as "Some x are y'", or "Some y' are x", whichever we prefer.

(3)

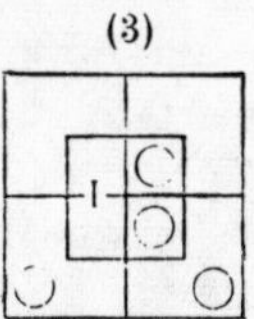

In the N.W. Quarter, we have *no* information. (The "I", sitting on the fence, is of no use to us until we know on *which* side he means to jump down!)

In the N.E. Quarter, we have not enough information to use.

Neither have we in the S.W. Quarter.

The S.E. Quarter is the only one that yields enough information to use. It is certainly *empty:* so we mark it as such on the Biliteral Diagram.

We may read off the result as "No x' are y'", or "No y' are x'", whichever we prefer.

(4)

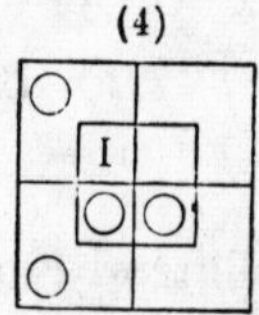

The N.W. Quarter is *occupied*, in spite of the "O" in the Outer Cell. So we mark it with a "I" on the Biliteral Diagram.

The N.E. Quarter yields no information.

The S.W. Quarter is certainly *empty*. So we mark it as such on the Biliteral Diagram.

The S.E. Quarter does not yield enough information to use.

We read off the result as "All y are x."]

[Review Tables V, VI. (pp. 46, 47). Work Examples §**1**, 13—16 (p. 97); §**2**, 21—32 (p. 98); §**3**, 1—20 (p. 99.)].

BOOK V.

SYLLOGISMS.

CHAPTER I.

INTRODUCTORY

WHEN a Trio of Biliteral Propositions of Relation is such that

(1) all their six Terms are Species of the same Genus,

(2) every two of them contain between them a Pair of codivisional Classes,

(3) the three Propositions are so related that, if the first two were true, the third would be true,

the Trio is called a '**Syllogism**'; the Genus, of which each of the six Terms is a Species, is called its '**Universe of Discourse**', or, more briefly, its '**Univ.**'; the first two Propositions are called its '**Premisses**', and the third its '**Conclusion**'; also the Pair of codivisional Terms in the Premisses are called its '**Eliminands**', and the other two its '**Retinends**'.

The Conclusion of a Syllogism is said to be '**consequent**' from its Premisses: hence it is usual to prefix to it the word "Therefore" (or the Symbol "∴").

[Note that the 'Eliminands' are so called because they are *eliminated*, and do not appear in the Conclusion ; and that the 'Retinends' are so called because they are *retained*, and *do* appear in the Conclusion.

Note also that the question, whether the Conclusion is or is not *consequent* from the Premisses, is not affected by the *actual* truth or falsity of any of the Trio, but depends entirely on their *relationship to each other*.

As a specimen-Syllogism, let us take the Trio

"No x-Things are m-Things ;
No y-Things are m'-Things.
No x-Things are y-Things."

which we may write, as explained at p. 26, thus :—

"No x are m ;
No y are m'.
No x are y".

Here the first and second contain the Pair of codivisional Classes m and m' ; the first and third contain the Pair x and x ; and the second and third contain the Pair y and y.

Also the three Propositions are (as we shall see hereafter) so related that, if the first two were true, the third would also be true.

Hence the Trio is a *Syllogism ;* the two Propositions, "No x are m" and "No y are m'", are its *Premisses ;* the Proposition "No x are y" is its *Conclusion ;* the Terms m and m' are its *Eliminands ;* and the Terms x and y are its *Retinends.*

Hence we may write it thus :—

"No x are m ;
No y are m'.
∴ No x are y".

As a second specimen, let us take the Trio

"All cats understand French ;
Some chickens are cats.
Some chickens understand French".

These, put into normal form, are

"All cats are creatures understanding French ;
Some chickens are cats.
Some chickens are creatures understanding French".

Here all the six Terms are Species of the Genus "creatures."

Also the first and second Propositions contain the Pair of codivisional Classes "cats" and "cats"; the first and third contain the Pair "creatures understanding French" and "creatures understanding French"; and the second and third contain the Pair "chickens" and "chickens".

Also the three Propositions are (as we shall see at p. 64) so related that, if the first two were true, the third would be true. (The first two are, as it happens, *not* strictly true in *our* planet. But there is nothing to hinder them from being true in some *other* planet, say *Mars* or *Jupiter*—in which case the third would *also* be true in that planet, and its inhabitants would probably engage chickens as nursery-governesses. They would thus secure a singular *contingent* privilege, unknown in England, namely, that they would be able, at any time when provisions ran short, to utilise the nursery-governess for the nursery-dinner!)

Hence the Trio is a *Syllogism;* the Genus "creatures" is its 'Univ.'; the two Propositions, "All cats understand French" and "Some chickens are cats", are its *Premisses;* the Proposition "Some chickens understand French" is its *Conclusion;* the Terms "cats" and "cats" are its *Eliminands;* and the Terms, "creatures understanding French" and "chickens", are its *Retinends*.

Hence we may write it thus:—

"All cats understand French;
Some chickens are cats;
∴ Some chickens understand French".

CHAPTER II.

PROBLEMS IN SYLLOGISMS.

---

§ 1.

Introductory.

WHEN the Terms of a Proposition are represented by *words*, it is said to be '**concrete**'; when by *letters*, '**abstract.**'

To translate a Proposition from concrete into abstract form, we fix on a Univ., and regard each Term as a *Species* of it, and we choose a letter to represent its *Differentia.*

[For example, suppose we wish to translate "Some soldiers are brave" into abstract form. We may take "men" as Univ., and regard "soldiers" and "brave men" as *Species* of the *Genus* "men"; and we may choose x to represent the peculiar Attribute (say "military") of "soldiers," and y to represent "brave." Then the Proposition may be written "Some military men are brave men"; *i.e.* "Some x-men are y-men"; *i.e.* (omitting "men," as explained at p. 26) "Some x are y."

In practice, we should merely say "Let Univ. be "men", x = soldiers y = brave", and at once translate "Some soldiers are brave" into "Some x are y."]

The Problems we shall have to solve are of two kinds, viz.

(1) "Given a Pair of Propositions of Relation, which contain between them a pair of codivisional Classes, and which are proposed as Premisses: to ascertain what Conclusion, if any, is consequent from them."

(2) "Given a Trio of Propositions of Relation, of which every two contain a pair of codivisional Classes, and which are proposed as a Syllogism: to ascertain whether the proposed Conclusion is consequent from the proposed Premisses, and, if so, whether it is *complete.*"

These Problems we will discuss separately.

---

§ 2.

Given a Pair of Propositions of Relation, which contain between them a pair of codivisional Classes, and which are proposed as Premisses: to ascertain what Conclusion, if any, is consequent from them.

The Rules, for doing this, are as follows:—

(1) Determine the 'Universe of Discourse'.

(2) Construct a Dictionary, making m and m (or m and m') represent the pair of codivisional Classes, and x (or x') and y (or y') the other two.

(3) Translate the proposed Premisses into abstract form.

(4) Represent them, together, on a Triliteral Diagram.

(5) Ascertain what Proposition, if any, in terms of x and y, is *also* represented on it.

(6) Translate this into concrete form.

It is evident that, if the proposed Premisses were true, this other Proposition would *also* be true. Hence it is a *Conclusion* consequent from the proposed Premisses.

[Let us work some examples.

(1)

"No son of mine is dishonest;
People always treat an honest man with respect".

Taking "men" as Univ., we may write these as follows:—

"No sons of mine are dishonest men;
All honest men are men treated with respect".

We can now construct our Dictionary, viz. m = honest; x = sons of mine; y = treated with respect.

(Note that the expression "x = sons of mine" is an abbreviated form of "x = the Differentia of 'sons of mine', when regarded as a Species of 'men'".)

The next thing is to translate the proposed Premisses into abstract form, as follows:—

"No x are m';
All m are y".

Next, by the process described at p. 50, we represent these on a Triliteral Diagram, thus:—

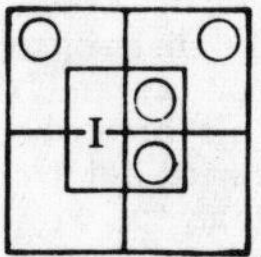

Next, by the process described at p. 53, we transfer to a Biliteral Diagram all the information we can.

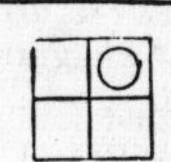

The result we can read either as "No x are y'" or as "No y' are x," whichever we prefer. So we refer to our Dictionary, to see which will look best; and we choose

"No x are y'",

which, translated into concrete form, is

"No son of mine ever fails to be treated with respect.

(2)

"All cats understand French
Some chickens are cats".

Taking "creatures" as Univ., we write these as follows:—

"All cats are creatures understanding French;
Some chickens are cats".

We can now construct our Dictionary, viz. m = cats; x = understanding French; y = chickens.

The proposed Premisses, translated into abstract form, are

'All m are x;
Some y are m".

In order to represent these on a Triliteral Diagram, we break up the first into the two Propositions to which it is equivalent, and thus get the *three* Propositions

(1) "Some m are x;
(2) No m are x';
(3) Some y are m".

The Rule, given at p. 50, would make us take these in the order 2, 1, 3.

This, however, would produce the result

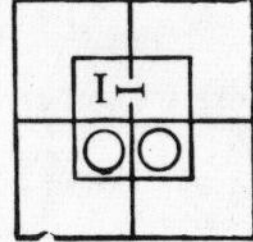

So it would be better to take them in the order 2, 3, 1. Nos. (2) and (3) give us the result here shown; and now we need not trouble about No. (1), as the Proposition "Some *m* are *x*" is *already* represented on the Diagram.

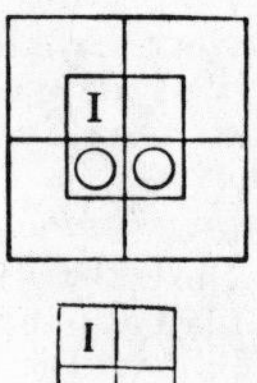

Transferring our information to a Biliteral Diagram, we get

This result we can read either as "Some *x* are *y*" or "Some *y* are *x*".

After consulting our Dictionary, we choose

"Some *y* are *x*",

which, translated into concrete form, is

"Some chickens understand French."

(3)

"All diligent students are successful;
All ignorant students are unsuccessful".

Let Univ. be "students"; *m* = successful; *x* = diligent; *y* = ignorant.

These Premisses, in abstract form, are

"All *x* are *m*;
All *y* are *m′*".

These, broken up, give us the four Propositions

(1) "Some *x* are *m*;
(2) No *x* are *m′*;
(3) Some *y* are *m′*;
(4) No *y* are *m*".

which we will take in the order 2, 4, 1, 3.

Representing these on a Triliteral Diagram, we get

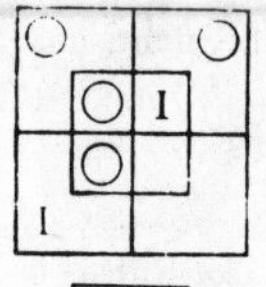

And this information, transferred to a Biliteral Diagram, is

Here we get *two* Conclusions, viz.

"All *x* are *y′*;
All *y* are *x′*."

And these, translated into concrete form, are

"All diligent students are (not-ignorant, i.e.) learned;
All ignorant students are (not-diligent, i.e.) idle".

(See p. 4.)

(4)

"Of the prisoners who were put on their trial at the last Assizes, all, against whom the verdict 'guilty' was returned, were sentenced to imprisonment;
Some, who were sentenced to imprisonment, were also sentenced to hard labour".

Let Univ. be "the prisoners who were put on their trial at the last Assizes"; m = who were sentenced to imprisonment; x = against whom the verdict 'guilty' was returned; y = who were sentenced to hard labour.

The Premisses, translated into abstract form, are

"All x are m;
Some m are y".

Breaking up the first, we get the three

(1) "Some x are m;
(2) No x are m';
(3) Some m are y".

Representing these, in the order 2, 1, 3, on a Triliteral Diagram, we get

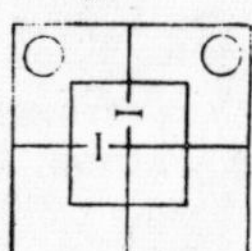

Here we get no Conclusion at all.

You would very likely have guessed, if you had seen *only* the Premisses, that the Conclusion would be

"Some, against whom the verdict 'guilty' was returned, were sentenced to hard labour".

But this Conclusion is not even *true*, with regard to the Assizes I have here invented.

"Not *true!*" you exclaim. "Then who *were* they, who were sentenced to imprisonment and were also sentenced to hard labour? They *must* have had the verdict 'guilty' returned against them, or how could they be sentenced?"

Well, it happened like *this*, you see. They were three ruffians, who had committed highway-robbery. When they were put on their trial, they *pleaded* 'guilty'. So no *verdict* was returned at all; and they were sentenced at once.]

I will now work out, in their briefest form, as models for the Reader to imitate in working examples, the above four concrete Problems.

(1) [see p. 60]

" No son of mine is dishonest;

People always treat an honest man with respect."

Univ. "men"; m = honest; x = my sons; y = treated with respect.

"No x are m';
All m are y."

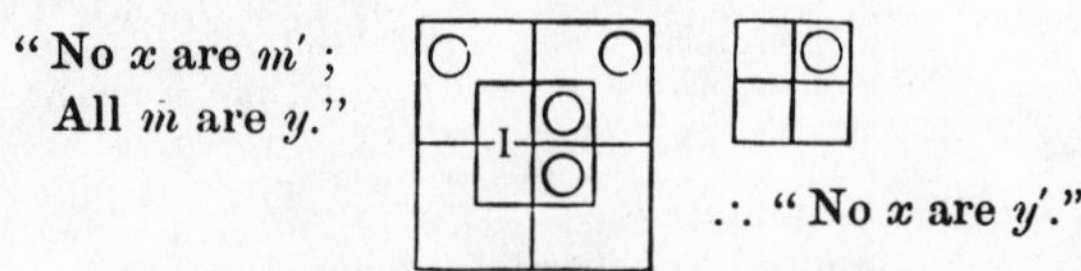

∴ "No x are y'."

i.e. " No son of mine ever fails to be treated with respect."

(2) [see p. 61]

All cats understand French;

Some chickens are cats".

Univ. "creatures"; m = cats; x = understanding French; y = chickens.

" All m are x;
Some y are m."

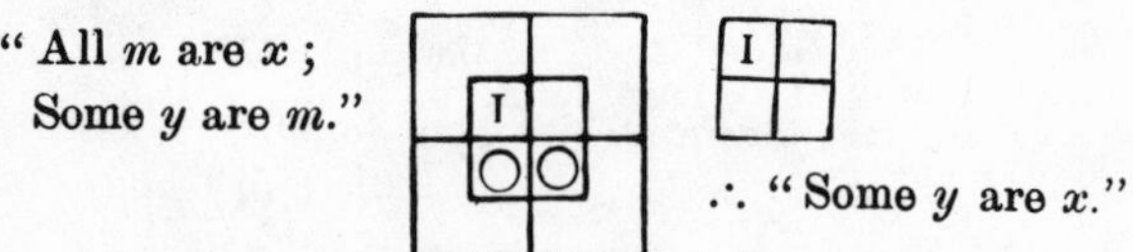

∴ "Some y are x."

i.e. " Some chickens understand French."

(3) [see p. 62]

" All diligent students are successful;

All ignorant students are unsuccessful".

Univ. "students"; m = successful; x = diligent; y = ignorant.

" All x are m;
All y are m'."

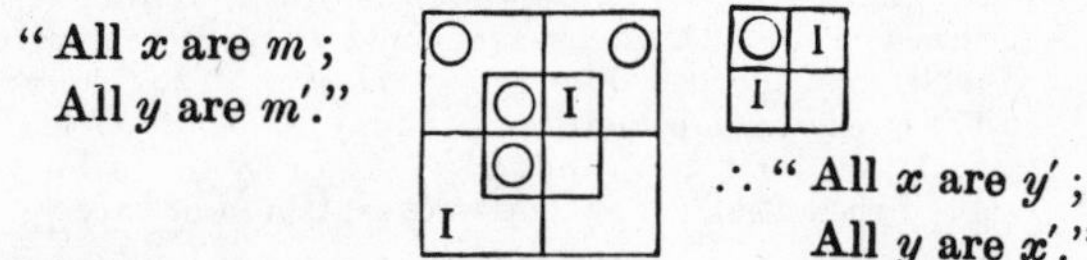

∴ " All x are y';
All y are x'."

i.e. All diligent students are learned; and all ignorant students are idle".

(4) [see p. 63]

"Of the prisoners who were put on their trial at the last Assizes, all, against whom the verdict 'guilty' was returned, were sentenced to imprisonment;

Some, who were sentenced to imprisonment, were also sentenced to hard labour".

Univ. "prisoners who were put on their trial at the last Assizes"; m = sentenced to imprisonment; x = against whom the verdict 'guilty' was returned; y = sentenced to hard labour.

"All x are m;
Some m are y."

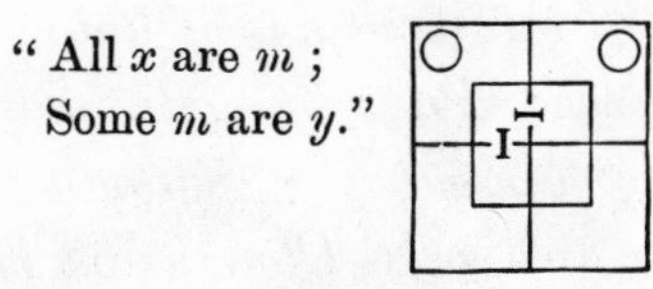

There is no Conclusion.

[Review Tables VII, VIII (pp. 48, 49). Work Examples § **1**, 17–21 (p. 97); § **4**, 1–6 (p. 100); § **5**, 1–6 (p. 101).]

---

§ 3.

Given a Trio of Propositions of Relation, of which every two contain a Pair of codivisional Classes, and which are proposed as a Syllogism; to ascertain whether the proposed Conclusion is consequent from the proposed Premisses, and, if so, whether it is complete.

The Rules, for doing this, are as follows:—

(1) Take the proposed Premisses, and ascertain, by the process described at p. 60, what Conclusion, if any, is consequent from them.

(2) If there be *no* Conclusion, say so.

(3) If there *be* a Conclusion, compare it with the proposed Conclusion, and pronounce accordingly.

I will now work out, in their briefest form, as models for the Reader to imitate in working examples, six Problems.

(1).

"All soldiers are strong;
All soldiers are brave.
Some strong men are brave."

Univ. "men"; m = soldiers; x = strong; y = brave.

"All m are x;
All m are y.
Some x are y."

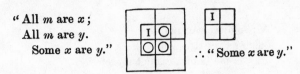

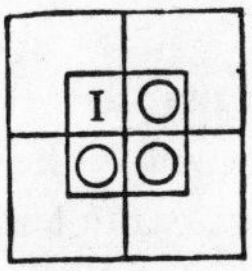

∴ "Some x are y."

Hence proposed Conclusion is right.

(2)

"I admire these pictures;
When I admire anything I wish to examine it thoroughly.
I wish to examine some of these pictures thoroughly."

Univ. "things"; m = admired by me; x = these pictures; y = things which I wish to examine thoroughly.

"All x are m;
All m are y.
Some x are y."

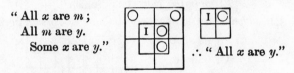

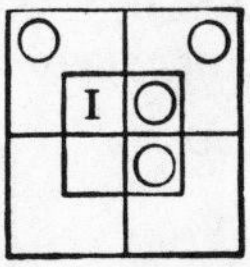

∴ "All x are y."

Hence proposed Conclusion is *incomplete*, the *complete* one being "I wish to examine *all* these pictures thoroughly"

(3)

"None but the brave deserve the fair;
Some braggarts are cowards.
Some braggarts do not deserve the fair."

Univ. "persons"; m = brave; x = deserving of the fair; y = braggarts.

"No m' are x;
Some y are m'.
Some y are x'."

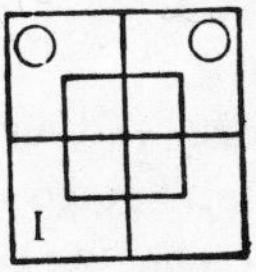

∴ "Some y are x'."

Hence proposed Conclusion is right.

(4)

"All soldiers can march;
Some babies are not soldiers.
Some babies cannot march".

Univ. "persons"; m = soldiers; x = able to march; y = babies.

"All m are x;
Some y are m'.
Some y are x'."

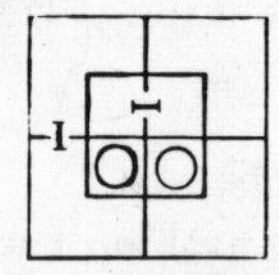

There is no Conclusion.

(5)

"All selfish men are unpopular;
All obliging men are popular.
All obliging men are unselfish".

Univ. "men"; m = popular; x = selfish; y = obliging.

"All x are m';
All y are m.
All y are x'."

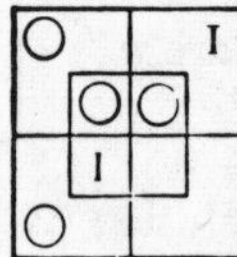

∴ "All x are y';
All y are x'."

Hence proposed Conclusion is *incomplete*, the *complete* one containing, in addition, "All selfish men are disobliging".

(6)

"No one, who means to go by the train and cannot get a conveyance, and has not enough time to walk to the station, can do without running;
This party of tourists mean to go by the train and cannot get a conveyance, but they have plenty of time to walk to the station.
This party of tourists need not run."

Univ. "persons meaning to go by the train, and unable to get a conveyance"; m = having enough time to walk to the station; x = needing to run; y = these tourists.

"No m' are x';
All y are m.
All y are x'."

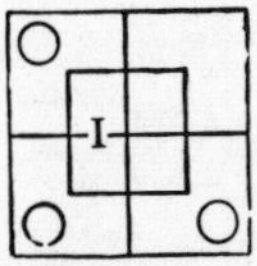

○	
I	
○	○

There is no Conclusion.

[Here is *another* opportunity, gentle Reader, for playing a trick on your innocent friend. Put the proposed Syllogism before him, and ask him what he thinks of the Conclusion.

He will reply "Why, it's perfectly correct, of course! And if your precious Logic-book tells you it *isn't*, don't believe it! You don't mean to tell me those tourists *need* to run? If *I* were one of them, and knew the *Premisses* to be true, I should be *quite* clear that I *needn't* run—and I *should walk!*"

And *you* will reply "But suppose there was a mad bull behind you?"

And then your innocent friend will say "Hum! Ha! I must think that over a bit!"

You may then explain to him, as a convenient *test* of the soundness of a Syllogism, that, if circumstances can be invented which, without interfering with the truth of the *Premisses*, would make the *Conclusion* false, the Syllogism *must* be unsound.]

[Review Tables V—VIII (pp. 46—49). Work Examples § **4**, 7—12 (p. 100); § **5**, 7—12 (p. 101); § **6**, 1—10 (p. 106); § **7**, 1—6 (p. 107, 108).]

BOOK VI.

THE METHOD OF SUBSCRIPTS.

CHAPTER I.

INTRODUCTORY.

LET us agree that "x_1" shall mean "Some existing Things have the Attribute x", i.e. (more briefly) "Some x exist"; also that "xy_1" shall mean "Some xy exist", and so on. Such a Proposition may be called an '**Entity.**'

[Note that, when there are *two* letters in the expression, it does not in the least matter which stands *first*: "xy_1" and "yx_1" mean exactly the same.]

Also that "x_0" shall mean "No existing Things have the Attribute x", i.e. (more briefly) "No x exist"; also that "xy_0" shall mean "No xy exist", and so on. Such a Proposition may be called a '**Nullity**'.

Also that "†" shall mean "and".

[Thus "ab_1 † cd_0" means "Some *ab* exist and no *cd* exist".]

Also that "ℙ" shall mean "would, if true, prove".

[Thus, "x_0 ℙ xy_0" means "The Proposition 'No x exist' would, if true, prove the Proposition 'No xy exist'".]

When two Letters are both of them accented, or both *not* accented, they are said to have '**Like Signs**', or to be '**Like**': when one is accented, and the other not, they are said to have '**Unlike Signs**', or to be '**Unlike**'.

CHAPTER II.

REPRESENTATION OF PROPOSITIONS OF RELATION

LET us take, first, the Proposition "Some x are y".

This, we know, is equivalent to the Proposition of Existence "Some xy exist". (See p. 31.) Hence it may be represented by the expression "xy_1".

The Converse Proposition "Some y are x" may of course be represented by the *same* expression, viz. "xy_1".

Similarly we may represent the three similar Pairs of Converse Propositions, viz.—

"Some x are y'" = "Some y' are x",
"Some x' are y" = "Some y are x'",
"Some x' are y'" = "Some y' are x'".

Let us take, next, the Proposition "No x are y".

This, we know, is equivalent to the Proposition of Existence "No xy exist". (See p. 33.) Hence it may be represented by the expression "xy_0".

The Converse Proposition "No y are x" may of course be represented by the *same* expression, viz. "xy_0".

Similarly we may represent the three similar Pairs of Converse Propositions, viz.

"No x are y'" = "No y' are x",
"No x' are y" = "No y are x'",
"No x' are y'" = "No y' are x'".

Let us take, next, the Proposition "All x are y".

Now it is evident that the Double Proposition of Existence "Some x exist and no xy' exist" tells us that *some* x-Things exist, but that *none* of them have the Attribute y': that is, it tells us that *all* of them have the Attribute y: that is, it tells us that "All x are y".

Also it is evident that the expression "$x_1 \dagger xy'_0$" represents this Double Proposition.

Hence it also represents the Proposition "All x are y".

[The Reader will perhaps be puzzled by the statement that the Proposition "All x are y" is equivalent to the Double Proposition "Some x exist and no xy' exist," remembering that it was stated, at p. 33, to be equivalent to the Double Proposition "Some x are y and no x are y'" (i.e. "Some xy exist and no xy' exist"). The explanation is that the Proposition "Some xy exist" contains *superfluous information.* "Some x exist" is enough for our purpose.]

This expression may be written in a shorter form, viz. "$x_1y'_0$", since *each* Subscript takes effect back to the *beginning* of the expression.

Similarly we may represent the seven similar Propositions "All x are y'", "All x' are y", "All x' are y'", "All y are x", "All y are x'", "All y' are x", and "All y' are x'".

[The Reader should make out all these for himself.]

It will be convenient to remember that, in translating a Proposition, beginning with "All", from abstract form into subscript form, or *vice versâ*, the Predicate *changes sign* (that is, changes from positive to negative, or else from negative to positive).

[Thus, the Proposition "All y are x'" becomes "y_1x_0", where the Predicate changes from x' to x.

Again, the expression "$x'_1y'_0$" becomes "All x' are y", where the Predicate changes from y' to y.]

CHAPTER III.

SYLLOGISMS.

---

§ 1.

Representation of Syllogisms.

We already know how to represent each of the three Propositions of a Syllogism in subscript form. When that is done, all we need, besides, is to write the three expressions in a row, with "†" between the Premisses, and "₱" before the Conclusion.

[Thus the Syllogism

"No x are m';
All m are y.
∴ No x are y'."

may be represented thus:—

xm'_0 † $m_1y'_0$ ₱ xy'_0

When a Proposition has to be translated from concrete form into subscript form, the Reader will find it convenient, just at first, to translate it into *abstract* form, and *thence* into subscript form. But, after a little practice, he will find it quite easy to go straight from concrete form to subscript form.]

---

§ 2.

Formulæ for solving Problems in Syllogisms.

When once we have found, by Diagrams, the Conclusion to a given Pair of Premisses, and have represented the Syllogism in subscript form, we have a *Formula*, by which we can at once find, without having to use Diagrams again, the Conclusion to any *other* Pair of Premisses having the *same* subscript forms.

[Thus, the expression

$$xm_0 \dagger ym'_0 \text{ ℙ } xy_0$$

is a *Formula*, by which we can find the Conclusion to any Pair of Premisses whose subscript forms are

$$xm_0 \dagger ym'_0$$

For example, suppose we had the Pair of Propositions

"No gluttons are healthy;
No unhealthy men are strong".

proposed as Premisses. Taking "men" as our 'Universe, and making m = healthy; x = gluttons; y = strong; we might translate the Pair into abstract form, thus:—

"No x are m;
No m' are y."

These, in subscript form, would be

$$xm_0 \dagger m'y_0$$

which are identical with those in our *Formula*. Hence we at once know the Conclusion to be

$$xy_0$$

that is, in abstract form,

"No x are y";

that is, in concrete form,

"No gluttons are strong".]

I shall now take three different forms of Pairs of Premisses, and work out their Conclusions, once for all, by Diagrams; and thus obtain some useful Formulæ. I shall call them "Fig. I", "Fig. II", and "Fig. III".

Fig. I.

This includes any Pair of Premisses which are both of them Nullities, and which contain Unlike Eliminands.

The simplest case is

$$xm_0 \dagger ym'_0$$

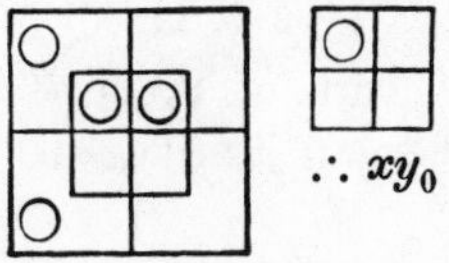

In this case we see that the Conclusion is a Nullity, and that the Retinends have kept their Signs.

And we should find this Rule to hold good with *any* Pair of Premisses which fulfil the given conditions.

> [The Reader had better satisfy himself of this, by working out, on Diagrams, several varieties, such as
>
> $m_1x_0 \dagger ym'_0$ (which $\mathbb{P}$ xy_0)
> $xm'_0 \dagger m_1y_0$ (which $\mathbb{P}$ xy_0)
> $x'm_0 \dagger ym'_0$ (which $\mathbb{P}$ $x'y_0$)
> $m'_1x'_0 \dagger m_1y'_0$ (which $\mathbb{P}$ $x'y'_0$).]

If either Retinend is asserted in the *Premisses* to exist, of course it may be so asserted in the *Conclusion*.

Hence we get two *Variants* of Fig. I, viz.

(*a*) where *one* Retinend is so asserted ;

(β) where *both* are so asserted.

> [The Reader had better work out, on Diagrams, examples of these two Variants, such as
>
> $m_1x_0 \dagger y_1m'_0$ (which proves y_1x_0)
> $x_1m'_0 \dagger m_1y_0$ (which proves x_1y_0)
> $x'_1m_0 \dagger y_1m'_0$ (which proves $x'_1y_0 \dagger y_1x'_0$).]

The Formula, to be remembered, is

$$xm_0 \dagger ym'_0 \ \mathbb{P}\ xy_0$$

with the following two Rules:—

(1) *Two Nullities, with Unlike Eliminands, yield a Nullity, in which both Retinends keep their Signs.*

(2) *A Retinend, asserted in the Premisses to exist, may be so asserted in the Conclusion.*

[Note that Rule (1) is merely the Formula expressed in words.]

Fig. II.

This includes any Pair of Premisses, of which one is a Nullity and the other an Entity, and which contain Like Eliminands.

The simplest case is

$$xm_0 \dagger ym_1$$

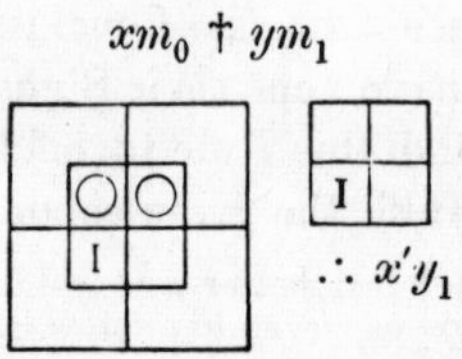

In this case we see that the Conclusion is an Entity, and that the Nullity-Retinend has changed its Sign.

And we should find this Rule to hold good with *any* Pair of Premisses which fulfil the given conditions.

[The Reader had better satisfy himself of this, by working out, on Diagrams, several varieties, such as

$x'm_0 \dagger ym_1$ (which $\Vdash xy_1$)
$x_1m'_0 \dagger y'm'_1$ (which $\Vdash x'y'_1$)
$m_1x_0 \dagger y'm_1$ (which $\Vdash x'y'_1$).]

The Formula, to be remembered, is,

$$xm_0 \dagger ym_1 \Vdash x'y_1$$

with the following Rule:—

A Nullity and an Entity, with Like Eliminands, yield an Entity, in which the Nullity-Retinend changes its Sign.

[Note that this Rule is merely the Formula expressed in words.]

Fig. III.

This includes any Pair of Premisses which are both of them Nullities, and which contain Like Eliminands asserted to exist.

The simplest case is

$$xm_0 \dagger ym_0 \dagger m_1$$

[Note that "m_1" is here stated *separately*, because it does not matter in *which* of the two Premisses it occurs: so that this includes the *three* forms "$m_1x_0 \dagger ym_0$", "$xm_0 \dagger m_1y_0$", and "$m_1x_0 \dagger m_1y_0$".]

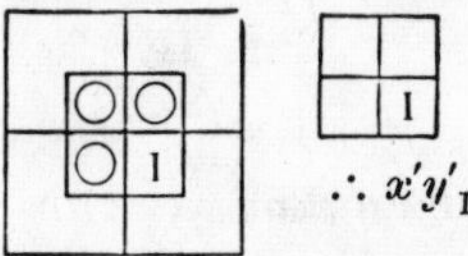

$\therefore x'y'_1$

In this case we see that the Conclusion is an Entity, and that *both* Retinends have changed their Signs.

And we should find this Rule to hold good with *any* Pair of Premisses which fulfil the given conditions.

[The Reader had better satisfy himself of this, by working out, on Diagrams, several varieties, such as

$x'm_0 \dagger m_1y_0$ (which $\Vdash xy'_1$)
$m'_1x_0 \dagger m'y'_0$ (which $\Vdash x'y_1$)
$m_1x'_0 \dagger m_1y'_0$ (which $\Vdash xy_1$).]

The Formula, to be remembered, is

$$xm_0 \dagger ym_0 \dagger m_1 \Vdash x'y'_1$$

with the following Rule (which is merely the Formula expressed in words):—

Two Nullities, with Like Eliminands asserted to exist, yield an Entity, in which both Retinends change their Signs.

In order to help the Reader to remember the peculiarities and Formulæ of these three Figures, I will put them all together in one Table.

TABLE IX.

Fig. I.

$$xm_0 \dagger ym'_0 \P xy_0$$

Two Nullities, with Unlike Eliminands, yield a Nullity, in which both Retinends keep their Signs.

A Retinend, asserted in the Premisses to exist, may be so asserted in the Conclusion.

Fig. II.

$$xm_0 \dagger ym_1 \P x'y_1$$

A Nullity and an Entity, with Like Eliminands, yield an Entity, in which the Nullity-Retinend changes its Sign.

Fig. III.

$$xm_0 \dagger ym_0 \dagger m_1 \P x'y'_1$$

Two Nullities, with Like Eliminands asserted to exist, yield an Entity, in which both Retinends change their Signs.

I will now work out, by these Formulæ, as models for the Reader to imitate, some Problems in Syllogisms which have been already worked, by Diagrams, in Book V., Chap. II.

(1) [see p. 64]

"No son of mine is dishonest;

People always treat an honest man with respect."

Univ. "men"; m = honest; x = my sons; y = treated with respect.

$$xm'_0 \dagger m_1y'_0 \P xy'_0 \text{ [Fig. I.}$$

i.e. "No son of mine ever fails to be treated with respect."

(2) [see p. 64]

"All cats understand French;
Some chickens are cats."

Univ. "creatures"; m = cats; x = understanding French y = chickens

$$m_1 x'_0 \dagger y m_1 \text{ ⁋ } x y_1 \text{ [Fig II.}$$

i.e. "Some chickens understand French."

(3) [see p. 64]

"All diligent students are successful;
All ignorant students are unsuccessful."

Univ. "students"; m = successful; x = diligent; y = ignorant.

$$x_1 m'_0 \dagger y_1 m_0 \text{ ⁋ } x_1 y_0 \dagger y_1 x_0 \text{ [Fig. I } (\beta).$$

i.e. "All diligent students are learned; and all ignorant students are idle."

(4) [see p. 66]

"All soldiers are strong;
All soldiers are brave.
Some strong men are brave."

Univ. "men"; m = soldiers; x = strong; y = brave.

$$m_1 x'_0 \dagger m_1 y'_0 \text{ ⁋ } x y_1 \text{ [Fig. III.}$$

Hence proposed Conclusion is right.

(5) [see p. 67]

"I admire these pictures;
When I admire anything, I wish to examine it thoroughly.
I wish to examine some of these pictures thoroughly."

Univ. "things"; m = admired by me; x = these; y = things which I wish to examine thoroughly.

$$x_1 m'_0 \dagger m_1 y'_0 \text{ ⁋ } x_1 y'_0 \text{ [Fig. I } (a).$$

Hence proposed Conclusion, xy_1, is *incomplete*, the *complete* one being "I wish to examine *all* these pictures thoroughly."

(6) [see p. 67]

"None but the brave deserve the fair;
Some braggarts are cowards.
Some braggarts do not deserve the fair."

Univ. "persons"; m = brave; x = deserving of the fair; y = braggarts.

$$m'x_0 \dagger ym'_1 \Vdash x'y_1 \text{ [Fig. II.}$$

Hence proposed Conclusion is right.

(7) [see p. 69]

"No one, who means to go by the train and cannot get a conveyance, and has not enough time to walk to the station, can do without running;
This party of tourists mean to go by the train and cannot get a conveyance, but they have plenty of time to walk to the station.
This party of tourists need not run."

Univ. "persons meaning to go by the train, and unable to get a conveyance"; m = having enough time to walk to the station; x = needing to run; y = these tourists.

$m'x'_0 \dagger y_1m'_0$ do not come under any of the three Figures. Hence it is necessary to return to the Method of Diagrams, as shown at p. 69.

Hence there is no Conclusion.

[Work Examples § **4**, 12–20 (p. 100); § **5**, 13–24 (p. 101, 102); § **6**, 1–6 (p. 106); § **7**, 1–3 (p. 107, 108). Also read Note (A), at p. 164.]

§ 3.

Fallacies.

Any argument which *deceives* us, by seeming to prove what it does not really prove, may be called a '**Fallacy**' (derived from the Latin verb *fallo* "I deceive"): but the particular kind, to be now discussed, consists of a Pair of Propositions, which are proposed as the Premisses of a Syllogism, but yield no Conclusion.

When each of the proposed Premisses is a Proposition in *I*, or *E*, or *A*, (the only kinds with which we are now concerned,) the Fallacy may be detected by the 'Method of Diagrams,' by simply setting them out on a Triliteral Diagram, and observing that they yield no information which can be transferred to the Biliteral Diagram.

But suppose we were working by the 'Method of *Subscripts*,' and had to deal with a Pair of proposed Premisses, which happened to be a 'Fallacy,' how could we be certain that they would not yield any Conclusion?

Our best plan is, I think, to deal with *Fallacies* in the same way as we have already dealt with *Syllogisms*: that is, to take certain forms of Pairs of Propositions, and to work them out, once for all, on the Triliteral Diagram, and ascertain that they yield *no* Conclusion; and then to record them, for future use, as *Formulæ for Fallacies,* just as we have already recorded our three *Formulæ for Syllogisms.*

Now, if we were to record the two Sets of Formulæ in the *same* shape, viz. by the Method of Subscripts, there would be considerable risk of confusing the two kinds. Hence, in order to keep them distinct, I propose to record the Formulæ for *Fallacies* in *words,* and to call them "Forms" instead of "Formulæ."

Let us now proceed to find, by the Method of Diagrams, three "Forms of Fallacies," which we will then put on record for future use. They are as follows:—

(1) Fallacy of Like Eliminands not asserted to exist.
(2) Fallacy of Unlike Eliminands with an Entity-Premiss.
(3) Fallacy of two Entity-Premisses.

These shall be discussed separately, and it will be seen that each fails to yield a Conclusion

(1) *Fallacy of Like Eliminands not asserted to exist.*

It is evident that neither of the given Propositions can be an *Entity,* since that kind asserts the *existence* of both of its Terms (see p. 20). Hence they must both be *Nullities.*

Hence the given Pair may be represented by ($xm_0 \dagger ym_0$), with or without x_1, y_1.

These, set out on Triliteral Diagrams, are

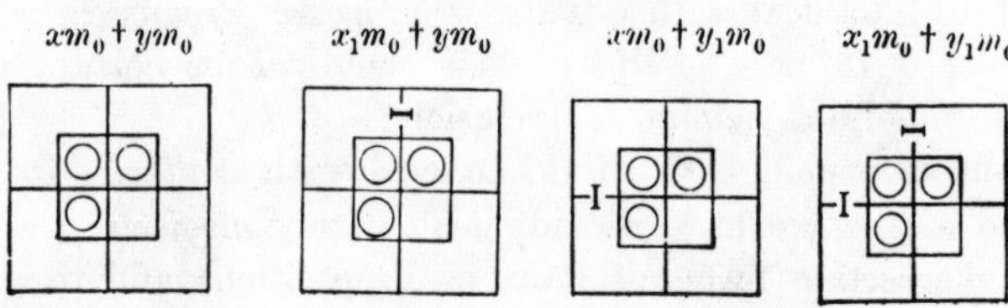

(2) *Fallacy of Unlike Eliminands with an Entity-Premiss.*

Here the given Pair may be represented by $(xm_0 \dagger ym'_1)$ with or without x_1 or m_1.

These, set out on Triliteral Diagrams, are

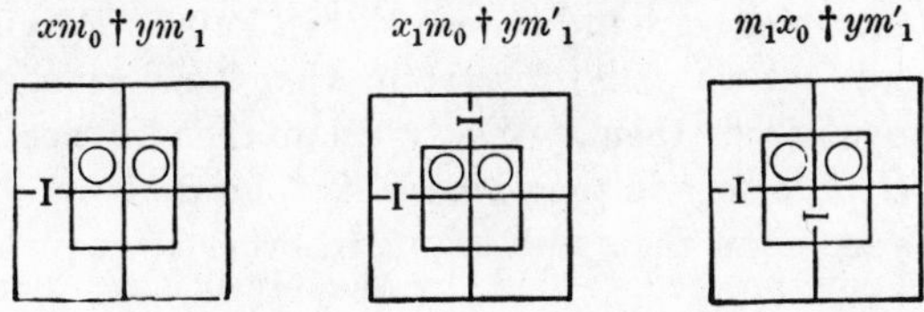

(3) *Fallacy of two Entity-Premisses.*

Here the given Pair may be represented by either $(xm_1 \dagger ym_1)$ or $(xm_1 \dagger ym'_1)$.

These, set out on Triliteral Diagrams, are

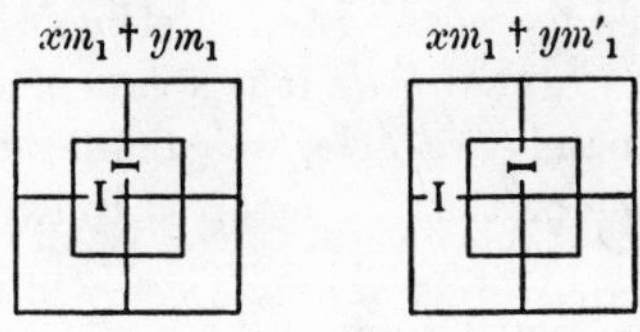

---

§ 4.

Method of proceeding with a given Pair of Propositions.

Let us suppose that we have before us a Pair of Propositions of Relation, which contain between them a Pair of codivisional Classes, and that we wish to ascertain what Conclusion, if any, is consequent from them. We translate them, if necessary, into subscript-form, and then proceed as follows :—

(1) We examine their Subscripts, in order to see whether they are

(*a*) a Pair of Nullities;
or (*b*) a Nullity and an Entity;
or (*c*) a Pair of Entities.

(2) If they are a Pair of Nullities, we examine their Eliminands, in order to see whether they are Unlike or Like.

If their Eliminands are *Unlike,* it is a case of Fig. I. We then examine their Retinends, to see whether one or both of them are asserted to *exist.* If *one* Retinend is so asserted, it is a case of Fig. I (α); if *both,* it is a case of Fig. I (β).

If their Eliminands are *Like,* we examine them, in order to see whether either of them is asserted to exist. If so, it is a case of Fig. III.; if not, it is a case of "Fallacy of Like Eliminands not asserted to exist."

(3) If they are a Nullity and an Entity, we examine their Eliminands, in order to see whether they are Like or Unlike.

If their Eliminands are *Like,* it is a case of Fig. II.; if *Unlike,* it is a case of "Fallacy of Unlike Eliminands with an Entity-Premiss."

(4) If they are a Pair of Entities, it is a case of "Fallacy of two Entity-Premisses."

[Work Examples § **4**, 1—11 (p. 100); § **5**, 1—12 (p. 101); § **6**, 7—12 (p. 106); § **7**, 7—12 (p. 108).]

BOOK VII.

SORITESES.

CHAPTER I.

INTRODUCTORY.

WHEN a Set of three or more Biliteral Propositions are such that all their Terms are Species of the same Genus, and are also so related that two of them, taken together, yield a Conclusion, which, taken with another of them, yields another Conclusion, and so on, until all have been taken, it is evident that, if the original Set were true, the last Conclusion would *also* be true.

Such a Set, with the last Conclusion tacked on, is called a '**Sorites**'; the original Set of Propositions is called its '**Premisses**'; each of the intermediate Conclusions is called a '**Partial Conclusion**' of the Sorites; the last Conclusion is called its '**Complete Conclusion,**' or, more briefly, its '**Conclusion**'; the Genus, of which all the Terms are Species, is called its "**Universe of Discourse**', or, more briefly, its '**Univ.**'; the Terms, used as Eliminands in the Syllogisms, are called its '**Eliminands**'; and the two Terms, which are *retained*, and therefore appear in the Conclusion, are called its '**Retinends**'.

[Note that each *Partial* Conclusion contains one or two *Eliminands;* but that the *Complete* Conclusion contains *Retinends* only.]

The Conclusion is said to be '**consequent**' from the Premisses; for which reason it is usual to prefix to it the word "Therefore" (or the symbol "∴").

[Note that the question, whether the Conclusion is or is not *consequent* from the Premisses, is not affected by the *actual* truth or falsity of any one of the Propositions which make up the Sorites, but depends entirely on their *relationship to one another*.

As a specimen-Sorites, let us take the following Set of 5 Propositions :—

(1) "No *a* are *b'*;
(2) All *b* are *c*;
(3) All *c* are *d*;
(4) No *e'* are *a'*;
(5) All *h* are *e'*".

Here the first and second, taken together, yield "No *a* are *c'*
This, taken along with the third, yields "No *a* are *d'*".
This, taken along with the fourth, yields "No *d'* are *e'*".
And this, taken along with the fifth, yields "All *h* are *d*".
Hence, if the original Set were true, this would *also* be true.

Hence the original Set, with this tacked on, is a *Sorites*; the original Set is its *Premisses*; the Proposition "All *h* are *d*" is its *Conclusion*; the Terms *a*, *b*, *c*, *e* are its *Eliminands*; and the Terms *d* and *h* are its *Retinends*.

Hence we may write the whole Sorites thus :—

"No *a* are *b'*;
All *b* are *c*;
All *c* are *d*;
No *e'* are *a'*;
All *h* are *e'*.
∴ All *h* are *d*".

In the above Sorites, the 3 Partial Conclusions are the Propositions "No *a* are *c'*", "No *a* are *d'*", "No *d'* are *e'*"; but, if the Premisses were arranged in other ways, other Partial Conclusions might be obtained. Thus, the order 41523 yields the Partial Conclusions "No *c'* are *b'*", "All *h* are *b*", "All *h* are *c*". There are altogether *nine* Partial Conclusions to this Sorites, which the Reader will find it an interesting task to make out for himself.]

CHAPTER II.

PROBLEMS IN SORITESES.

---

§ 1.

Introductory.

THE Problems we shall have to solve are of the following form :—

"Given three or more Propositions of Relation, which are proposed as Premisses : to ascertain what Conclusion, if any, is consequent from them."

We will limit ourselves, at present, to Problems which can be worked by the Formulæ of Fig. I. (See p. 75.) Those, that require *other* Formulæ, are rather too hard for beginners.

Such Problems may be solved by either of two Methods, viz.

(1) The Method of Separate Syllogisms ;

(2) The Method of Underscoring.

These shall be discussed separately.

---

§ 2.

Solution by Method of Separate Syllogisms.

The Rules, for doing this, are as follows:—

(1) Name the 'Universe of Discourse'.

(2) Construct a Dictionary, making a, b, c, &c. represent the Terms.

(3) Put the Proposed Premisses into subscript form.

(4) Select two which, containing between them a pair of codivisional Classes, can be used as the Premisses of a Syllogism.

(5) Find their Conclusion by Formula.

(6) Find a third Premiss which, along with this Conclusion, can be used as the Premisses of a second Syllogism.

(7) Find a second Conclusion by Formula.

(8) Proceed thus, until all the proposed Premisses have been used.

(9) Put the last Conclusion, which is the Complete Conclusion of the Sorites, into concrete form.

[As an example of this process, let us take, as the proposed Set of Premisses,

(1) "All the policemen on this beat sup with our cook;
(2) No man with long hair can fail to be a poet;
(3) Amos Judd has never been in prison;
(4) Our cook's 'cousins' all love cold mutton;
(5) None but policemen on this beat are poets;
(6) None but her 'cousins' ever sup with our cook;
(7) Men with short hair have all been in prison."

Univ. "men"; a = Amos Judd; b = cousins of our cook;
c = having been in prison; d = long-haired;
e = loving cold mutton; h = poets;
k = policemen on this beat; l = supping with our cook

We now have to put the proposed Premisses into *subscript* form. Let us begin by putting them into *abstract* form. The result is

(1) "All k are l;
(2) No d are h';
(3) All a are c';
(4) All b are c;
(5) No k' are h;
(6) No b' are l;
(7) All d' are c'

And it is now easy to put them into *subscript* form, as follows:—

(1) $k_1 l'_0$
(2) dh'_0
(3) $a_1 c_0$
(4) $b_1 c'_0$
(5) $k'h_0$
(6) $b'l_0$
(7) $d'_1 c'_0$

We now have to find a pair of Premisses which will yield a Conclusion. Let us begin with No. (1), and look down the list, till we come to one which we can take along with it, so as to form Premisses belonging to Fig. I. We find that No. (5) will do, since we can take k as our Eliminand. So our first syllogism is.

(1) $k_1 l'_0$
(5) $k'h_0$
$\therefore l'h_0$ . . . (8)

We must now begin again with $l'h_0$, and find a Premiss to go along with it. We find that No. (2) will do, h being our Eliminand. So our next Syllogism is

(8) $l'h_0$
(2) dh'_0
$\therefore l'd_0$ . . . (9)

We have now used up Nos. (1), (5), and (2), and must search among the others for a partner for $l'd_0$. We find that No. (6) will do. So we write

(9) $l'd_0$
(6) $b'l_0$
$\therefore db'_0$ . . . (10)

Now what can we take along with db'_0? No. (4) will do.

(10) db'_0
(4) $b_1 c'_0$
$\therefore dc'_0$ . . . (11)

Along with *this* we may take No. (7).

(11) dc'_0
(7) $d'_1c'_0$
$\therefore e'c'_0$ . . . (12)

And along with *this* we may take No. (3).

(12) $c'c'_0$
(3) a_1c_0
$\therefore a_1c'_0$

This Complete Conclusion, translated into *abstract* form, is

"All a are c";

and this, translated into *concrete* form, is

"Amos Judd loves cold mutton."

In actually *working* this Problem, the above explanations would, of course, be omitted, and all, that would appear on paper, would be as follows:—

(1) $k_1l'_0$
(2) dh'_0
(3) a_1c_0
(4) $b_1c'_0$
(5) $k'h_0$
(6) $b'l_0$
(7) $d'_1c'_0$

(1) $k_1l'_0$	(8) $l'h_0$	(9) $l'd_0$
(5) $k'h_0$	(2) dh'_0	(6) $b'l_0$
$\therefore l'h_0$ . . (8)	$\therefore l'd_0$ . . (9)	$\therefore db'_0$. (10)
(10) db'_0	(11) dc'_0	(12) $c'c'_0$
(4) $b_1c'_0$	(7) $d'_1c'_0$	(3) a_1c_0
$\therefore dc'_0$ . . (11)	$\therefore c'c'_0$ . . (12)	$\therefore a_1c'_0$

Note that, in working a Sorites by this Process, we may begin with *any* Premiss we choose.]

§ 3.

Solution by Method of Underscoring.

Consider the Pair of Premisses

$$xm_0 \dagger ym'_0$$

which yield the Conclusion xy_0

We see that, in order to get this Conclusion, we must eliminate m and m', and write x and y together in one expression.

Now, if we agree to *mark* m and m' as eliminated, and to read the two expressions together, as if they were written in one, the two Premisses will then exactly represent the *Conclusion*, and we need not write it out separately.

Let us agree to mark the eliminated letters by *underscoring* them, putting a *single* score under the *first*, and a *double* one under the *second*.

The two Premisses now become

$$x\underline{m}_0 \dagger y\underline{\underline{m}}'_0$$

which we read as "xy_0".

In copying out the Premisses for underscoring, it will be convenient to *omit all subscripts*. As to the "0's" we may always *suppose* them written, and, as to the "1"s, we are not concerned to know *which* Terms are asserted to *exist*, except those which appear in the *Complete* Conclusion; and for *them* it will be easy enough to refer to the original list.

[I will now go through the process of solving, by this method, the example worked in § 2.

The Data are

$$\overset{1}{k_1 l'_0} \dagger \overset{2}{dh'_0} \dagger \overset{3}{a_1 c_0} \dagger \overset{4}{b_1 e'_0} \dagger \overset{5}{k'h_0} \dagger \overset{6}{b'l_0} \dagger \overset{7}{d'_1 c'_0}$$

The Reader should take a piece of paper, and write out this solution for himself. The first line will consist of the above Data ; the second must be composed, bit by bit, according to the following directions.

We begin by writing down the first Premiss, with its numeral over it, but omitting the subscripts.

We have now to find a Premiss which can be combined with this, *i.e.*, a Premiss containing either k' or l. The first we find is No. 5 ; and this we tack on, with a †.

To get the *Conclusion* from these, k and k' must be eliminated, and what remains must be taken as one expression. So we *underscore* them, putting a *single* score under k, and a *double* one under k'. The result we read as $l'h$.

We must now find a Premiss containing either l or h'. Looking along the row, we fix on No. 2, and tack it on.

Now these 3 Nullities are really equivalent to ($l'h \dagger dh'$), in which h and h' must be eliminated, and what remains taken as one expression. So we *underscore* them. The result reads as $l'd$.

We now want a Premiss containing l or d'. No. 6 will do.

These 4 Nullities are really equivalent to ($l'd \dagger b'l$). So we underscore l' and l. The result reads as db'.

We now want a Premiss containing d' or b. No. 4 will do.

Here we underscore b' and b. The result reads as dc'.

We now want a Premiss containing d' or c. No. 7 will do.

Here we underscore d and d'. The result reads as $c'c'$.

We now want a Premiss containing c or c. No. 3 will do—in fact *must* do, as it is the only one left.

Here we underscore c' and c ; and, as the whole thing now reads as $c'a$, we may tack on $c'a_0$ as the *Conclusion*, with a $\Vdash$.

We now look along the row of Data, to see whether c' or a has been given as *existent*. We find that a has been so given in No. 3. So we add this fact to the Conclusion, which now stands as $\Vdash c'a_0 \dagger a_1$, *i.e.* $\Vdash a_1 c'_0$; i.e. "All a are c."

If the Reader has faithfully obeyed the above directions, his written solution will now stand as follows :—

$$\overset{1}{k_1 l'_0} \dagger \overset{2}{dh'_0} \dagger \overset{3}{a_1 c_0} \dagger \overset{4}{b_1 c'_0} \dagger \overset{5}{k'h_0} \dagger \overset{6}{b'l_0} \dagger \overset{7}{d'_1 c'_0}$$

$$\overset{1}{\underline{k}\,\underline{l'}} \dagger \overset{5}{\underline{\underline{k'}}\,\underline{h}} \dagger \overset{2}{\underline{d}\,\underline{\underline{h'}}} \dagger \overset{6}{\underline{b'}\,\underline{\underline{l}}} \dagger \overset{4}{\underline{\underline{b}}\,c'} \dagger \overset{7}{\underline{\underline{d'}}\,\underline{c'}} \dagger \overset{3}{a\,\underline{\underline{c}}} \Vdash c'a_0 \dagger a_1 \text{ i.e. } \Vdash a_1 c'_0$$

i.e. "All a are c."

The Reader should now take a second piece of paper, and copy the Data only, and try to work out the solution for himself, beginning with some other Premiss.

If he fails to bring out the Conclusion $a_1 c'_0$, I would advise him to take a third piece of paper, and *begin again!*]

I will now work out, in its briefest form, a Sorites of 5 Premisses, to serve as a model for the Reader to imitate in working examples.

(1) "I greatly value everything that John gives me;
(2) Nothing but this bone will satisfy my dog;
(3) I take particular care of everything that I greatly value;
(4) This bone was a present from John;
(5) The things, of which I take particular care, are things I do *not* give to my dog".

Univ. "things"; a = given by John to me; b = given by me to my dog; c = greatly valued by me; d = satisfactory to my dog"; e = taken particular care of by me; h = this bone.

$$\overset{1}{a_1 c'_0} \dagger \overset{2}{h'd_0} \dagger \overset{3}{c_1 e'_0} \dagger \overset{4}{h_1 a'_0} \dagger \overset{5}{e_1 b_0}$$

$$\overset{1}{\underline{a}\,\underline{c}'} \dagger \overset{3}{\underline{\underline{c}}\,e'} \dagger \overset{4}{\underline{h}\,\underline{\underline{a}}'} \dagger \overset{2}{\underline{\underline{h}}'d} \dagger \overset{5}{\underline{\underline{e}}\,b} \Vdash db_0$$

i.e. "Nothing, that I give my dog, satisfies him," or, "My dog is not satisfied with *anything* that I give him!"

[Note that, in working a Sorites by this process, we may begin with *any* Premiss we choose. For instance, we might begin with No. 5, and the result would then be

$$\overset{5}{\underline{e}b} \dagger \overset{3}{\underline{c}\,\underline{\underline{e}}'} \dagger \overset{1}{\underline{a}\,\underline{\underline{c}}'} \dagger \overset{4}{\underline{h}\,\underline{\underline{a}}'} \dagger \overset{2}{\underline{\underline{h}}'d} \Vdash bd_0]$$

[Work Examples § **4**, 25—30 (p. 100); § **5**, 25—30 (p. 102); § **6**, 13—15 (p. 106); § **7**, 13—15 (p. 108); § **8**, 1—4, 13, 14, 19, 24 (p. 110, 111); § **9**, 1—4, 26, 27, 40, 48 (p. 112, 116, 119, 121).]

The Reader, who has successfully grappled with all the Examples hitherto set, and who thirsts, like Alexander the Great, for "more worlds to conquer," may employ his spare energies on the following 17 Examination-Papers. He is recommended not to attempt more than *one* Paper on any one day. The answers to the questions about words and phrases may be found by referring to the Index at p. 197.

I. § **4**, 31 (p. 100); § **5**, 31—34 (p. 102); § **6**, 16, 17 (p. 106); § **7**, 16 (p. 108); § **8**, 5, 6 (p. 110); § **9**, 5, 22, 42 (pp. 112, 115, 119). What is "Classification'? And what is a 'Class'?

II. § **4**, 32 (p. 100); § **5**, 35—38 (pp. 102, 103); § **6**, 18 (p. 107) § **7**, 17, 18 (p. 108); § **8**, 7, 8 (p. 110); § **9**, 6, 23, 43 (pp. 112, 115, 119). What are 'Genus', 'Species', and 'Differentia'

III. § **4**, 33 (p. 100); § **5**, 39—42 (p. 103); § **6**, 19, 20 (p. 107); § **7**, 19 (p. 109); § **8**, 9, 10 (p. 111); § **9**, 7, 24, 44 (pp. 113, 116, 120). What are 'Real' and 'Imaginary' Classes?

IV. § **4**, 34 (p. 100); § **5**, 43—46 (p. 103); § **6**, 21 (p. 107); § **7**, 20, 21 (p. 109); § **8**, 11, 12 (p. 111); § **9**, 8, 25, 45 (pp. 113, 116, 120). What is 'Division'? When are Classes said to be 'Codivisional'?

V. § **4**, 35 (p. 100); § **5**, 47—50 (p. 103); § **6**, 22, 23 (p. 107); § **7**, 22 (p. 109); § **8**, 15, 16 (p. 111); § **9**, 9, 28, 46 (pp. 113, 116, 120). What is 'Dichotomy'? What arbitrary rule does sometimes require?

VI. § **4**, 36 (p. 100); § **5**, 51—54 (p. 103); § **6**, 24 (p. 107); § **7**, 23, 24 (p. 109); § **8**, 17 (p. 111); § **9**, 10, 29, 47 (pp. 113, 117, 120). What is a 'Definition'?

VII. § **4**, 37 (p. 100); § **5**, 55—58 (pp. 103, 104); § **6**, 25, 26 (p. 107); § **7**, 25 (p. 109); § **8**, 18 (p. 111); § **9**, 11, 30, 49 (pp. 113, 117, 121). What are the 'Subject' and the 'Predicate' of a Proposition? What is its 'Normal' form?

VIII. § **4**, 38 (p. 100); § **5**, 59—62 (p. 104); § **6**, 27 (p. 107); § **7**, 26, 27 (p. 109); § **8**, 20 (p. 111); § **9**, 12, 31, 50 (pp. 113, 117, 121). What is a Proposition 'in *I*'? 'In *E*'? And 'in *A*'?

IX. § **4**, 39 (p. 100); § **5**, 63—66 (p. 104); § **6**, 28, 29 (p. 107); § **7**, 28 (p. 109); § **8**, 21 (p. 111); § **9**, 13, 32, 51 (pp. 114, 117, 121). What is the 'Normal' form of a Proposition of Existence?

X. § **4**, 40 (p. 100); § **5**, 67—70 (p. 104); § **6**, 30 (p. 107); § **7**, 29, 30 (p. 109); § **8**, 22 (p. 111); § **9**, 14, 33, 52 (pp. 114, 117, 122). What is the 'Universe of Discourse'?

XI. § **4**, 41 (p. 100); § **5**, 71—74 (p. 104); § **6**, 31, 32 (p. 107); § **7**, 31 (p. 109); § **8**, 23 (p. 111); § **9**, 15, 34, 53 (pp. 114, 118, 122). What is implied, in a Proposition of Relation, as to the Reality of its Terms?

XII. § **4**, 42 (p. 100); § **5**, 75—78 (p. 105); § **6**, 33 (p. 107); § **7**, 32, 33 (pp. 109, 110); § **8**, 25 (p. 111); § **9**, 16, 35, 54 (pp. 114, 118, 122). Explain the phrase "sitting on the fence".

XIII. § **5**, 79—83 (p. 105); § **6**, 34, 35 (p. 107); § **7**, 34 (p. 110); § **8**, 26 (p. 111); § **9**, 17, 36, 55 (pp. 114, 118, 122). What are 'Converse' Propositions?

XIV. § **5**, 84—88 (p. 105); § **6**, 36 (p. 107); § **7**, 35, 36 (p. 110); § **8**, 27 (p. 111); § **9**, 18, 37, 56 (pp. 114, 118, 123). What are 'Concrete' and 'Abstract' Propositions?

XV. § **5**, 89—93 (p. 105); § **6**, 37, 38 (p. 107); § **7**, 37 (p. 110); § **8**, 28 (p. 111); § **9**, 19, 38, 57 (pp. 115, 118, 123). What is a 'Syllogism'? And what are its 'Premisses' and its 'Conclusion'?

XVI. § **5**, 94—97 (p. 106); § **6**, 39 (p. 107); § **7**, 38, 39 (p. 110); § **8**, 29 (p. 111); § **9**, 20, 39, 58 (pp. 115, 119, 123). What is a 'Sorites'? And what are its 'Premisses', its 'Partial Conclusions', and its 'Complete Conclusion'?

XVII. § **5**, 98—101 (p. 106); § **6**, 40 (p. 107); § **7**, 40 (p. 110); § **8**, 30 (p. 111); § **9**, 21, 41, 59, 60 (pp. 115, 119, 124). What are the 'Universe of Discourse', the 'Eliminands', and the 'Retinends', of a Syllogism? And of a Sorites?

BOOK VIII.

EXAMPLES, ANSWERS, AND SOLUTIONS.

[N.B. The numbers at the foot of each page indicate the pages where the corresponding matter may be found.]

CHAPTER I.

EXAMPLES.

---

§ 1.

Propositions of Relation, to be reduced to normal form.

---

1. I have been out for a walk.
2. I am feeling better.
3. No one has read the letter but John.
4. Neither you nor I are old.
5. No fat creatures run well.
6. None but the brave deserve the fair.
7. No one looks poetical unless he is pale.
8. Some judges lose their tempers.
9. I never neglect important business.
10. What is difficult needs attention.
11. What is unwholesome should be avoided.
12. All the laws passed last week relate to excise.
13. Logic puzzles me.
14. There are no Jews in the house.
15. Some dishes are unwholesome if not well-cooked.
16. Unexciting books make one drowsy.
17. When a man knows what he's about, he can detect a sharper.
18. You and I know what we're about.
19. Some bald people wear wigs.
20. Those who are fully occupied never talk about their grievances.
21. No riddles interest me if they can be solved.

Ans. 125; Sol. 134—136.]

§ 2.

Pairs of Abstract Propositions, one in terms of* x *and* m, *and the other in terms of* y *and* m, *to be represented on the same Triliteral Diagram.

1. No *x* are *m*;
   No *m′* are y.
2. No *x′* are *m′*;
   All *m′* are *y*.
3. Some *x′* are *m*;
   No *m* are *y*.
4. All *m* are *x*;
   All *m′* are *y′*.
5. All *m′* are *x*;
   All *m′* are *y′*.
6. All *x′* are *m′*;
   No *y′* are *m*.
7. All *x* are *m*;
   All *y′* are *m′*.
8. Some *m′* are *x′*;
   No *m* are *y*.
9. All *m* are *x′*;
   No *m* are *y*.
10. No *m* are *x′*;
    No *y* are *m′*.
11. No *x′* are *m′*;
    No *m* are *y*.
12. Some *x* are *m*;
    All *y′* are *m*.
13. All *x′* are *m*;
    All *m* are *y*.
14. Some *x* are *m′*;
    All *m* are *y*.
15. No *m′* are *x′*;
    All *y* are *m*.
16. All *x* are *m′*;
    No *y* are *m*.
17. Some *m′* are *x*;
    No *m′* are *y′*.
18. All *x* are *m′*;
    Some *m′* are *y′*.
19. All *m* are *x*;
    Some *m* are *y′*.
20. No *x′* are *m*;
    Some *y* are *m*.
21. Some *x′* are *m′*;
    All *y′* are *m*.
22. No *m* are *x*;
    Some *m* are *y*.
23. No *m′* are *x*;
    All *y* are *m′*.
24. All *m* are *x*;
    No *y′* are *m′*.
25. Some *m* are *x*;
    No *y′* are *m*.
26. All *m′* are *x′*;
    Some *y* are *m′*.
27. Some *m* are *x′*;
    No *y′* are *m′*.
28. No *x* are *m′*;
    All *m* are *y′*.
29. No *x′* are *m*;
    No *m* are *y′*.
30. No *x* are *m*;
    Some *y′* are *m′*.
31. Some *m′* are *x*;
    All *y′* are *m*.
32. All *x* are *m′*;
    All *y* are *m*.

[Ans. 126, 127.

§ 3.

Marked Triliteral Diagrams, to be interpreted in terms of x *and* y.

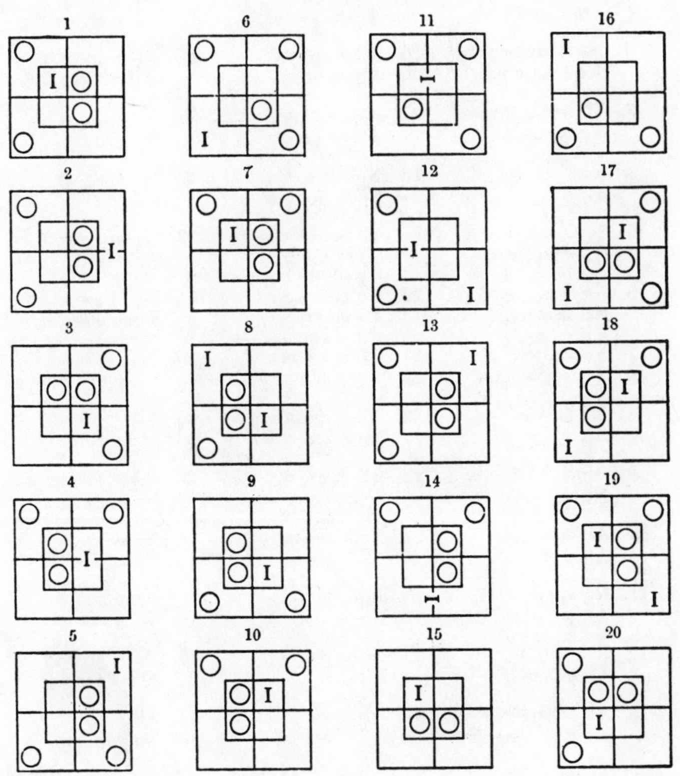

Ans. 127.]

§ 4.

Pairs of Abstract Propositions, proposed as Premisses: Conclusions to be found.

---

1 No m are x';
All m' are y.

2. No m' are x;
Some m' are y'.

3. All m' are x;
All m' are y'.

4. No x' are m';
All y' are m.

5. Some m are x';
No y are m.

6. No x' are m;
No m are y.

7. No m are x';
Some y' are m.

8. All m' are x';
No m' are y.

9. Some x' are m';
No m are y'.

10. All x are m;
All y' are m'.

11. No m are x;
All y' are m'.

12. No x are m;
All y are m.

13. All m' are x;
No y are m.

14. All m are x;
All m' are y.

15. No x are m;
No m' are y.

16. All x are m';
All y are m.

17. No x are m;
All m' are y.

18. No x are m';
No m are y.

19. All m are x;
All m are y'.

20. No m are x;
All m' are y.

21. All x are m;
Some m' are y.

22. Some x are m;
All y are m.

23. All m are x;
Some y are m.

24. No x are m;
All y are m.

25. Some m are x';
No m are y'.

26. No m are x';
All y are m.

27. All x are m';
All y' are m.

28. All m are x';
Some m are y.

29. No m are x;
All y are m'.

30. All x are m;
Some y are m.

31. All x are m;
All y are m.

32. No x are m';
All m are y.

33. No m are x;
No m are y.

34. No m are x;
Some y are m.

35. No m are x;
All y are m.

36. All m are x';
Some y are m.

37. All m are x;
No y are m.

38. No m are x;
No m' are y.

39. Some m are x';
No m are y.

40. No x' are m;
All y' are m.

41. All x are m';
No y are m'.

42. No m' are x;
No y are m.

[Ans. 127, 128; Sol. (1 to 12) 136—138; (1 to 42) 146, 147.

§ 5

Pairs of Concrete Propositions, proposed as Premisses: Conclusions to be found.

---

1. I have been out for a walk;
   I am feeling better.

2. No one has read the letter but John;
   No one, who has *not* read it, knows what it is about.

3. Those who are not old like walking;
   You and I are young.

4. Your course is always honest;
   Your course is always the best policy.

5. No fat creatures run well;
   Some greyhounds run well.

6. Some, who deserve the fair, get their deserts;
   None but the brave deserve the fair.

7. Some Jews are rich;
   All Esquimaux are Gentiles.

8. Sugar-plums are sweet;
   Some sweet things are liked by children.

9. John is in the house;
   Everybody in the house is ill.

10. Umbrellas are useful on a journey;
    What is useless on a journey should be left behind.

11. Audible music causes vibration in the air;
    Inaudible music is not worth paying for.

12. Some holidays are rainy;
    Rainy days are tiresome.

13. No Frenchmen like plumpudding;
    All Englishmen like plumpudding.

14. No portrait of a lady, that makes her simper or scowl, is satisfactory;
    No photograph of a lady ever fails to make her simper or scowl.

15. All pale people are phlegmatic;
    No one looks poetical unless he is pale.

16. No old misers are cheerful;
    Some old misers are thin.

17. No one, who exercises self-control, fails to keep his temper;
    Some judges lose their tempers.

Ans. 128; Sol. (1—12) 138—141; (13 &c) 147.]

18. All pigs are fat;
Nothing that is fed on barley-water is fat.

19. All rabbits, that are not greedy, are black;
No old rabbits are free from greediness.

20. Some pictures are not first attempts;
No first attempts are really good.

21. I never neglect important business;
Your business is unimportant.

22. Some lessons are difficult;
What is difficult needs attention.

23. All clever people are popular;
All obliging people are popular.

24. Thoughtless people do mischief;
No thoughtful person forgets a promise.

25. Pigs cannot fly;
Pigs are greedy.

26. All soldiers march well:
Some babies are not soldiers.

27. No bride-cakes are wholesome;
What is unwholesome should be avoided.

28. John is industrious;
No industrious people are unhappy.

29. No philosophers are conceited;
Some conceited persons are not gamblers.

30. Some excise laws are unjust;
All the laws passed last week relate to excise

31. No military men write poetry;
None of my lodgers are civilians.

32. No medicine is nice;
Senna is a medicine.

33. Some circulars are not read with pleasure;
No begging-letters are read with pleasure.

34. All Britons are brave;
No sailors are cowards.

35. Nothing intelligible ever puzzles *me;*
Logic puzzles me.

36. Some pigs are wild;
All pigs are fat.

[Ans. 128, 129; Sol. (18—24) 148.

37. All wasps are unfriendly;
All unfriendly creatures are unwelcome.

38 No old rabbits are greedy;
All black rabbits are greedy.

39. Some eggs are hard-boiled;
No eggs are uncrackable.

40. No antelope is ungraceful;
Graceful creatures delight the eye.

41. All well-fed canaries sing loud;
No canary is melancholy if it sings loud.

42. Some poetry is original;
No original work is producible at will.

43. No country, that has been explored, is infested by dragons;
Unexplored countries are fascinating.

44. No coals are white;
No niggers are white.

45. No bridges are made of sugar;
Some bridges are picturesque.

46. No children are patient;
No impatient person can sit still.

47. No quadrupeds can whistle;
Some cats are quadrupeds.

48. Bores are terrible;
You are a bore.

49. Some oysters are silent;
No silent creatures are amusing.

50. There are no Jews in the house;
No Gentiles have beards a yard long.

51. Canaries, that do not sing loud, are unhappy;
No well-fed canaries fail to sing loud.

52. All my sisters have colds;
No one can sing who has a cold.

53. All that is made of gold is precious;
Some caskets are precious.

54. Some buns are rich;
All buns are nice.

55. All my cousins are unjust;
All judges are just.

Ans. 129.]

56. Pain is wearisome ;
No pain is eagerly wished for.

57. All medicine is nasty ;
Senna is a medicine.

58. Some unkind remarks are annoying ;
No critical remarks are kind.

59. No tall men have woolly hair ;
Niggers have woolly hair.

60. All philosophers are logical ;
An illogical man is always obstinate.

61. John is industrious ;
All industrious people are happy.

62. These dishes are all well-cooked ;
Some dishes are unwholesome if not well-cooked.

63. No exciting books suit feverish patients ;
Unexciting books make one drowsy.

64. No pigs can fly ;
All pigs are greedy.

65. When a man knows what he's about, he can detect a sharper ;
You and I know what we're about,

66. Some dreams are terrible ;
No lambs are terrible.

67. No bald creature needs a hairbrush ;
No lizards have hair.

68. All battles are noisy ;
What makes no noise may escape notice.

69. All my cousins are unjust ;
No judges are unjust.

70. All eggs can be cracked ;
Some eggs are hard-boiled.

71. Prejudiced persons are untrustworthy ;
Some unprejudiced persons are disliked.

72. No dictatorial person is popular ;
She is dictatorial.

73. Some bald people wear wigs ;
All your children have hair.

74. No lobsters are unreasonable ;
No reasonable creatures expect impossibilities.

[Ans. 129, 130.

75. No nightmare is pleasant;
Unpleasant experiences are not eagerly desired.

76. No plumcakes are wholesome;
Some wholesome things are nice.

77. Nothing that is nice need be shunned;
Some kinds of jam are nice.

78. All ducks waddle;
Nothing that waddles is graceful.

79. Sandwiches are satisfying;
Nothing in this dish is unsatisfying.

80. No rich man begs in the street;
Those who are not rich should keep accounts.

81. Spiders spin webs;
Some creatures, that do not spin webs, are savage

82. Some of these shops are not crowded;
No crowded shops are comfortable.

83. Prudent travelers carry plenty of small change;
Imprudent travelers lose their luggage.

84. Some geraniums are red;
All these flowers are red.

85. None of my cousins are just;
All judges are just.

86. No Jews are mad;
All my lodgers are Jews.

87. Busy folk are not always talking about their grievances;
Discontented folk are always talking about their grievances.

88. None of my cousins are just;
No judges are unjust.

89. All teetotalers like sugar;
No nightingale drinks wine.

90. No riddles interest me if they can be solved;
All these riddles are insoluble.

91. All clear explanations are satisfactory;
Some excuses are unsatisfactory.

92. All elderly ladies are talkative;
All good-tempered ladies are talkative.

93. No kind deed is unlawful;
What is lawful may be done without scruple.

Ans. 130.]

94 No babies are studious;
No babies are good violinists.

95. All shillings are round;
All these coins are round.

96. No honest men cheat;
No dishonest men are trustworthy.

97. None of my boys are clever;
None of my girls are greedy.

98. All jokes are meant to amuse;
No Act of Parliament is a joke.

99. No eventful tour is ever forgotten;
Uneventful tours are not worth writing a book about.

100. All my boys are disobedient;
All my girls are discontented.

101. No unexpected pleasure annoys me;
Your visit is an unexpected pleasure.

---

§ 6.

Trios of Abstract Propositions, proposed as Syllogisms: to be examined.

1. Some x are m; No m are y'. Some x are y.
2. All x are m; No y are m'. No y are x'.
3. Some x are m'; All y' are m. Some x are y.
4. All x are m; No y are m. All x are y'.
5. Some m' are x'; No m' are y. Some x' are y'.
6. No x' are m; All y are m'. All y are x'.
7. Some m' are x'; All y' are m'. Some x' are y'.
8. No m' are x'; All y' are m'. All y' are x.
9. Some m are x'; No m are y. Some x' are y'.
10. All m' are x'; All m' are y. Some y are x'.
11. All x are m'; Some y are m. Some y are x'.
12. No x are m; No m' are y'. No x are y'.
13. No x are m; All y' are m. All y' are x'.
14. All m' are x'; All m' are y. Some y are x'.
15. Some m are x'; All y are m'. Some x' are y'.
16. No x' are m; All y' are m'. Some y' are x.
17. No m' are x; All m' are y'. Some x' are y'.

[Ans. 130, 131; Sol. (1—10) 141—143.

18. No x' are m ;	Some m are y.	Some x are y.
19. Some m are x ;	All m are y.	Some y are x'.
20. No x' are m' ;	Some m' are y'.	Some x are y'.
21. No m are x ;	All m are y'.	Some x' are y'.
22. All x' are m ;	Some y are m'.	All x' are y'.
23. All m are x ;	No m' are y'.	No x' are y'.
24. All x are m' ;	All m' are y.	All x are y.
25. No x are m' ;	All m are y.	No x are y'.
26. All m are x' ;	All y are m.	All y are x'.
27. All x are m ;	No m are y'.	All x are y.
28. All x are m ;	No y' are m'.	All x are y.
29. No x' are m ;	No m' are y'.	No x' are y'.
30. All x are m ;	All m are y'.	All x are y'.
31. All x' are m' ;	No y' are m'.	All x' are y.
32. No x are m ;	No y' are m'.	No x are y'.
33. All m are x' ;	All y' are m.	All y' are x'.
34. All x are m' ;	Some y are m'.	Some y are x.
35. Some x are m ;	All m are y.	Some x are y.
36. All m are x' ;	All y are m.	All y are x'.
37. No m are x' ;	All m are y'.	Some x are y'.
38. No x are m ;	No m are y'.	No x are y'.
39. No m are x ;	Some m are y'.	Some x' are y'.
40. No m are x' ;	Some y are m.	Some x are y.

§ 7.

Trios of Concrete Propositions, proposed as Syllogisms: to be examined.

1. No doctors are enthusiastic ;
   You are enthusiastic.
       You are not a doctor.

2. Dictionaries are useful ;
   Useful books are valuable.
       Dictionaries are valuable.

3. No misers are unselfish.
   None but misers save egg-shells.
       No unselfish people save egg-shells.

4. Some epicures are ungenerous ;
   All my uncles are generous.
       My uncles are not epicures.

Ans. 131 ; Sol. (§7) 144, 145, 150.]

5. Gold is heavy;
Nothing but gold will silence him
 Nothing light will silence him

6. Some healthy people are fat;
No unhealthy people are strong.
 Some fat people are not strong.

7. "I saw it in a newspaper."
"All newspapers tell lies."
 It was a lie.

8. Some cravats are not artistic;
I admire anything artistic.
 There are some cravats that I do not admire.

9. His songs never last an hour;
A song, that lasts an hour, is tedious.
 His songs are never tedious.

10. Some candles give very little light;
Candles are *meant* to give light.
 Some things, that are meant to give light, give very little.

11. All, who are anxious to learn, work hard;
Some of these boys work hard.
 Some of these boys are anxious to learn.

12. All lions are fierce;
Some lions do not drink coffee.
 Some creatures that drink coffee are not fierce.

13. No misers are generous;
Some old men are ungenerous.
 Some old men are misers.

14. No fossil can be crossed in love;
An oyster may be crossed in love.
 Oysters are not fossils.

15. All uneducated people are shallow;
Students are all educated.
 No students are shallow.

16. All young lambs jump;
No young animals are healthy, unless they jump.
 All young lambs are healthy.

17. Ill-managed business is unprofitable;
Railways are never ill-managed.
 All railways are profitable.

18. No Professors are ignorant;
All ignorant people are vain.
 No professors are vain.

[Ans. 131; Sol. 145, 150—152.

19. A prudent man shuns hyænas;
No banker is imprudent.
No banker fails to shun hyænas.

20. All wasps are unfriendly;
No puppies are unfriendly.
Puppies are not wasps

21. No Jews are honest;
Some Gentiles are rich.
Some rich people are dishonest.

22. No idlers win fame;
Some painters are not idle.
Some painters win fame.

23. No monkeys are soldiers;
All monkeys are mischievous.
Some mischievous creatures are not soldiers.

24. All these bonbons are chocolate-creams;
All these bonbons are delicious.
Chocolate-creams are delicious.

25. No muffins are wholesome;
All buns are unwholesome.
Buns are not muffins.

26. Some unauthorised reports are false;
All authorised reports are trustworthy.
Some false reports are not trustworthy.

27. Some pillows are soft;
No pokers are soft.
Some pokers are not pillows.

28. Improbable stories are not easily believed;
None of his stories are probable.
None of his stories are easily believed.

29. No thieves are honest;
Some dishonest people are found out.
Some thieves are found out.

30. No muffins are wholesome;
All puffy food is unwholesome.
All muffins are puffy.

31. No birds, except peacocks, are proud of their tails;
Some birds, that are proud of their tails, cannot sing.
Some peacocks cannot sing.

32. Warmth relieves pain;
Nothing, that does not relieve pain, is useful in toothache.
Warmth is useful in toothache.

Ans. 131; Sol. 152—154.]

33. No bankrupts are rich;
Some merchants are not bankrupts.
Some merchants are rich.

34. Bores are dreaded;
No bore is ever begged to prolong his visit.
No one, who is dreaded, is ever begged to prolong his visit.

35. All wise men walk on their feet;
All unwise men walk on their hands.
No man walks on both.

36. No wheelbarrows are comfortable;
No uncomfortable vehicles are popular.
No wheelbarrows are popular.

37. No frogs are poetical;
Some ducks are unpoetical.
Some ducks are not frogs.

38. No emperors are dentists;
All dentists are dreaded by children.
No emperors are dreaded by children.

39. Sugar is sweet;
Salt is not sweet.
Salt is not sugar.

40. Every eagle can fly;
Some pigs cannot fly.
Some pigs are not eagles.

---

§ 8.

Sets of Abstract Propositions, proposed as Premisses for Soriteses: Conclusions to be found.

[N.B. At the end of this Section instructions are given for varying these Examples.]

1.	3.	5.	7.
1. No *c* are *d*;	1. No *b* are *a*;	1. All *b'* are *a'*;	1. No *d* are *b'*;
2. All *a* are *d*;	2. No *c* are *d'*;	2. No *b* are *c*;	2. All *b* are *a*;
3. All *b* are *c*.	3. All *d* are *b*.	3. No *a'* are *d*.	3. No *c* are *d'*.

2.	4.	6.	8.
1. All *d* are *b*;	1. No *b* are *c*;	1. All *a* are *b'*;	1. No *b'* are *d*;
2. No *a* are *c'*;	2. All *a* are *b*;	2. No *b'* are *c*;	2. No *a'* are *b*;
3. No *b* are *c*.	3. No *c'* are *d*.	3. All *d* are *a*.	3. All *c* are *d*.

[Ans. 131, 132; Sol. 154—156.

9.

1. All *b'* are *a* ;
2. No *a* are *d* ;
3. All *b* are *c*.

10.

1. No *c* are *d* ;
2. All *b* are *c* ;
3. No *a* are *d'*.

11.

1. No *b* are *c* ;
2. All *d* are *a* ;
3. All *c'* are *a'*.

12.

1. No *e* are *b'* ;
2. All *e'* are *d'*;
3. All *b* are *a*.

13.

1. All *d* are *c* ;
2. All *e* are *a* ;
3. No *b* are *d'*;
4. All *c* are *a'*.

14.

1. All *e* are *b* ;
2. All *a* are *c* ;
3. All *d* are *b'*;
4. All *a'* are *e*.

15.

1. No *b'* are *d* ;
2. All *e* are *c* ;
3. All *b* are *a* ;
4. All *d'* are *c'*.

16.

1. No *a'* are *e* ;
2. All *d* are *c'*;
3. All *a* are *b* ;
4. All *e'* are *d*.

17.

1. All *d* are *c* ;
2. All *a* are *e* ;
3. No *b* are *d'*;
4. All *c* are *e'*.

18.

1. All *a* are *b* ;
2. All *d* are *e* ;
3. All *a'* are *c'* ;
4. No *b* are *e*.

19.

1. No *b* are *c* ;
2. All *e* are *h* ;
3. All *a* are *b* ;
4. No *d* are *h* ;
5. All *e'* are *c*.

20.

1. No *d* are *h'*;
2. No *c* are *e* ;
3. All *h* are *b* ;
4. No *a* are *d'*.
5. No *b* are *c'*.

21.

1. All *b* are *a* ;
2. No *d* are *h* ;
3. No *c* are *e* ;
4. No *a* are *h'*;
5. All *c'* are *b*.

22.

1. All *e* are *d'*;
2. No *b'* are *h'*;
3. All *c'* are *d* ;
4. All *a* are *e* ;
5. No *c* are *h*.

23.

1. All *b'* are *a'*;
2. No *d* are *e'*;
3. All *h* are *b'*;
4. No *c* are *e* ;
5. All *d'* are *a*.

24.

1. All *h'* are *k'*;
2. No *b'* are *a* ;
3. All *c* are *d* ;
4. All *e* are *h'*;
5. No *d* are *k'*;
6. No *b* are *c'*.

25.

1. All *a* are *d* ;
2. All *k* are *b* ;
3. All *e* are *h* ;
4. No *a'* are *b* ;
5. All *d* are *c* ;
6. All *h* are *k*.

26.

1. All *a'* are *h* ;
2. No *d'* are *k'*;
3. All *e* are *b'*;
4. No *h* are *k* ;
5. All *a* are *c* ;
6. No *b'* are *d*.

27.

1. All *e* are *d'*;
2. No *h* are *b* ;
3. All *a'* are *k* ;
4. No *c* are *e'*;
5. All *b'* are *d* ;
6. No *a* are *c'*.

28.

1. No *a'* are *k* ;
2. All *e* are *b* ;
3. No *h* are *k* ;
4. No *d'* are *c* ;
5. No *a* are *b* ;
6. All *c'* are *h*.

29.

1. No *e* are *k* ;
2. No *b'* are *m*;
3. No *a* are *c'*;
4. All *h'* are *e* ;
5. All *d* are *k* ;
6. No *c* are *b* ;
7. All *d'* are *l* ;
8. No *h* are *m'*.

30.

1. All *n* are *m*;
2 All *a'* are *e* ;
3. No *c'* are *l* ;
4. All *k* are *r'*;
5. No *a* are *h* ;
6. No *d* are *l'*;
7. No *c* are *n* ;
8. All *e* are *b* ;
9. All *m* are *r*;
10. All *h* are *d*.

[N.B. In each Example, in Sections 8 and 9, it is possible to begin with *any* Premiss, at pleasure, and thus to get as many different Solutions (all of course yielding the *same* Complete Conclusion) as there are Premisses in the Example. Hence § 8 really contains 129 different Examples, and § 9 contains 273.]

Ans. 132 ; Sol. 156, 157.]

§ 9.

Sets of Concrete Propositions, proposed as Premisses for Soriteses: Conclusions to be found.

1.

(1) Babies are illogical;
(2) Nobody is despised who can manage a crocodile;
(3) Illogical persons are despised.

Univ. "persons"; a = able to manage a crocodile; b = babies; c = despised; d = logical.

2.

(1) My saucepans are the only things I have that are made of tin;
(2) I find all *your* presents very useful;
(3) None of my saucepans are of the slightest use.

Univ. "things of mine"; a = made of tin; b = my saucepans; c = useful; d = your presents.

3.

(1) No potatoes of mine, that are new, have been boiled;
(2) All my potatoes in this dish are fit to eat;
(3) No unboiled potatoes of mine are fit to eat.

Univ. "my potatoes"; a = boiled; b = eatable; c = in this dish; d = new.

4.

(1) There are no Jews in the kitchen;
(2) No Gentiles say "shpoonj";
(3) My servants are all in the kitchen.

Univ. "persons"; a = in the kitchen; b = Jews; c = my servants; d = saying "shpoonj."

5.

(1) No ducks waltz;
(2) No officers ever decline to waltz;
(3) All my poultry are ducks.

Univ. "creatures"; a = ducks; b = my poultry; c = officers; d = willing to waltz.

6.

(1) Every one who is sane can do Logic;
(2) No lunatics are fit to serve on a jury;
(3) None of *your* sons can do Logic.

Univ. "persons"; a = able to do Logic; b = fit to serve on a jury; c = sane; d = your sons.

[Ans. 132; Sol. 157, 158.

7.

(1) There are no pencils of mine in this box;
(2) No sugar-plums of mine are cigars;
(3) The whole of my property, that is not in this box, consists of cigars.

Univ. "things of mine"; a = cigars; b = in this box;
c = pencils; d = sugar-plums.

8.

(1) No experienced person is incompetent;
(2) Jenkins is always blundering;
(3) No competent person is always blundering.

Univ. "persons"; a = always blundering; b = competent;
c = experienced; d = Jenkins.

9.

(1) No terriers wander among the signs of the zodiac;
(2) Nothing, that does not wander among the signs of the zodiac, is a comet;
(3) Nothing but a terrier has a curly tail.

Univ. "things"; a = comets; b = curly-tailed; c = terriers;
d = wandering among the signs of the zodiac.

10.

(1) No one takes in the *Times*, unless he is well-educated;
(2) No hedge-hogs can read;
(3) Those who cannot read are not well-educated.

Univ. "creatures"; a = able to read; b = hedge-hogs;
c = taking in the *Times*; d = well-educated.

11.

(1) All puddings are nice;
(2) This dish is a pudding;
(3) No nice things are wholesome.

Univ. "things"; a = nice; b = puddings;
c = this dish; d = wholesome.

12.

(1) My gardener is well worth listening to on military subjects;
(2) No one can remember the battle of Waterloo, unless he is very old;
(3) Nobody is really worth listening to on military subjects, unless he can remember the battle of Waterloo.

Univ. "persons"; a = able to remember the battle of Waterloo;
b = my gardener; c = well worth listening to on military subjects;
d = very old.

Ans. 132; Sol. 158.]

13.

(1) All humming-birds are richly coloured ;
(2) No large birds live on honey ;
(3) Birds that do not live on honey are dull in colour.

Univ. "birds" ; a = humming-birds ; b = large ; c = living on honey ; d = richly coloured.

14.

(1) No Gentiles have hooked noses ;
(2) A man who is a good hand at a bargain always makes money ;
(3) No Jew is ever a bad hand at a bargain.

Univ. "persons" ; a = good hands at a bargain ; b = hook-nosed ; c = Jews ; d = making money.

15.

(1) All ducks in this village, that are branded 'B,' belong to Mrs. Bond ;
(2) Ducks in this village never wear lace collars, unless they are branded 'B' ;
(3) Mrs. Bond has no gray ducks in this village.

Univ. "ducks in this village" ; a = belonging to Mrs. Bond ; b = branded 'B' ; c = gray ; d = wearing lace-collars.

16.

(1) All the old articles in this cupboard are cracked ;
(2) No jug in this cupboard is new ;
(3) Nothing in this cupboard, that is cracked, will hold water.

Univ. "things in this cupboard" ; a = able to hold water ; b = cracked ; c = jugs ; d = old.

17.

(1) All unripe fruit is unwholesome ;
(2) All these apples are wholesome ;
(3) No fruit, grown in the shade, is ripe.

Univ. "fruit" ; a = grown in the shade ; b = ripe ; c = these apples ; d = wholesome.

18.

(1) Puppies, that will not lie still, are always grateful for the loan of a skipping-rope ;
(2) A lame puppy would not say "thank you" if you offered to lend it a skipping-rope.
(3) None but lame puppies ever care to do worsted-work.

Univ. "puppies" ; a = caring to do worsted-work ; b = grateful for the loan of a skipping-rope; c = lame ; d = willing to lie still.

[Ans. 132 ; Sol. 158, 159.

19.

(1) No name in this list is unsuitable for the hero of a romance ;
(2) Names beginning with a vowel are always melodious ;
(3) No name is suitable for the hero of a romance, if it begins with a consonant.

Univ. "names" ; a=beginning with a vowel ; b=in this list ; c=melodious ; d = suitable for the hero of a romance.

20.

(1) All members of the House of Commons have perfect self-command ;
(2) No M.P., who wears a coronet, should ride in a donkey-race ;
(3) All members of the House of Lords wear coronets.

Univ. "M.P.'s" ; a=belonging to the House of Commons ; b=having perfect self-command ; c = one who may ride in a donkey-race ; d = wearing a coronet.

21.

(1) No goods in this shop, that have been bought and paid for, are still on sale ;
(2) None of the goods may be carried away, unless labeled "sold" ;
(3) None of the goods are labeled "sold," unless they have been bought and paid for.

Univ. "goods in this shop" ; a = allowed to be carried away ; b = bought and paid for ; c = labeled "sold" ; d = on sale.

22.

(1) No acrobatic feats, that are not announced in the bills of a circus, are ever attempted there ;
(2) No acrobatic feat is possible, if it involves turning a quadruple somersault ;
(3) No impossible acrobatic feat is ever announced in a circus bill.

Univ. "acrobatic feats" ; a = announced in the bills of a circus ; b = attempted in a circus ; c = involving the turning of a quadruple somersault ; d = possible.

23.

(1) Nobody, who really appreciates Beethoven, fails to keep silence while the Moonlight-Sonata is being played ;
(2) Guinea-pigs are hopelessly ignorant of music ;
(3) No one, who is hopelessly ignorant of music, ever keeps silence while the Moonlight-Sonata is being played.

Univ. "creatures" ; a = guinea-pigs ; b = hopelessly ignorant of music ; c=keeping silence while the Moonlight-Sonata is being played ; d=really appreciating Beethoven.

Ans. 132, 133 ; Sol. 159.]

24.

(1) Coloured flowers are always scented;
(2) I dislike flowers that are not grown in the open air;
(3) No flowers grown in the open air are colourless.

Univ. "flowers"; a = coloured; b = grown in the open air; c = liked by me; d = scented.

25.

(1) Showy talkers think too much of themselves;
(2) No really well-informed people are bad company;
(3) People who think too much of themselves are not good company.

Univ. "persons"; a = good company; b = really well-informed; c = showy talkers; d = thinking too much of one's self.

26.

(1) No boys under 12 are admitted to this school as boarders;
(2) All the industrious boys have red hair;
(3) None of the day-boys learn Greek;
(4) None but those under 12 are idle.

Univ. "boys in this school"; a = boarders; b = industrious; c = learning Greek; d = red-haired; e = under 12.

27.

(1) The only articles of food, that my doctor allows me, are such as are not very rich;
(2) Nothing that agrees with me is unsuitable for supper;
(3) Wedding-cake is always very rich;
(4) My doctor allows me all articles of food that are suitable for supper.

Univ. "articles of food"; a = agreeing with me; b = allowed by my doctor; c = suitable for supper; d = very rich; e = wedding-cake.

28.

(1) No discussions in our Debating-Club are likely to rouse the British Lion, so long as they are checked when they become too noisy;
(2) Discussions, unwisely conducted, endanger the peacefulness of our Debating-Club;
(3) Discussions, that go on while Tomkins is in the Chair, are likely to rouse the British Lion;
(4) Discussions in our Debating-Club, when wisely conducted, are always checked when they become too noisy.

Univ. "discussions in our Debating-Club"; a = checked when too noisy; b = dangerous to the peacefulness of our Debating-Club; c = going on while Tomkins is in the chair; d = likely to rouse the British Lion; e = wisely conducted.

[Ans. 133; Sol. 160.

29.

(1) All my sons are slim ;
(2) No child of mine is healthy who takes no exercise ;
(3) All gluttons, who are children of mine, are fat ;
(4) No daughter of mine takes any exercise.

Univ. "my children" ; a = fat ; b = gluttons ; c = healthy ; d = sons ; e = taking exercise.

30.

(1) Things sold in the street are of no great value ;
(2) Nothing but rubbish can be had for a song ;
(3) Eggs of the Great Auk are very valuable ;
(4) It is only what is sold in the street that is really *rubbish.*

Univ. "things" ; a = able to be had for a song ; b = eggs of the Great Auk ; c = rubbish ; d = sold in the street ; e = very valuable.

31.

(1) No books sold here have gilt edges, except what are in the front shop ;
(2) All the *authorised* editions have red labels ;
(3) All the books with red labels are priced at 5s. and upwards ;
(4) None but *authorised* editions are ever placed in the front shop.

Univ. "books sold here" ; a = authorised editions ; b = gilt-edged ; c = having red labels ; d = in the frontshop ; e = priced at 5*s*. and upwards.

32.

(1) Remedies for bleeding, which fail to check it, are a mockery ;
(2) Tincture of Calendula is not to be despised ;
(3) Remedies, which will check the bleeding when you cut your finger, are useful ;
(4) All mock remedies for bleeding are despicable.

Univ. "remedies for bleeding"; a = able to check bleeding ; b = despicable ; c = mockeries ; d = Tincture of Calendula ; e = useful when you cut your finger.

33.

(1) None of the unnoticed things, met with at sea, are mermaids ;
(2) Things entered in the log, as met with at sea, are sure to be worth remembering ;
(3) *I* have never met with anything worth remembering, when on a voyage ;
(4) Things met with at sea, that are noticed, are sure to be recorded in the log ;

Univ. "things met with at sea" ; a = entered in log ; b = mermaids ; c = met with by me ; d = noticed ; e = worth remembering.

Ans. 133 ; Sol. 160.]

34.

(1) The only books in this library, that I do *not* recommend for reading, are unhealthy in tone;
(2) The bound books are all well-written;
(3) All the romances are healthy in tone;
(4) I do not recommend you to read any of the unbound books.

Univ. "books in this library"; a = bound; b = healthy in tone; c = recommended by me; d = romances; e = well-written.

35.

(1) No birds, except ostriches, are 9 feet high;
(2) There are no birds in this aviary that belong to any one but *me*;
(3) No ostrich lives on mince-pies;
(4) I have no birds less than 9 feet high.

Univ. "birds"; a = in this aviary; b = living on mince-pies; c = my d = 9 feet high; e = ostriches.

36.

(1) A plum-pudding, that is not really solid, is mere porridge;
(2) Every plum-pudding, served at my table, has been boiled in a cloth;
(3) A plum-pudding that is mere porridge is indistinguishable from soup;
(4) No plum-puddings are really solid, except what are served at *my* table.

Univ. "plum-puddings"; a = boiled in a cloth; b = distinguishable from soup; c = mere porridge; d = really solid; e = served at my table.

37.

(1) No interesting poems are unpopular among people of real taste;
(2) No modern poetry is free from affectation;
(3) All *your* poems are on the subject of soap-bubbles;
(4) No affected poetry is popular among people of real taste;
(5) No ancient poem is on the subject of soap-bubbles.

Univ. "poems"; a = affected; b = ancient; c = interesting; d = on the subject of soap-bubbles; e = popular among people of real taste; h = written by you.

38.

(1) All the fruit at this Show, that fails to get a prize, is the property of the Committee;
(2) None of my peaches have got prizes;
(3) None of the fruit, sold off in the evening, is unripe;
(4) None of the ripe fruit has been grown in a hot-house;
(5) All fruit, that belongs to the Committee, is sold off in the evening.

Univ. "fruit at this Show"; a=belonging to the Committee; b=getting prizes; c = grown in a hot-house; d = my peaches; e = ripe; h = sold off in the evening.

[Ans. 133; Sol. 161.

39.

(1) Promise-breakers are untrustworthy;
(2) Wine-drinkers are very communicative;
(3) A man who keeps his promises is honest;
(4) No teetotalers are pawnbrokers;
(5) One can always trust a very communicative person.

Univ. "persons"; a = honest; b = pawnbrokers; c = promise-breakers; d = trustworthy; e = very communicative; h = wine-drinkers.

40.

(1) No kitten, that loves fish, is unteachable;
(2) No kitten without a tail will play with a gorilla;
(3) Kittens with whiskers always love fish;
(4) No teachable kitten has green eyes;
(5) No kittens have tails unless they have whiskers.

Univ. "kittens"; a = green-eyed; b = loving fish; c = tailed; d = teachable; e = whiskered; h = willing to play with a gorilla.

41.

(1) All the Eton men in this College play cricket;
(2) None but the Scholars dine at the higher table;
(3) None of the cricketers row;
(4) *My* friends in this College all come from Eton;
(5) All the Scholars are rowing-men.

Univ. "men in this College"; a = cricketers; b = dining at the higher table; c = Etonians; d = my friends; e = rowing-men; h = Scholars.

42.

(1) There is no box of mine here that I dare open;
(2) My writing-desk is made of rose-wood;
(3) All my boxes are painted, except what are here;
(4) There is no box of mine that I dare not open, unless it is full of live scorpions;
(5) All my rose-wood boxes are unpainted.

Univ. "my boxes"; a=boxes that I dare open; b=full of live scorpions; c = here; d = made of rose-wood; e = painted; h = writing-desks.

43.

(1) Gentiles have no objection to pork;
(2) Nobody who admires pigsties ever reads Hogg's poems;
(3) No Mandarin knows Hebrew;
(4) Every one, who does not object to pork, admires pigsties;
(5) No Jew is ignorant of Hebrew.

Univ. "persons"; a = admiring pigsties; b=Jews; c=knowing Hebrew; d = Mandarins; e = objecting to pork; h = reading Hogg's poems.

Ans. 133; Sol. 161.]

44.

(1) All writers, who understand human nature, are clever;
(2) No one is a true poet unless he can stir the hearts of men;
(3) Shakespeare wrote "Hamlet";
(4) No writer, who does not understand human nature, can stir the hearts of men;
(5) None but a true poet could have written "Hamlet."

Univ. "writers"; a = able to stir the hearts of men; b = clever; c = Shakespeare; d = true poets; e = understanding human nature; h = writer of 'Hamlet.'

45.

(1) I despise anything that cannot be used as a bridge;
(2) Everything, that is worth writing an ode to, would be a welcome gift to me;
(3) A rainbow will not bear the weight of a wheel-barrow;
(4) Whatever can be used as a bridge will bear the weight of a wheel-barrow;
(5) I would not take, as a gift, a thing that I despise.

Univ. "things"; a = able to bear the weight of a wheel-barrow; b = acceptable to me; c = despised by me; d = rainbows; e = useful as a bridge; h = worth writing an ode to.

46.

(1) When I work a Logic-example without grumbling, you may be sure it is one that I can understand;
(2) These Soriteses are not arranged in regular order, like the examples I am used to;
(3) No easy example ever makes my head ache;
(4) I ca'n't understand examples that are not arranged in regular order, like those I am used to;
(5) I never grumble at an example, unless it gives me a headache.

Univ. "Logic-examples worked by me"; a = arranged in regular order, like the examples I am used to; b = easy; c = grumbled at by me; d = making my head ache; e = these Soriteses; h = understood by me.

47.

(1) Every idea of mine, that cannot be expressed as a Syllogism, is really ridiculous;
(2) None of my ideas about Bath-buns are worth writing down;
(3) No idea of mine, that fails to come true, can be expressed as a Syllogism;
(4) I never have any really ridiculous idea, that I do not at once refer to my solicitor;
(5) My dreams are all about Bath-buns;
(6) I never refer any idea of mine to my solicitor, unless it is worth writing down.

Univ. "my ideas"; a = able to be expressed as a Syllogism; b = about Bath-buns; c = coming true; d = dreams; e = really ridiculous; h = referred to my solicitor; k = worth writing down.

[Ans. 133; Sol. 162.

48.

(1) None of the pictures here, except the battle-pieces, are valuable;
(2) None of the unframed ones are varnished;
(3) All the battle-pieces are painted in oils;
(4) All those that have been sold are valuable;
(5) All the English ones are varnished;
(6) All those in frames have been sold.

Univ. "the pictures here"; a = battle-pieces; b = English; c = framed; d = oil-paintings; e = sold; h = valuable; k = varnished.

49.

(1) Animals, that do not kick, are always unexcitable;
(2) Donkeys have no horns;
(3) A buffalo can always toss one over a gate;
(4) No animals that kick are easy to swallow;
(5) No hornless animal can toss one over a gate;
(6) All animals are excitable, except buffaloes.

Univ. "animals"; a = able to toss one over a gate; b = buffaloes; c = donkeys; d = easy to swallow; e = excitable; h = horned; k = kicking.

50.

(1) No one, who is going to a party, ever fails to brush his hair;
(2) No one looks fascinating, if he is untidy;
(3) Opium-eaters have no self-command;
(4) Every one, who has brushed his hair, looks fascinating;
(5) No one wears white kid gloves, unless he is going to a party;
(6) A man is always untidy, if he has no self-command.

Univ. "persons"; a = going to a party; b = having brushed one's hair; c = having self-command; d = looking fascinating; e = opium-eaters; h = tidy; k = wearing white kid gloves.

51.

(1) No husband, who is always giving his wife new dresses, can be a cross-grained man;
(2) A methodical husband always comes home for his tea;
(3) No one, who hangs up his hat on the gas-jet, can be a man that is kept in proper order by his wife;
(4) A good husband is always giving his wife new dresses;
(5) No husband can fail to be cross-grained, if his wife does not keep him in proper order;
(6) An unmethodical husband always hangs up his hat on the gas-jet.

Univ. "husbands"; a = always coming home for his tea; b = always giving his wife new dresses; c = cross-grained; d = good; e = hanging up his hat on the gas-jet; h = kept in proper order; k = methodical.

Ans. 133; Sol. 162.]

52.

(1) Everything, not absolutely ugly, may be kept in a drawing-room ;
(2) Nothing, that is encrusted with salt, is ever quite dry ;
(3) Nothing should be kept in a drawing-room, unless it is free from damp;
(4) Bathing-machines are always kept near the sea ;
(5) Nothing, that is made of mother-of-pearl, can be absolutely ugly ;
(6) Whatever is kept near the sea gets encrusted with salt.

Univ. "things"; a = absolutely ugly ; b = bathing-machines ; c = encrusted with salt ; d = kept near the sea ; e = made of mother-of-pearl ; h = quite dry ; k = things that may be kept in a drawing-room.

53.

(1) I call no day "unlucky," when Robinson is civil to me ;
(2) Wednesdays are always cloudy ;
(3) When people take umbrellas, the day never turns out fine ;
(4) The only days when Robinson is uncivil to me are Wednesdays ;
(5) Everybody takes his umbrella with him when it is raining ;
(6) My "lucky" days always turn out fine.

Univ. "days" ; a = called by me 'lucky' ; b = cloudy ; c = days when people take umbrellas ; d = days when Robinson is civil to me ; e = rainy ; h = turning out fine ; k = Wednesdays.

54.

(1) No shark ever doubts that it is well fitted out ;
(2) A fish, that cannot dance a minuet, is contemptible ;
(3) No fish is quite certain that it is well fitted out, unless it has three rows of teeth ;
(4) All fishes, except sharks, are kind to children.
(5) No heavy fish can dance a minuet ;
(6) A fish with three rows of teeth is not to be despised.

Univ. "fishes" ; a = able to dance a minuet ; b = certain that he is well fitted out ; c = contemptible ; d = having 3 rows of teeth ; e = heavy ; h = kind to children ; k = sharks.

55.

(1) All the human race, except my footmen, have a certain amount of common-sense ;
(2) No one, who lives on barley-sugar, can be anything but a mere baby ;
(3) None but a hop-scotch player knows what real happiness is ;
(4) No mere baby has a grain of common sense ;
(5) No engine-driver ever plays hop-scotch ;
(6) No footman of mine is ignorant of what true happiness is ;

Univ. "human beings" ; a = engine-drivers ; b = having common sense ; c = hop-scotch players ; d = knowing what real happiness is ; e = living on barley-sugar ; h = mere babies ; k = my footmen.

[Ans. 133 ; Sol. 162, 163.

56.

(1) I trust every animal that belongs to me;
(2) Dogs gnaw bones;
(3) I admit no animals into my study, unless they will beg when told to do so;
(4) All the animals in the yard are mine;
(5) I admit every animal, that I trust, into my study;
(6) The only animals, that are really willing to beg when told to do so, are dogs.

Univ. "animals"; a = admitted to my study; b = animals that I trust; c = dogs; d = gnawing bones; e = in the yard; h = my; k = willing to beg when told.

57.

(1) Animals are always mortally offended if I fail to notice them;
(2) The only animals that belong to *me* are in that field;
(3) No animal can guess a conundrum, unless it has been properly trained in a Board-School;
(4) None of the animals in that field are badgers;
(5) When an animal is mortally offended, it always rushes about wildly and howls;
(6) I never notice any animal, unless it belongs to me;
(7) No animal, that has been properly trained in a Board-School, ever rushes about wildly and howls.

Univ. "animals"; a = able to guess a conundrum; b = badgers; c = in that field; d = mortally offended if I fail to notice them; e = my; h = noticed by me; k = properly trained in a Board-School; l = rushing about wildly and howling.

58.

(1) I never put a cheque, received by me, on that file, unless I am anxious about it;
(2) All the cheques received by me, that are not marked with a cross, are payable to bearer;
(3) None of them are ever brought back to me, unless they have been dishonoured at the Bank;
(4) All of them, that are marked with a cross, are for amounts of over £100;
(5) All of them, that are not on that file, are marked "not negotiable";
(6) No cheque of yours, received by me, has ever been dishonoured;
(7) I am never anxious about a cheque, received by me, unless it should happen to be brought back to me;
(8) None of the cheques received by me, that are marked "not negotiable," are for amounts of over £100.

Univ. "cheques received by me"; a = brought back to me; b = cheques that I am anxious about; c = honoured; d = marked with a cross; e = marked 'not negotiable'; h = on that file; k = over £100; l = payable to bearer; m = your.

Ans. 133; Sol. 163.]

59.

(1) All the dated letters in this room are written on blue paper;
(2) None of them are in black ink, except those that are written in the third person;
(3) I have not filed any of them that I can read;
(4) None of them, that are written on one sheet, are undated;
(5) All of them, that are not crossed, are in black ink;
(6) All of them, written by Brown, begin with "Dear Sir";
(7) All of them, written on blue paper, are filed;
(8) None of them, written on more than one sheet, are crossed;
(9) None of them, that begin with "Dear Sir," are written in the third person.

"Univ. letters in this room"; a = beginning with "Dear Sir"; b = crossed; c = dated; d = filed; e = in black ink; h = in third person; k = letters that I can read; l = on blue paper; m = on one sheet; n = written by Brown.

60.

(1) The only animals in this house are cats;
(2) Every animal is suitable for a pet, that loves to gaze at the moon:
(3) When I detest an animal, I avoid it;
(4) No animals are carnivorous, unless they prowl at night;
(5) No cat fails to kill mice;
(6) No animals ever take to me, except what are in this house;
(7) Kangaroos are not suitable for pets;
(8) None but carnivora kill mice;
(9) I detest animals that do not take to me;
(10) Animals, that prowl at night, always love to gaze at the moon.

Univ. "animals"; a = avoided by me; b = carnivora; c = cats; d = detested by me; e = in this house; h = kangaroos; k = killing mice; l = loving to gaze at the moon; m = prowling at night; n = suitable for pets; r = taking to me.

[Ans. 133; Sol. 163.

CHAPTER II.

ANSWERS.

Answers to § 1.

---

1. "All" . . . . *Sign of Quantity.*
"persons represented by the Name 'I'" (or "I's") *Subject.*
"are" . . . . *Copula.*
"persons who have been out for a walk" . . . . *Predicate.*

or, more briefly,

"All | 'I's | are | persons who have been out for a walk".

2. "All | 'I's | are | persons who feel better".
3. "No | persons who are not 'John' | are | persons who have read the letter".
4. "No | Members of the Class 'you and I' | are | old persons".
5. "No | fat creatures | are | creatures that run well".
6. "No | not-brave persons | are | persons deserving of the fair".
7. "No | not-pale persons | are | persons who look poetical".
8. "Some | judges | are | persons who lose their tempers".
9. "All | 'I's | are | persons who do not neglect important business".
10. "All | difficult things | are | things that need attention".
11. "All | unwholesome things | are | things that should be avoided".
12. "All | laws passed last week | are | laws relating to excise".
13. "All | logical studies | are | things that puzzle me".
14. "No | persons in the house | are | Jews".
15. "Some | not well-cooked dishes | are | unwholesome dishes".
16. "All | unexciting books | are | books that make one drowsy".
17. "All | men who know what they're about | are | men who can detect a sharper".
18. "All | Members of the Class 'you and I' | are | persons who know what they're about".
19. "Some | bald persons | are | persons accustomed to wear wigs".
20. "All | fully occupied persons | are | persons who do not talk about their grievances".
21. "No | riddles that can be solved | are | riddles that interest me".

Ex. 97 ; Sol. 134—136.]

Answers to § 2.

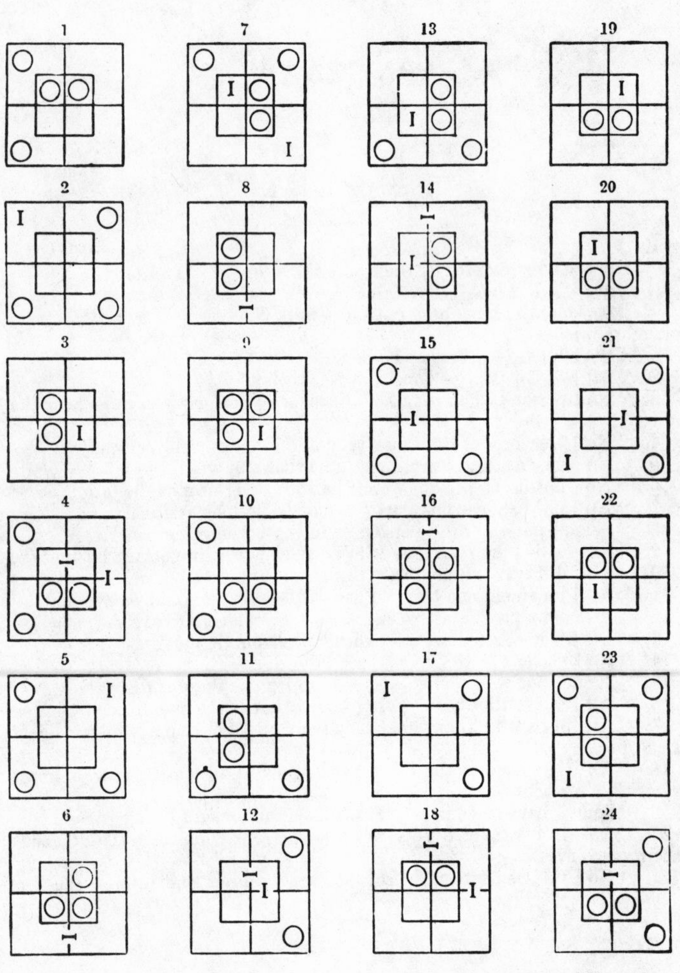

[Ex. 98.

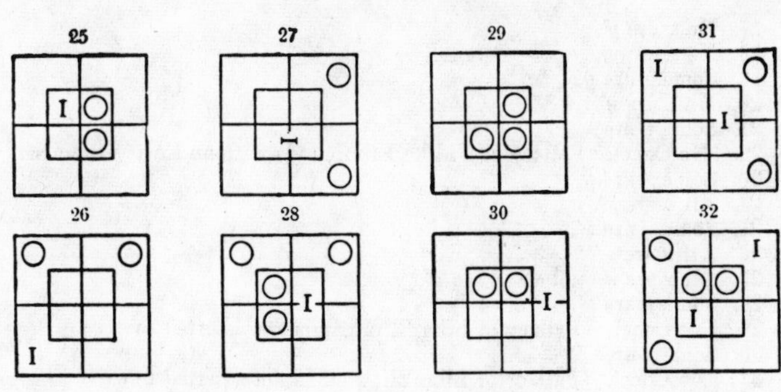

Answers to § 3.

1. Some xy exist, or some x are y, or some y are x.
2. No information.
3. All y' are x'.
4. No xy exist, &c.
5. All y' are x.
6. All x' are y.
7. All x are y.
8. All x' are y', and all y are x.
9. All x' are y'.
10. All x are y'.
11. No information.
12. Some $x'y'$ exist, &c.
13. Some xy' exist, &c.
14. No xy' exist, &c.
15. Some xy exist, &c.
16. All y are x.
17. All x' are y, and all y' are x.
18. All x are y' and all y are x'.
19. All x are y, and all y' are x'.
20. All y are x'.

Answers to § 4.

1. No x' are y'.
2. Some x' are y'.
3. Some x are y'.
4. [No Concl. Fallacy of Like Eliminands not asserted to exist.]
5. Some x' are y'.
6. [No Concl. Fallacy of Like Eliminands not asserted to exist.]
7. Some x are y'.
8. Some x' are y'.
9. [No Concl. Fallacy of Unlike Eliminands with an Entity-Premiss.]
10. All x are y, and all y' are x'.
11. [No Concl. Fallacy of Like Eliminands not asserted to exist.]
12. All y are x'.
13. No x' are y.
14. No x' are y'.
15. No x are y.
16. All x are y', and all y are x'.

Ex. 98—100 ; Sol. 136—138.]

17. No x are y'.
18. No x are y.
19. Some x are y'.
20. No x are y'.
21. Some y are x'.
22. [No Concl. Fallacy of Unlike Eliminands with an Entity-Premiss.
23. Some x are y.
24. All y are x'.
25. Some y are x'.
26. All y are x.
27. All x are y, and all y' are x'.
28. Some y are x'.
29. [No Concl. Fallacy of Like Eliminands not asserted to exist.]
30. Some y are x'.
31. [No Concl. Fallacy of Like Eliminands not asserted to exist.]
32. No x are y'.
33. [No Concl. Fallacy of Like Eliminands not asserted to exist.]
34. Some x are y.
35. All y are x'.
36. Some y are x'.
37. Some x are y'.
38. No x are y.
39. Some x are y'.
40. All y' are x.
41. All x are y'.
42. No x are y.

Answers to § 5.

1. Somebody who has been out for a walk is feeling better.
2. No one but John knows what the letter is about.
3. You and I like walking.
4. Honesty is sometimes the best policy.
5. Some greyhounds are not fat.
6. Some brave persons get their deserts.
7. Some rich persons are not Esquimaux.
8. [No Concl. Fallacy of Unlike Eliminands with an Entity-Premiss.
9. John is ill.
10. Some things, that are not umbrellas, should be left behind on a journey.
11. No music is worth paying for, unless it causes vibration in the air.
12. Some holidays are tiresome.
13. Englishmen are not Frenchmen.
14. No photograph of a lady is satisfactory.
15. No one looks poetical unless he is phlegmatic.
16. Some thin persons are not cheerful.
17. Some judges do not exercise self-control.
18. Pigs are not fed on barley-water.
19. Some black rabbits are not old.

[Ex. 100—102 ; Sol. 146—148.

20. [No Concl. Fallacy of Unlike Eliminands with an Entity-Premiss.]
21. [No Concl. Fallacy of Like Eliminands not asserted to exist.]
22. Some lessons need attention.
23. [No Concl. Fallacy of Like Eliminands not asserted to exist.]
24. No one, who forgets a promise, fails to do mischief.
25. Some greedy creatures cannot fly.
26. [No Concl. Fallacy of Unlike Eliminands with an Entity-Premiss.]
27. No bride-cakes are things that need not be avoided.
28. John is happy.
29. Some people, who are not gamblers, are not philosophers.
30. [No Concl. Fallacy of Unlike Eliminands with an Entity-Premiss.]
31. None of my lodgers write poetry.
32. Senna is not nice.
33. [No Concl. Fallacy of Unlike Eliminands with an Entity-Premiss.]
34. [No Concl. Fallacy of Like Eliminands not asserted to exist.]
35. Logic is unintelligible.
36. Some wild creatures are fat.
37. All wasps are unwelcome.
38. All black rabbits are young.
39. Some hard-boiled things can be cracked.
40. No antelopes fail to delight the eye.
41. All well-fed canaries are cheerful.
42. Some poetry is not producible at will.
43. No country infested by dragons fails to be fascinating.
44. [No Concl. Fallacy of Like Eliminands not asserted to exist.]
45. Some picturesque things are not made of sugar.
46. No children can sit still.
47. Some cats cannot whistle.
48. You are terrible.
49. Some oysters are not amusing.
50. Nobody in the house has a beard a yard long.
51. Some ill-fed canaries are unhappy.
52. My sisters cannot sing.
53. [No Concl. Fallacy of Unlike Eliminands with an Entity-Premiss.]
54. Some rich things are nice.
55. My cousins are none of them judges, and judges are none of them cousins of mine.
56. Something wearisome is not eagerly wished for.
57. Senna is nasty.
58. [No Concl. Fallacy of Unlike Eliminands with an Entity-Premiss.]
59. Niggers are not any of them tall.
60. Some obstinate persons are not philosophers.
61. John is happy.
62. Some unwholesome dishes are not present here (i.e. cannot be spoken of as "these").
63. No books suit feverish patients unless they make one drowsy.
64. Some greedy creatures cannot fly.
65. You and I can detect a sharper.
66. Some dreams are not lambs.

Ex. 102—104 ; Sol. 147, 148.]

67. No lizard needs a hairbrush.
68. Some things, that may escape notice, are not battles.
69 My cousins are not any of them judges.
70. Some hard-boiled things can be cracked.
71. [No Concl. Fallacy of Unlike Eliminands with an Entity-Premiss.]
72. She is unpopular.
73. Some people, who wear wigs, are not children of yours.
74. No lobsters expect impossibilities.
75. No nightmare is eagerly desired.
76. Some nice things are not plumcakes.
77. Some kinds of jam need not be shunned.
78. All ducks are ungraceful.
79. [No Concl. Fallacy of Like Eliminands not asserted to exist.]
80. No man, who begs in the street, should fail to keep accounts.
81. Some savage creatures are not spiders.
82. [No Concl. Fallacy of Unlike Eliminands with an Entity-Premiss.]
83. No travelers, who do not carry plenty of small change, fail to lose their luggage.
84. [No Concl. Fallacy of Unlike Eliminands with an Entity-Premiss.]
85. Judges are none of them cousins of mine.
86. All my lodgers are sane.
87. Those who are busy are contented, and discontented people are not busy.
88. None of my cousins are judges.
89. No nightingale dislikes sugar.
90. [No Concl. Fallacy of Like Eliminands not asserted to exist.]
91. Some excuses are not clear explanations.
92. [No Concl. Fallacy of Like Eliminands not asserted to exist.]
93. No kind deed need cause scruple.
94. [No Concl. Fallacy of Like Eliminands not asserted to exist.]
95. [No Concl. Fallacy of Like Eliminands not asserted to exist.]
96. No cheats are trustworthy.
97. No clever child of mine is greedy.
98. Some things, that are meant to amuse, are not Acts of Parliament.
99. No tour, that is ever forgotten, is worth writing a book about.
100. No obedient child of mine is contented.
101. Your visit does not annoy me.

Answers to § 6.

1. Conclusion right.
2. No Concl. Fallacy of Like Eliminands not asserted to exist.

3, 4, 5. Concl. right.

6. No Concl. Fallacy of Like Eliminands not asserted to exist.
7. No Concl. Fallacy of Unlike Eliminands with an Entity-Premiss.

8—15. Concl. right.

[Ex. 104—106 ; Sol. 148, 149.

16. No Concl. Fallacy of Like Eliminands not asserted to exist.
17—21. Concl. right.
22. Concl. wrong: the right one is "Some x are y."
23—27. Concl. right.
28. No Concl. Fallacy of Like Eliminands not asserted to exist.
29—33. Concl. right.
34. No Concl. Fallacy of Unlike Eliminands with an Entity-Premiss.
35, 36, 37. Concl. right.
38. No Concl. Fallacy of Like Eliminands not asserted to exist.
39, 40. Concl. right.

Answers to § 7.

1, 2, 3. Concl. right.
4. Concl. wrong: right one is "Some epicures are not uncles of mine.
5. Concl. right.
6. No Concl. Fallacy of Unlike Eliminands with an Entity-Premiss.
7. Concl. wrong: right one is "The publication, in which I saw it, tells lies."
8. No Concl. Fallacy of Unlike Eliminands with an Entity-Premiss.
9. Concl. wrong: right one is "Some tedious songs are not his."
10. Concl. right.
11. No Concl. Fallacy of Unlike Eliminands with an Entity-Premiss.
12. Concl. wrong: right one is "Some fierce creatures do not drink coffee."
13. No Concl. Fallacy of Unlike Eliminands with an Entity-Premiss.
14. Concl. right.
15. Concl. wrong: right one is "Some shallow persons are not students."
16 No Concl. Fallacy of Like Eliminands not asserted to exist.
17. Concl. wrong: right one is "Some business, other than railways, is unprofitable."
18. Concl. wrong: right one is "Some vain persons are not Professors."
19. Concl. right.
20. Concl. wrong: right one is "Wasps are not puppies."
21. No Concl. Fallacy of Unlike Eliminands with an Entity-Premiss.
22. No Concl. Same Fallacy.
23. Concl. right.
24. Concl. wrong: right one is "Some chocolate-creams are delicious.
25. No Concl. Fallacy of Like Eliminands not asserted to exist.
26. No Concl. Fallacy of Unlike Eliminands with an Entity-Premiss,
27. Concl. wrong: right one is "Some pillows are not pokers."
28. Concl. right.
29. No Concl. Fallacy of Unlike Eliminands with an Entity-Premiss
30. No Concl Fallacy of Like Eliminands not asserted to exist.
31. Concl. right.
32. No Concl. Fallacy of Like Eliminands not asserted to exist.
33. No Concl. Fallacy of Unlike Eliminands with an Entity-Premiss.

Ex. 106—110 ; Sol. 149—154.]

34. Concl. wrong: right one is "Some dreaded persons are not begged to prolong their visits."
35. Concl. wrong: right one is "No man walks on neither."
36. Concl. right.
37. No Concl. Fallacy of Unlike Eliminands with an Entity-Premiss.
38. Concl. wrong: right one is "Some persons, dreaded by children, are not emperors."
39. Concl. incomplete: the omitted portion is "Sugar is not salt."
40. Concl. right.

Answers to § 8.

1. $a_1 b_0 \dagger b_1 a_0$.
2. $d_1 a_0$.
3. ac_0.
4. $a_1 d_0$.
5. cd_0.
6. $d_1 c_0$.
7. $a'c_0$.
8. $c_1 a'_0$.
9. $c'd_0$.
10. $b_1 a_0$.
11. $d_1 b_0$.
12. $a'd_0$.
13. $c_1 b_0$.
14. $d_1 e'_0$.
15. $c_1 a'_0$.
16. $b'c_0$.
17. $a_1 b_0$.
18. $d_1 c_0$.
19. $a_1 d_0$.
20. ac_0.
21. dc_0.
22. $a_1 b'_0$.
23. $h_1 c_0$.
24. $c_1 a_0$.
25. $c_1 c'_0$.
26. $c_1 c'_0$.
27. hk'_0.
28. $c_1 d'_0$.
29. $l'a_0$.
30. $k_1 b'_0$.

Answers to § 9.

1. Babies cannot manage crocodiles.
2. *Your* presents to me are not made of tin.
3. All my potatoes in this dish are old ones.
4. My servants never say "shpoonj."
5. My poultry are not officers.
6. None of *your* sons are fit to serve on a jury.
7. No pencils of mine are sugar-plums.
8. Jenkins is inexperienced.
9. No comet has a curly tail.
10. No hedge-hog takes in the *Times*.
11. This dish is unwholesome.
12. My gardener is very old.
13. All humming-birds are small.
14. No one with a hooked nose ever fails to make money.
15. No gray ducks in this village wear lace collars.
16. No jug in this cupboard will hold water.
17. These apples were grown in the sun.
18. Puppies, that will not lie still, never care to do worsted work.
19. No name in this list is unmelodious.
20. No M.P. should ride in a donkey-race, unless he has perfect self-command.
21. No goods in this shop, that are still on sale, may be carried away.

[Ex. 110—115; Sol. 154—159.

22. No acrobatic feat, which involves turning a quadruple somersault, is ever attempted in a circus.
23. Guinea-pigs never really appreciate Beethoven.
24. No scentless flowers please me.
25. Showy talkers are not really well-informed.
26. None but red-haired boys learn Greek in this school.
27. Wedding-cake always disagrees with me.
28. Discussions, that go on while Tomkins is in the chair, endanger the peacefulness of our Debating-Club.
29. All gluttons, who are children of mine, are unhealthy.
30. An egg of the Great Auk is not to be had for a song.
31. No books sold here have gilt edges, unless they are priced at 5*s.* and upwards.
32. When you cut your finger, you will find Tincture of Calendula useful.
33. *I* have never come across a mermaid at sea.
34. All the romances in this library are well-written.
35. No bird in this aviary lives on mince-pies.
36. No plum-pudding, that has not been boiled in a cloth, can be distinguished from soup.
37. All *your* poems are uninteresting.
38. None of my peaches have been grown in a hot-house.
39. No pawnbroker is dishonest.
40. No kitten with green eyes will play with a gorilla.
41. All *my* friends dine at the lower table.
42. My writing-desk is full of live scorpions.
43. No Mandarin ever reads Hogg's poems.
44. Shakespeare was clever.
45. Rainbows are not worth writing odes to.
46. These Sorites-examples are difficult.
47. All my dreams come true.
48. All the English pictures here are painted in oils.
49. Donkeys are not easy to swallow.
50. Opium-eaters never wear white kid gloves.
51. A good husband always comes home for his tea.
52. Bathing-machines are never made of mother-of-pearl.
53. Rainy days are always cloudy.
54. No heavy fish is unkind to children.
55. No engine-driver lives on barley-sugar.
56. All the animals in the yard gnaw bones.
57. No badger can guess a conundrum.
58. No cheque of yours, received by me, is payable to order.
59. I cannot read any of Brown's letters.
60. I always avoid a kangaroo.

CHAPTER III.

SOLUTIONS.

---

§ 1.

Propositions of Relation reduced to normal form.

Solutions for § 1.

---

1. The Univ. is "persons." The Individual "I" may be regarded as a Class, of persons, whose peculiar Attribute is "represented by the Name 'I'", and may be called the Class of "I's". It is evident that this Class cannot possibly contain more than one Member: hence the Sign of Quantity is "all". The verb "have been" may be replaced by the phrase "are persons who have been". The Proposition may be written thus:—

"All" . . . . *Sign of Quantity.*
"I's" . . . . *Subject.*
"are" . . . . *Copula.*
"persons who have been out for a walk" . . . . . *Predicate.*

or, more briefly,

"All | I's | are | persons who have been out for a walk".

2. The Univ. and the Subject are the same as in Ex. 1. The Proposition may be written

"All | I's | are | persons who feel better".

3. Univ. is "persons". The Subject is evidently the Class of persons from which John is *excluded: i.e.* it is the Class containing all persons who are *not* "John".

The Sign of Quantity is "no".

The verb "has read" may be replaced by the phrase "are persons who have read".

The Proposition may be written

"No | persons who are not 'John' | are | persons who have read the letter".

4. Univ. is "persons". The Subject is evidently the Class of persons whose only two Members are "you and I".

Hence the Sign of Quantity is "no".

The Proposition may be written

"No | Members of the Class 'you and I' | are | old persons"

[Ex. 97; Ans. 125.

5. Univ. is "creatures". The verb "run well" may be replaced by the phrase "are creatures that run well".
The Proposition may be written
"No | fat creatures | are | creatures that run well".

6. Univ. is "persons". The Subject is evidently the Class of persons who are *not* brave.
The verb "deserve" may be replaced by the phrase "are deserving of".
The Proposition may be written
"No | not-brave persons | are | persons deserving of the fair".

7. Univ. is "persons". The phrase "looks poetical" evidently belongs to the *Predicate:* and the *Subject* is the Class, of persons, whose peculiar Attribute is "*not*-pale".
The Proposition may be written
"No | not-pale persons | are | persons who look poetical".

8. Univ. is "persons".
The Proposition may be written
"Some | judges | are | persons who lose their tempers".

9. Univ. is "persons". The phrase "never neglect" is merely a stronger form of the phrase "am a person who does not neglect".
The Proposition may be written
"All | 'I's' | are | persons who do not neglect important business".

10. Univ. is "things". The phrase "what is difficult" (*i.e.* "that which is difficult") is equivalent to the phrase "all difficult things".
The Proposition may be written
"All | difficult things | are | things that need attention".

11. Univ. is "things". The phrase "what is unwholesome" may be interpreted as in Ex. 10.
The Proposition may be written
"All | unwholesome things | are | things that should be avoided".

12. Univ. is "laws". The Predicate is evidently a Class whose peculiar Attribute is "relating to excise".
The Proposition may be written
"All | laws passed last week | are | laws relating to excise".

13. Univ. is "things". The Subject is evidently the Class, of studies, whose peculiar Attribute is "logical": hence the Sign of Quantity is "all".
The Proposition may be written
"All | logical studies | are | things that puzzle me".

14. Univ. is "persons". The Subject is evidently "persons in the house".
The Proposition may be written
"No | persons in the house | are | Jews".

15. Univ. is "dishes". The phrase "if not well-cooked" is equivalent to the Attribute "not well-cooked".
The Proposition may be written
"Some | not well-cooked dishes | are | unwholesome dishes".

Ex. 97 ; Ans. 125.]

16. Univ. is "books". The phrase "make one drowsy" may be replaced by the phrase "are books that make one drowsy".
The Sign of Quantity is evidently "all".
The Proposition may be written
"All | unexciting books | are | books that make one drowsy".

17. Univ. is "men". The Subject is evidently "a man who knows what he's about"; and the word "when" shows that the Proposition is asserted of *every* such man, *i.e.* of *all* such men. The verb "can" may be replaced by "are men who can".
The Proposition may be written
"All | men who know what they're about | are | men who can detect a sharper".

18. The Univ. and the Subject are the same as in Ex. 4.
The Proposition may be written
"All | Members of the Class 'you and I' | are | persons who know what they're about".

19. Univ. is "persons. The verb "wear" may be replaced by the phrase "are accustomed to wear".
The Proposition may be written
"Some | bald persons | are | persons accustomed to wear wigs".

20. Univ. is "persons". The phrase "never talk" is merely a stronger form of "are persons who do not talk".
The Proposition may be written
"All | fully occupied persons | are | persons who do not talk about their grievances".

21. Univ. is "riddles". The phrase "if they can be solved" is equivalent to the Attribute "that can be solved".
The Proposition may be written
"No | riddles that can be solved | are | riddles that interest me".

---

§ 2.

Method of Diagrams.

Solutions for § 4, *Nos.* 1—12.

1. No m are x';
All m' are y.

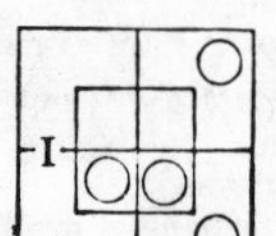

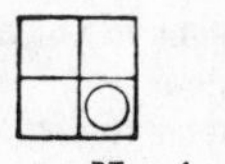

∴ No x' are y'.

[Ex. 97; Ans. 125, 127.

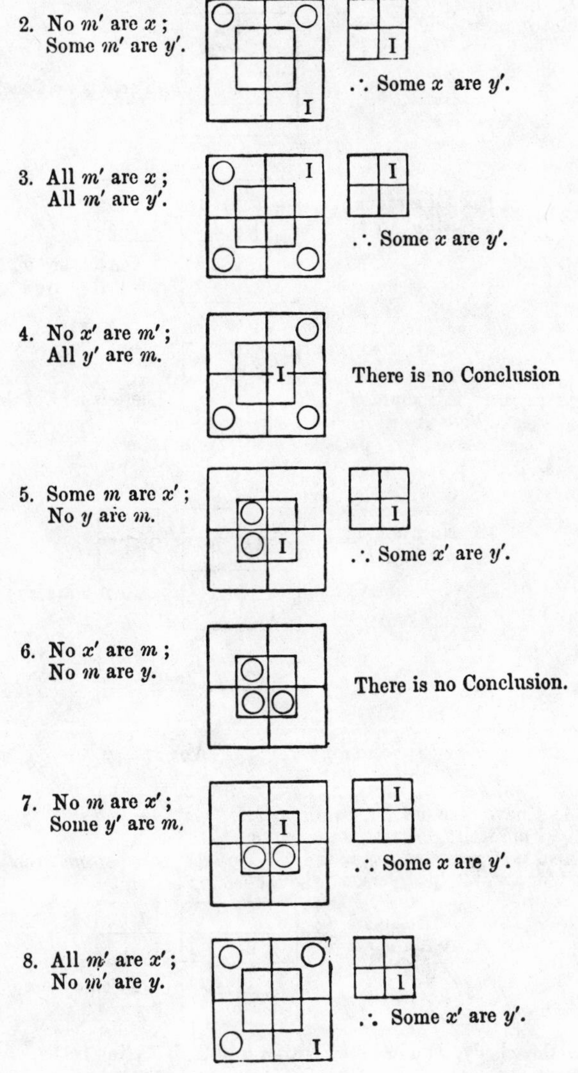

2. No m' are x;
Some m' are y'.
∴ Some x are y'.

3. All m' are x;
All m' are y'.
∴ Some x are y'.

4. No x' are m';
All y' are m.
There is no Conclusion

5. Some m are x';
No y are m.
∴ Some x' are y'.

6. No x' are m;
No m are y.
There is no Conclusion.

7. No m are x';
Some y' are m.
∴ Some x are y'.

8. All m' are x';
No m' are y.
∴ Some x' are y'.

Ex. 100; Ans. 127.]

9. Some x' are m';
No m are y'.

There is no Conclusion.

10. All x are m;
All y' are m'.

∴ All x are y;
All y' are x'.

11. No m are x;
All y' are m'.

There is no Conclusion.

12. No x are m;
All y are m.

∴ All y are x'.

Solutions for § 5, *Nos.* 1—12.

1. I have been out for a walk;
I am feeling better.

Univ. is "persons"; m = the Class of I's; x = persons who have been out for a walk; y = persons who are feeling better.

All m are x;
All m are y.

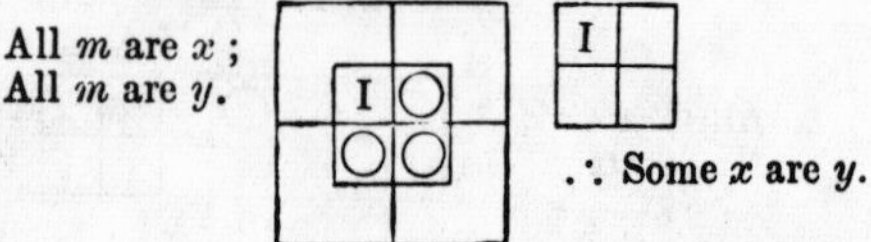

∴ Some x are y.

i.e. Somebody, who has been out for a walk, is feeling better.

[Ex. 100, 101; Ans. 127, 128.

2. No one has read the letter but John;
   No one, who has *not* read it, knows what it is about.

Univ. is "persons"; m = persons who have read the letter; x = the Class of Johns; y = persons who know what the letter is about.

No x' are m
No m' are y

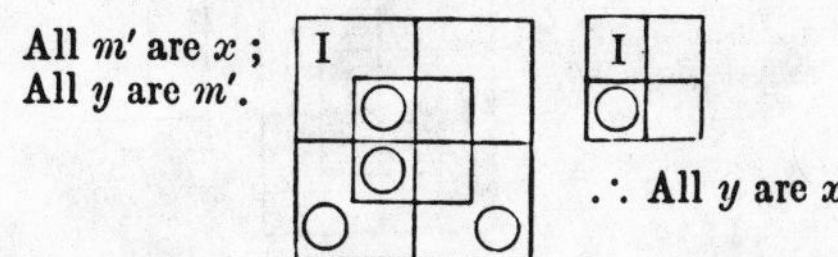

∴ No x' are y

i.e. No one, but John, knows what the letter is about.

3. Those who are not old like walking;
   You and I are young.

Univ. is "persons"; m = old; x = persons who like walking; y = you and I.

All m' are x;
All y are m'.

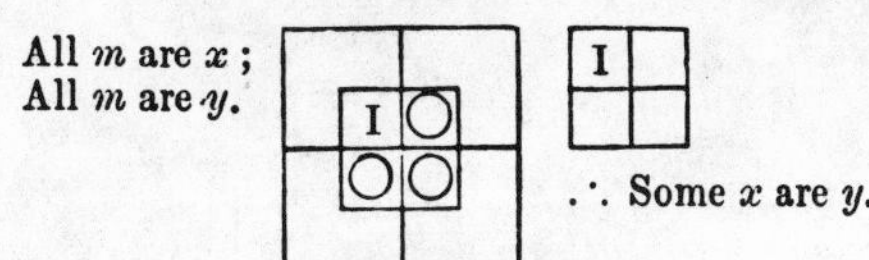

∴ All y are x.

i.e. You and I like walking.

4. Your course is always honest;
   Your course is always the best policy.

Univ. is "courses"; m = your; x = honest; y = courses which are the best policy.

All m are x;
All m are y.

∴ Some x are y.

i.e. Honesty is sometimes the best policy.

5. No fat creatures run well;
   Some greyhounds run well.

Univ. is "creatures"; m = creatures that run well: x = fat; y = greyhounds.

No x are m;
Some y are m.

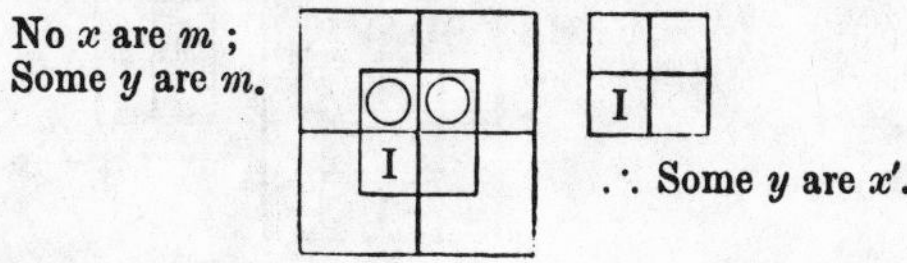

∴ Some y are x'.

i.e. Some greyhounds are not fat.

Ex. 101; Ans. 128.]

6. Some, who deserve the fair, get their deserts;
   None but the brave deserve the fair.

Univ. is "persons"; m = persons who deserve the fair; x = persons who get their deserts; y = brave.

Some m are x;
No y' are m.

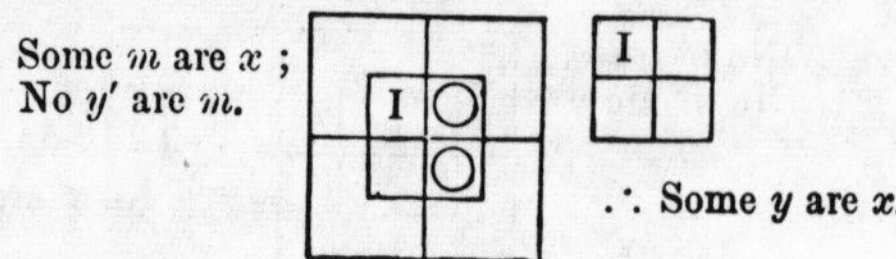

∴ Some y are x.

i.e. Some brave persons get their deserts.

7. Some Jews are rich;
   All Esquimaux are Gentiles.

Univ. is "persons"; m = Jews; x = rich; y = Esquimaux.

Some m are x;
All y are m'.

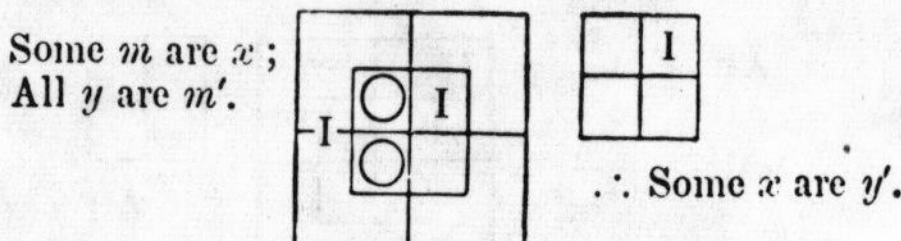

∴ Some x are y'.

i.e. Some rich persons are not Esquimaux.

8. Sugar-plums are sweet;
   Some sweet things are liked by children.

Univ. is "things"; m = sweet; x = sugar-plums; y = things that are liked by children.

All x are m;
Some m are y.

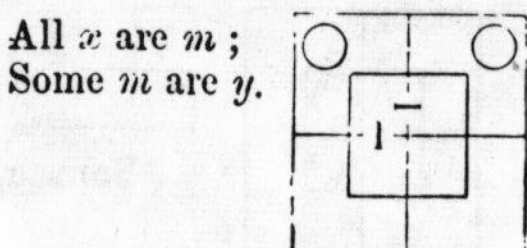

There is no Conclusion.

9. John is in the house;
   Everybody in the house is ill.

Univ. is "persons"; m = persons in the house; x = the Class of Johns; y = ill.

All x are m;
All m are y.

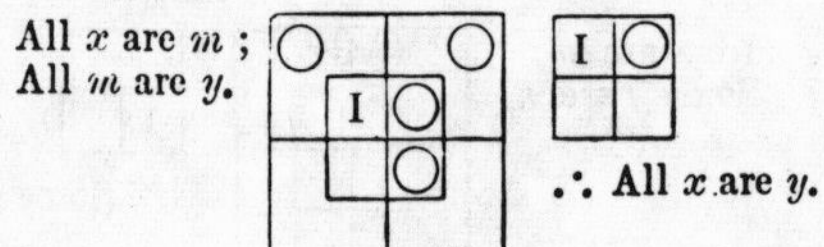

∴ All x are y.

i.e. John is ill.

[Ex. 101; Ans. 128.

10. Umbrellas are useful on a journey;
What is useless on a journey should be left behind.
Univ. is "things"; m = useful on a journey; x = umbrellas; y = things that should be left behind.

All x are m;
All m' are y.

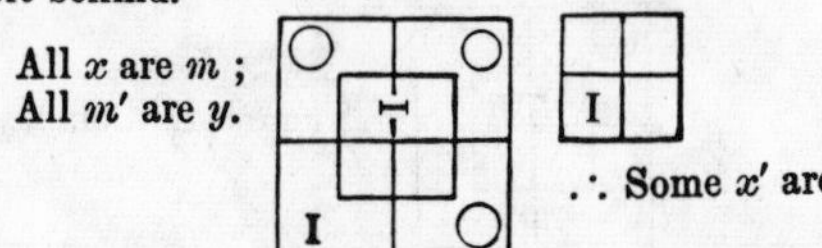

∴ Some x' are y.

i.e. Some things, that are not umbrellas, should be left behind on a journey.

11. Audible music causes vibration in the air;
Inaudible music is not worth paying for.
Univ. is "music"; m = audible; x = music that causes vibration in the air; y = worth paying for.

All m are x;
All m' are y'.

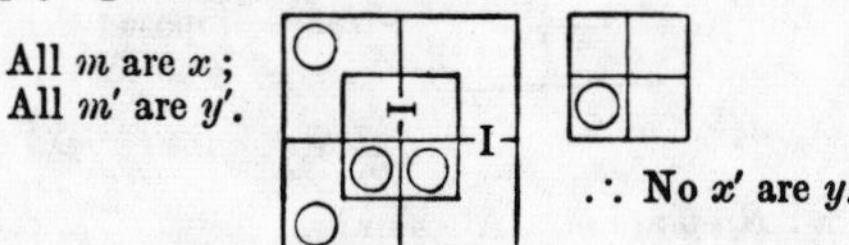

∴ No x' are y.

i.e. No music is worth paying for, unless it causes vibration in the air.

12. Some holidays are rainy;
Rainy days are tiresome.
Univ. is "days"; m = rainy; x = holidays; y = tiresome.

Some x are m;
All m are y.

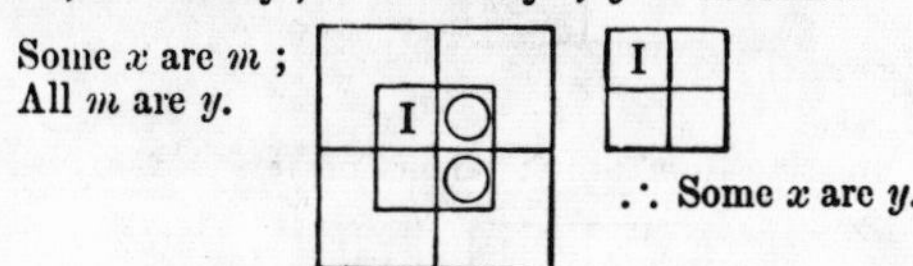

∴ Some x are y.

i.e. Some holidays are tiresome.

Solutions for § 6, *Nos.* 1—10.

1.

Some x are m; No m are y'. Some x are y.

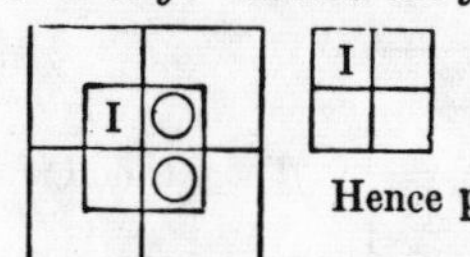

Hence proposed Conclusion is right.

Ex. 101, 106; Ans. 128, 130.]

2.

All x are m; No y are m'. No y are x'.

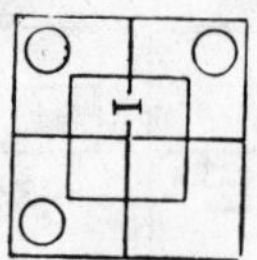

There is no Conclusion.

3.

Some x are m'; All y' are m. Some x are y.

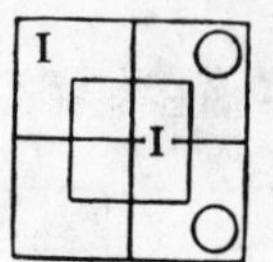

Hence proposed Conclusion is right.

4.

All x are m; No y are m. All x are y'.

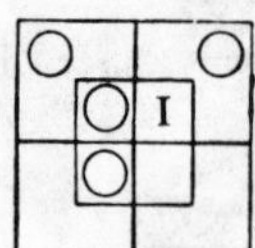

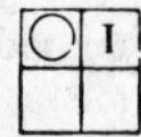

Hence proposed Conclusion is right.

5.

Some m' are x'; No m' are y. Some x' are y'.

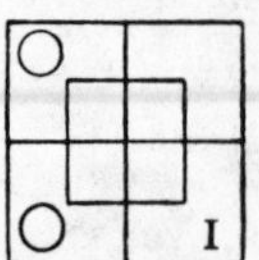

Hence proposed Conclusion is right.

6.

No x' are m; All y are m'. All y are x.

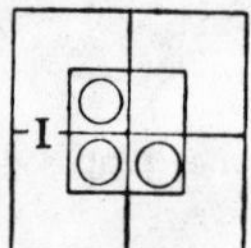

There is no Conclusion.

[Ex. 106; Ans. 130.

7.

Some m' are x'; All y' are m'. Some x' are y'.

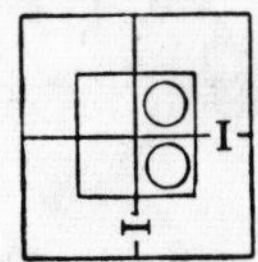

There is no Conclusion.

8.

No m' are x'; All y' are m'. All y' are x.

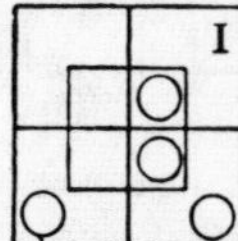

Hence proposed Conclusion is right.

9.

Some m are x'; No m are y. Some x' are y'.

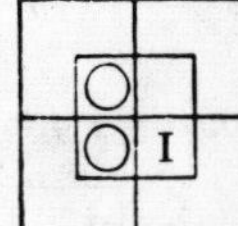

Hence proposed Conclusion is right.

10.

All m' are x'; All m are y. Some y are x'.

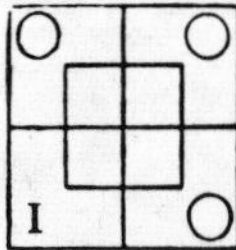

Hence proposed Conclusion is right

Solutions for § 7, *Nos.* 1–6.

1.

No doctors are enthusiastic ;
You are enthusiastic.
  You are not a doctor.

Univ. "persons" ; m = enthusiastic ; x = doctors ; y = you.

No x are m ;
All y are m.
  All y are x'.

∴ All y are x'.

Hence proposed Conclusion is right.

2.

All dictionaries are useful ;
Useful books are valuable.
  Dictionaries are valuable.

Univ. "books" ; m = useful ; x = dictionaries ; y = valuable.

All x are m ;
All m are y.
  All x are y.

∴ All x are y.

Hence proposed Conclusion is right.

3.

No misers are unselfish ;
None but misers save egg-shells.
  No unselfish people save egg-shells.

Univ. "people" ; m = misers ; x = selfish ; y = people who save egg-shells.

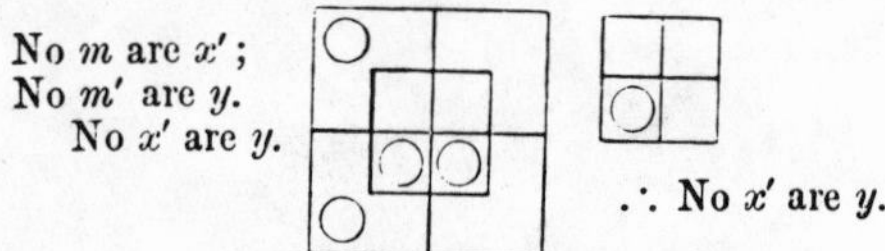

No m are x' ;
No m' are y.
  No x' are y.

∴ No x' are y.

Hence proposed Conclusion is right.

[Ex. 107 ; Ans. 131.

4.

Some epicures are ungenerous;
All my uncles are generous.
My uncles are not epicures.

Univ. "persons"; m = generous; x = epicures; y = my uncles.

Some x are m';
All y are m.
All y are x'.

∴ Some x are y'.

Hence proposed Conclusion is wrong, the right one being "Some epicure are not uncles of mine."

5.

Gold is heavy;
Nothing but gold will silence him.
Nothing light will silence him.

Univ. "things"; m = gold; x = heavy; y = able to silence him.

All m are x;
No m' are y.
No x' are y.

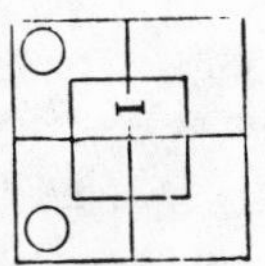

∴ No x' are y

Hence proposed Conclusion is right.

6.

Some healthy people are fat;
No unhealthy people are strong.
Some fat people are not strong.

Univ. "persons"; m = healthy; x = fat; y = strong.

Some m are x;
No m' are y.
Some x are y'.

There is no Conclusion.

---

§ 3.

Method of Subscripts.

Solutions for § 4.

1. $mx'_0 \dagger m'_1y'_0$ ⁋ $x'y'_0$ [Fig. I.
i.e. "No x' are y'."

2. $m'x_0 \dagger m'y'_1$ ⁋ $x'y'_1$ [Fig. II.
i.e. "Some x' are y'."

3. $m'_1x'_0 \dagger m'_1y_0$ ⁋ xy'_1 [Fig. III.
i.e. "Some x are y'."

4. $x'm'_0 \dagger y'_1m'_0$ ⁋ nothing.
[Fallacy of Like Eliminands not asserted to exist.]

5. $mx'_1 \dagger ym_0$ ⁋ $x'y'_1$ [Fig. II.
i.e. "Some x' are y'."

6. $x'm_0 \dagger my_0$ ⁋ nothing.
[Fallacy of Like Eliminands not asserted to exist.]

7. $mx'_0 \dagger y'm_1$ ⁋ xy'_1 [Fig. II.
i.e. "Some x are y'."

8. $m'_1x_0 \dagger m'y_0$ ⁋ $x'y'_1$ [Fig. III.
i.e. "Some x' are y'."

9. $x'm'_1 \dagger my_0$ ⁋ nothing.
[Fallacy of Unlike Eliminands with an Entity-Premiss.]

10. $x_1m'_0 \dagger y'_1m_0$ ⁋ $x_1y'_0 \dagger y'_1x_0$
[Fig. I. (β).
i.e. "All x are y, and all y' are x'."

11. $mx_0 \dagger y'_1m_0$ ⁋ nothing.
[Fallacy of Like Eliminands not asserted to exist.]

12. $xm_0 \dagger y_1m'_0$ ⁋ y_1x_0 [Fig. I. (α).
i.e. "All y are x'."

13. $m'_1x'_0 \dagger ym_0$ ⁋ $x'y_0$ [Fig. I.
i.e. "No x' are y."

14. $m_1x'_0 \dagger m'_1y'_0$ ⁋ $x'y'_0$ [Fig. I.
i.e. "No x' are y'."

15. $xm_0 \dagger m'y_0$ ⁋ xy_0 [Fig. I.
i.e. "No x are y."

16. $x_1m_0 \dagger y_1m'_0$ ⁋ $(x_1y_0 \dagger y_1x_0)$
[Fig. I. (β)
i.e. "All x are y' and all y are x'."

17. $xm_0 \dagger m'_1y'_0$ ⁋ xy'_0 [Fig. I.
i.e. "No x are y'."

18. $xm'_0 \dagger my_0$ ⁋ xy_0 [Fig. I.
i.e. "No x are y."

19. $m_1x'_0 \dagger m_1y_0$ ⁋ xy'_1 [Fig. III.
i.e. "Some x are y'."

20. $mx_0 \dagger m'_1y'_0$ ⁋ xy'_0 [Fig. I.
i.e. "No x are y'."

21. $x_1m'_0 \dagger m'y_1$ ⁋ $x'y_1$ Fig. II.
i.e. "Some x' are y."

22. $xm_1 \dagger y_1m'_0$ ⁋ nothing.
[Fallacy of Unlike Eliminands with an Entity-Premiss.]

23. $m_1x'_0 \dagger ym_1$ ⁋ xy_1 [Fig. II.
i.e. "Some x are y."

24. $xm_0 \dagger y_1m'_0$ ⁋ y_1x_0 [Fig. I. (α).
i.e. "All y are x'."

25. $mx'_1 \dagger my'_0$ ⁋ $x'y_1$ Fig. II.
i.e. "Some x' are y."

26. $mx'_0 \dagger y_1m'_0$ ⁋ $y_1x'_0$ [Fig. I. (α)
i.e. "All y are x."

27. $x_1m_0 \dagger y'_1m'_0$ ⁋ $(x_1y'_0 \dagger y'_1x_0)$
[Fig. I. (β)
i.e. "All x are y, and all y' are x'."

28. $m_1x_0 \dagger my_1$ ⁋ $x'y_1$ [Fig. II.
i.e. "Some x' are y."

29. $mx_0 \dagger y_1m_0$ ⁋ nothing.
[Fallacy of Like Eliminands not asserted to exist.]

30. $x_1m'_0 \dagger ym_1$ ⁋ $x'y_1$ Fig. II.
i.e. "Some y are x'."

31. $x_1m'_0 \dagger y_1m'_0$ ⁋ nothing.
[Fallacy of Like Eliminands not asserted to exist.]

[Ex. 100; Ans. 127, 128.

32. $xm_0 \dagger m_1y'_0 \mathbb{P} xy'_0$ [Fig. I.
i.e. "No x are y'."

33. $mx_0 \dagger my_0 \mathbb{P}$ nothing.
[Fallacy of Like Eliminands not asserted to exist.]

34. $mx'_0 \dagger ym_1 \mathbb{P} xy_1$ [Fig. II.
i.e. "Some x are y."

35. $mx_0 \dagger y_1m'_0 \mathbb{P} y_1x_0$ [Fig. I. (α).
i.e. "All y are x'."

36. $m_1x_0 \dagger ym_1 \mathbb{P} x'y_1$ [Fig. II.
i.e. "Some x' are y."

37. $m_1x'_0 \dagger ym_0 \mathbb{P} xy'_1$ [Fig. III.
i.e. "Some x are y'."

38. $mx_0 \dagger m'y_0 \mathbb{P} xy_0$ [Fig. I.
i.e. "No x are y."

39. $mx'_1 \dagger my_0 \mathbb{P} x'y'_1$ [Fig. II.
i.e. "Some x' are y'."

40. $x'm_0 \dagger y'_1m'_0 \mathbb{P} y'_1x'_0$ [Fig. I. (α)
i.e. "All y' are x."

41. $x_1m_0 \dagger ym'_0 \mathbb{P} x_1y_0$ [Fig. I. (α).
i.e. "All x are y'."

42. $m'x_0 \dagger ym_0 \mathbb{P} xy_0$ [Fig. I.
i.e "No x are y."

Solutions for § 5, *Nos.* 13—24.

---

13. No Frenchmen like plumpudding;
All Englishmen like plumpudding.

Univ. "men"; m = liking plumpudding; x = French; y = English.

$$xm_0 \dagger y_1m'_0 \mathbb{P} y_1x_0 \quad \text{[Fig. I}(\alpha).$$

i.e. Englishmen are not Frenchmen.

14. No portrait of a lady, that makes her simper or scowl, is satisfactory:
No photograph of a lady ever fails to make her simper or scowl.

Univ. "portraits of ladies"; m = making the subject simper or scowl; x = satisfactory; y = photographic.

$$mx_0 \dagger ym'_0 \mathbb{P} xy_0 \quad \text{[Fig. I.}$$

i.e. No photograph of a lady is satisfactory.

15. All pale people are phlegmatic;
No one looks poetical unless he is pale.

Univ. "people"; m = pale; x = phlegmatic; y = looking poetical.

$$m_1x'_0 \dagger m'y_0 \mathbb{P} x'y_0 \quad \text{[Fig. I.}$$

i.e. No one looks poetical unless he is phlegmatic.

16. No old misers are cheerful;
Some old misers are thin.

Univ. "persons"; m = old misers; x = cheerful; y = thin.

$$mx_0 \dagger my_1 \mathbb{P} x'y_1 \quad \text{[Fig. II.}$$

i.e. Some thin persons are not cheerful.

17. No one, who exercises self-control, fails to keep his temper;
Some judges lose their tempers.

Univ. "persons"; m = keeping their tempers : x = exercising self-control; y = judges.

$$xm'_0 \dagger ym'_1 \mathbb{P} x'y_1 \quad \text{[Fig. II.}$$

i.e. Some judges do not exercise self-control.

Ex. 100, 101; Ans. 28.]

18. All pigs are fat;
Nothing that is fed on barley-water is fat.

Univ. is "things"; m = fat; x = pigs; y = fed on barley-water.

$x_1m'_0 \dagger ym_0 \P x_1y_0$ [Fig. I. (*a*).

i.e. Pigs are not fed on barley-water.

19. All rabbits, that are not greedy, are black;
No old rabbits are free from greediness.

Univ. is "rabbits"; m = greedy; x = black; y = old.

$m'_1x'_0 \dagger ym'_0 \P xy'_1$ [Fig. III.

i.e. Some black rabbits are not old.

20. Some pictures are not first attempts;
No first attempts are really good.

Univ. is "things"; m = first attempts; x = pictures; y = really good.

$xm'_1 \dagger my_0 \P$ nothing.

[Fallacy of Unlike Eliminands with an Entity-Premiss]

21. I never neglect important business;
Your business is unimportant.

Univ. is "business"; m = important; x = neglected by me; y = your.

$mx_0 \dagger y_1m_0 \P$ nothing.

[Fallacy of Like Eliminands not asserted to exist.]

22. Some lessons are difficult;
What is difficult needs attention.

Univ. is "things"; m = difficult; x = lessons; y = needing attention.

$xm_1 \dagger m_1y'_0 \P xy_1$ [Fig II.

i.e. Some lessons need attention.

23. All clever people are popular;
All obliging people are popular.

Univ. is "people"; m = popular; x = clever; y = obliging.

$x_1m'_0 \dagger y_1m'_0 \P$ nothing.

[Fallacy of Like Eliminands not asserted to exist.]

24. Thoughtless people do mischief;
No thoughtful person forgets a promise.

Univ. is "persons"; m = thoughtful; x = mischievous; y = forgetful of promises.

$m'_1x'_0 \dagger my_0 \P x'y_0$

i.e. No one, who forgets a promise, fails to do mischief.

Solutions for § 6.

1. $xm_1 \dagger my'_0 \P xy_1$ [Fig. II.] Concl. right.
2. $x_1m'_0 \dagger ym'_0$ Fallacy of Like Eliminands not asserted to exist.
3. $xm'_1 \dagger y'_1m'_0 \P xy_1$ [Fig. II.] Concl. right.

[Ex. 102, 106; Ans. 128—130.

4. $x_1m'_0 \dagger ym_0$ ℙ x_1y_0 [Fig. I (α).] Concl. right.
5. $m'x'_1 \dagger m'y_0$ ℙ $x'y'_1$ [Fig. II.] ,,
6. $x'm_0 \dagger y_1m_0$ Fallacy of Like Eliminands not asserted to exist.
7. $m'x'_1 \dagger y'_1m_0$ Fallacy of Unlike Eliminands with an Entity-Premiss.
8. $m'x'_0 \dagger y'_1m_0$ ℙ $y'_1x'_0$ [Fig. I (α).] Concl. right.
9. $mx'_1 \dagger my_0$ ℙ $x'y'_1$ [Fig. II.] ,,
10. $m'_1x_0 \dagger m'_1y'_0$ ℙ $x'y_1$ [Fig. III.] ,,
11. $x_1m_0 \dagger ym_1$ ℙ $x'y_1$ [Fig. II.] ,,
12. $xm_0 \dagger m'y'_0$ ℙ xy'_0 [Fig. I.] ,,
13. $xm_0 \dagger y_1'm'_0$ ℙ y'_1x_0 [Fig. I (α).] ,,
14. $m'_1x_0 \dagger m'_1y'_0$ ℙ $x'y_1$ [Fig. III.] ,,
15. $mx'_1 \dagger y_1m_0$ ℙ $x'y'_1$ [Fig. II.] ,,
16. $x'm_0 \dagger y'_1m_0$ Fallacy of Like Eliminands not asserted to exist.
17. $m'x_0 \dagger m'_1y_0$ ℙ $x'y'_1$ [Fig. III.] Concl. right.
18. $x'm_0 \dagger my_1$ ℙ xy_1 [Fig. II.] ,,
19. $mx'_1 \dagger m_1y'_0$ ℙ $x'y_1$ [,,] ,,
20. $x'm'_0 \dagger m'y'_1$ ℙ xy'_1 [,,] ,,
21. $mx_0 \dagger m_1y_0$ ℙ $x'y'_1$ [Fig. III.] ,,
22. $x'_1m'_0 \dagger ym'_1$ ℙ xy_1 [Fig. II.] Concl. wrong: the right one is "Some x are y."
23. $m_1x'_0 \dagger m'y'_0$ ℙ $x'y'_0$ [Fig. I.] Concl. right.
24. $x_1m_0 \dagger m'_1y'_0$ ℙ $x_1y'_0$ [Fig. I. (α)] ,,
25. $xm'_0 \dagger m_1y'_0$ ℙ xy'_0 [Fig. I.] ,
26. $m_1x_0 \dagger y_1m'_0$ ℙ y_1x_0 [Fig. I (α).] ,,
27. $x_1m'_0 \dagger my'_0$ ℙ $x_1y'_0$ [,,] ,,
28. $x_1m'_0 \dagger y'm'_0$ Fallacy of Like Eliminands not asserted to exist.
29. $x'm_0 \dagger m'y'_0$ ℙ $x'y'_0$ [Fig. I.] Concl. right.
30. $x_1m'_0 \dagger m_1y_0$ ℙ x_1y_0 [Fig. I (α).] ,,
31. $x'_1m_0 \dagger y'm'_0$ ℙ $x'_1y'_0$ [,,] ,,
32. $xm_0 \dagger y'm'_0$ ℙ xy'_0 [Fig. I.] ,,
33. $m_1x_0 \dagger y'_1m'_0$ ℙ y'_1x_0 [Fig. I. (α)] ,,
34. $x_1m_0 \dagger ym'_1$ Fallacy of Unlike Eliminands with an Entity-Premiss.
35. $xm_1 \dagger m_1y'_0$ ℙ xy_1 [Fig. II.] Concl. right.
36. $m_1x_0 \dagger y_1m'_0$ ℙ y_1x_0 [Fig. I (α).] ,,
37. $mx'_0 \dagger m_1y_0$ ℙ xy'_1 [Fig. III.] ,,
38. $xm_0 \dagger my'_0$ Fallacy of Like Eliminands not asserted to exist.
39. $mx_0 \dagger my'_1$ ℙ $x'y'_1$ [Fig. II.] Concl. right.
40. $mx'_0 \dagger ym_1$ ℙ xy_1 [Fig. II.] ,,

Ex. 106, 107 ; Ans. 130, 131.]

Solutions for § 7.

---

1. No doctors are enthusiastic;
You are enthusiastic.
You are not a doctor.

Univ. "persons"; m = enthusiastic; x = doctors; y = you.

$xm_0 \dagger y_1 m'_0$ ⁋ $y_1 x_0$ [Fig. I(α).

Conclusion right.

2. Dictionaries are useful;
Useful books are valuable.
Dictionaries are valuable.

Univ. "books"; m = useful; x = dictionaries; y = valuable.

$x_1 m'_0 \dagger m_1 y'_0$ ⁋ $x_1 y'_0$ [Fig. I(α).

Conclusion right.

3. No misers are unselfish;
None but misers save egg-shells.
No unselfish people save egg-shells.

Univ. "people"; m = misers; x = selfish; y = people who save egg-shells.

$mx'_0 \dagger m'y_0$ ⁋ $x'y_0$ [Fig. I.

Conclusion right.

4. Some epicures are ungenerous;
All my uncles are generous.
My uncles are not epicures.

Univ. "persons"; m = generous; x = epicures; y = my uncles.

$xm'_1 \dagger y_1 m'_0$ ⁋ xy'_1 [Fig. II.

Conclusion wrong: right one is "Some epicures are not uncles of mine."

5. Gold is heavy;
Nothing but gold will silence him.
Nothing light will silence him.

Univ. "things"; m = gold; x = heavy; y = able to silence him.

$m_1 x'_0 \dagger m'y_0$ ⁋ $x'y_0$ [Fig. I.

Conclusion right.

6. Some healthy people are fat;
No unhealthy people are strong.
Some fat people are not strong.

Univ. "people"; m = healthy; x = fat; y = strong.

$mx_1 \dagger m'y_0$

No Conclusion. [Fallacy of Unlike Eliminands with an Entity-Premiss.]

7. I saw it in a newspaper;
All newspapers tell lies.
It was a lie.

Univ. "publications"; m = newspapers; x = publications in which I saw it; y = telling lies.

$x_1 m'_0 \dagger m_1 y'_0$ ⁋ $x_1 y'_0$ [Fig. I(α).

Conclusion wrong: right one is "The publication, in which I saw it, tells lies."

[Ex. 107, 108; Ans. 131.

8. Some cravats are not artistic;
I admire anything artistic.
There are some cravats that I do not admire.

Univ. "things"; m = artistic; x = cravats; y = things that I admire.

$$xm'_1 \dagger m_1y'_0$$

No Conclusion. [Fallacy of Unlike Eliminands with an Entity-Premiss.]

9. His songs never last an hour.
A song, that lasts an hour, is tedious.
His songs are never tedious.

Univ. "songs"; m = lasting an hour; x = his; y = tedious.

$$x_1m_0 \dagger m_1y'_0 \text{ ℙ } x'y_1 \quad \text{[Fig. III.}$$

Conclusion wrong: right one is "Some tedious songs are not his."

10. Some candles give very little light;
Candles are *meant* to give light.
Some things, that are meant to give light, give very little.

Univ. "things"; m = candles; x = giving &c.; y = meant &c.

$$mx_1 \dagger m_1y'_0 \text{ ℙ } xy_1 \quad \text{[Fig. II.}$$

Conclusion right.

11. All, who are anxious to learn, work hard.
Some of these boys work hard.
Some of these boys are anxious to learn.

Univ. "persons"; m = hard-working; x = anxious to learn; y = these boys.

$$x_1m'_0 \dagger ym_1$$

No Conclusion. [Fallacy of Unlike Eliminands with an Entity-Premiss.]

12. All lions are fierce;
Some lions do not drink coffee.
Some creatures that drink coffee are not fierce.

Univ. "creatures"; m = lions; x = fierce; y = creatures that drink coffee.

$$m_1x'_0 \dagger my'_1 \text{ ℙ } xy'_1 \quad \text{[Fig. II.}$$

Conclusion wrong: right one is "Some fierce creatures do not drink coffee."

13. No misers are generous;
Some old men are ungenerous.
Some old men are misers

Univ. "persons"; m = generous; x = misers; y = old men.

$$xm_0 \dagger ym'_1$$

No Conclusion. [Fallacy of Unlike Eliminands with an Entity-Premiss.]

14. No fossil can be crossed in love;
An oyster may be crossed in love.
Oysters are not fossils.

Univ. "things"; m = things that can be crossed in love; x = fossils; y = oysters.

$$xm_0 \dagger y_1m'_0 \text{ ℙ } y_1x_0 \quad \text{[Fig. I}(\alpha).$$

Conclusion right.

Ex. 108; Ans. 131.]

15. All uneducated people are shallow;
Students are all educated.
No students are shallow.

Univ. "people"; m = educated; x = shallow; y = students.

$m'_1 x'_0 \dagger y_1 m'_0 ¶ x y'_1$ [Fig. III.

Conclusion wrong: right one is "Some shallow people are not students."

16. All young lambs jump;
No young animals are healthy, unless they jump.
All young lambs are healthy.

Univ. "young animals"; m = young animals that jump; x = lambs y = healthy.

$x_1 m'_0 \dagger m' y_0$

No Conclusion. [Fallacy of Like Eliminands not asserted to exist.]

17. Ill-managed business is unprofitable;
Railways are never ill-managed.
All railways are profitable.

Univ. "business"; m = ill-managed; x = profitable; y = railways.

$m_1 x_0 \dagger y_1 m_0 ¶ x' y'_1$ [Fig. III.

Conclusion wrong: right one is "Some business, other than railways, is unprofitable."

18. No Professors are ignorant;
All ignorant people are vain.
No Professors are vain.

Univ. "people"; m = ignorant; x = Professors; y = vain.

$x m_0 \dagger m_1 y'_0 ¶ x' y_1$ [Fig. III.

Conclusion wrong: right one is "Some vain persons are not Professors."

19. A prudent man shuns hyænas;
No banker is imprudent.
No banker fails to shun hyænas.

Univ. "men"; m = prudent; x = shunning hyænas; y = bankers.

$m_1 x'_0 \dagger y m'_0 ¶ x' y_0$ [Fig. 1.

Conclusion right.

20. All wasps are unfriendly;
No puppies are unfriendly.
No puppies are wasps.

Univ. "creatures"; m = friendly; x = wasps; y = puppies.

$x_1 m_0 \dagger y m'_0 ¶ x_1 y_0$ [Fig. I(*α*).

Conclusion incomplete: complete one is "Wasps are not puppies".

21. No Jews are honest;
Some Gentiles are rich.
Some rich people are dishonest.

Univ. "persons"; m = Jews; x = honest; y = rich.

$m x_0 \dagger m' y_1$

No Conclusion. [Fallacy of Unlike Eliminands with an Entity-Premiss.]

[Ex. 108, 109; Ans. 131.

22. No idlers win fame;
Some painters are not idle.
Some painters win fame.

Univ. "persons"; m = idlers; x = persons who win fame; y = painters.

$mx_0 \dagger ym'_1$

No Conclusion. [Fallacy of Unlike Eliminands with an Entity-Premiss.]

23. No monkeys are soldiers;
All monkeys are mischievous.
Some mischievous creatures are not soldiers.

Univ. "creatures"; m = monkeys; x = soldiers; y = mischievous.

$mx_0 \dagger m_1y'_0$ ⁋ $x'y_1$ [Fig. III.

Conclusion right.

24. All these bonbons are chocolate-creams;
All these bonbons are delicious.
Chocolate-creams are delicious.

Univ. "food"; m = these bonbons; x = chocolate-creams; y = delicious.

$m_1x'_0 \dagger m_1y'_0$ ⁋ xy_1 [Fig. III.

Conclusion wrong, being in excess of the right one, which is "*Some* chocolate-creams are delicious."

25. No muffins are wholesome;
All buns are unwholesome.
Buns are not muffins.

Univ. "food"; m = wholesome; x = muffins; y = buns.

$xm_0 \dagger y_1m_0$

No Conclusion. [Fallacy of Like Eliminands not asserted to exist.]

26. Some unauthorised reports are false;
All authorised reports are trustworthy.
Some false reports are not trustworthy.

Univ. "reports"; m = authorised; x = true; y = trustworthy.

$m'x'_1 \dagger m_1y'_0$

No Conclusion. [Fallacy of Unlike Eliminands with an Entity-Premiss.]

27. Some pillows are soft;
No pokers are soft.
Some pokers are not pillows.

Univ. "things"; m = soft; x = pillows; y = pokers.

$xm_1 \dagger ym_0$ ⁋ xy'_1 [Fig. II.

Conclusion wrong: right one is "Some pillows are not pokers."

28. Improbable stories are not easily believed;
None of his stories are probable.
None of his stories are easily believed.

Univ. "stories"; m = probable; x = easily believed; y = his.

$m'_1x_0 \dagger ym_0$ ⁋ xy_0 [Fig. I.

Conclusion right.

Ex. 109; Ans. 131.]

29. No thieves are honest;
Some dishonest people are found out.
Some thieves are found out.

Univ. "people"; m = honest; x = thieves; y = found out.

$$xm_0 \dagger m'y_1$$

No Conclusion. [Fallacy of Unlike Eliminands with an Entity-Premiss.]

30. No muffins are wholesome;
All puffy food is unwholesome.
All muffins are puffy.

Univ. is "food"; m = wholesome; x = muffins; y = puffy.

$$xm_0 \dagger y_1m_0$$

No Conclusion. [Fallacy of Like Eliminands not asserted to exist.]

31. No birds, except peacocks, are proud of their tails;
Some birds, that are proud of their tails, cannot sing.
Some peacocks cannot sing.

Univ. "birds"; m = proud of their tails; x = peacocks; y = birds that can sing.

$$x'm_0 \dagger my'_1 \Vdash xy'_1 \quad \text{[Fig. II.}$$

Conclusion right.

32. Warmth relieves pain;
Nothing, that does not relieve pain, is useful in toothache.
Warmth is useful in toothache.

Univ. "applications"; m = relieving pain; x = warmth; y = useful in toothache.

$$x_1m'_0 \dagger m'y_0$$

No Conclusion. [Fallacy of Like Eliminands not asserted to exist.]

33. No bankrupts are rich;
Some merchants are not bankrupts.
Some merchants are rich.

Univ. "persons"; m = bankrupts; x = rich; y = merchants.

$$mx_0 \dagger ym'_1$$

No Conclusion. [Fallacy of Unlike Eliminands with an Entity-Premiss.]

34. Bores are dreaded;
No bore is ever begged to prolong his visit.
No one, who is dreaded, is ever begged to prolong his visit.

Univ. "persons"; m = bores; x = dreaded; y = begged to prolong their visits.

$$m_1x'_0 \dagger my_0 \Vdash xy'_1 \quad \text{[Fig. III.}$$

Conclusion wrong: the right one is "Some dreaded persons are not begged to prolong their visits."

35. All wise men walk on their feet;
All unwise men walk on their hands.
No man walks on both.

Univ. "men"; m = wise; x = walking on their feet; y = walking on their hands.

$$m_1x'_0 \dagger m'_1y'_0 \Vdash x'y'_0 \quad \text{[Fig. I.}$$

Conclusion wrong: right one is "No man walks on neither."

[Ex. 109, 110; Ans. 131, 132.

36. No wheelbarrows are comfortable ;
No uncomfortable vehicles are popular.
No wheelbarrows are popular.

Univ. "vehicles" ; m = comfortable ; x = wheelbarrows ; y = popular.

$$xm_0 \dagger m'x_0 \Vdash xy_0 \quad \text{[Fig. I.}$$

Conclusion right.

37. No frogs are poetical ;
Some ducks are unpoetical.
Some ducks are not frogs.

Univ. "creatures" ; m = poetical ; x = frogs ; y = ducks.

$$xm_0 \dagger ym'_1$$

No Conclusion. [Fallacy of Unlike Eliminands with an Entity-Premiss.]

38. No emperors are dentists ;
All dentists are dreaded by children.
No emperors are dreaded by children.

Univ. "persons" ; m = dentists ; x = emperors ; y = dreaded by children.

$$xm_0 \dagger m_1y'_0 \Vdash x'y_1 \quad \text{[Fig. III.}$$

Conclusion wrong : right one is "Some persons, dreaded by children, are not emperors."

39. Sugar is sweet ;
Salt is not sweet.
Salt is not sugar.

Univ. "things" ; m = sweet ; x = sugar ; y = salt.

$$x_1m'_0 \dagger y_1m_0 \Vdash (x_1y_0 \dagger y_1x_0) \quad \text{[Fig. I } (\beta).$$

Conclusion incomplete : omitted portion is "Sugar is not salt."

40. Every eagle can fly ;
Some pigs cannot fly.
Some pigs are not eagles.

Univ. "creatures" ; m = creatures that can fly ; x = eagles ; y = pigs.

$$x_1m'_0 \dagger ym'_1 \Vdash x'y_1 \quad \text{[Fig. II.}$$

Conclusion right.

Solutions for § 8.

1. $\overset{1}{cd_0} \dagger \overset{2}{a_1d'_0} \dagger \overset{3}{b_1c'_0}$; $\overset{1}{\underline{c}\,\underline{d}} \dagger \overset{2}{a\,\underline{\underline{d'}}} \dagger \overset{3}{b\,\underline{\underline{c'}}} \Vdash ab_0 \dagger a_1 \dagger b_1$
i.e. $\Vdash a_1b_0 \dagger b_1a_0$

2. $\overset{1}{d_1b'_0} \dagger \overset{2}{ac'_0} \dagger \overset{3}{bc_0}$; $\overset{1}{d\,\underline{b'}} \dagger \overset{3}{\underline{\underline{b}}\,\underline{c}} \dagger \overset{2}{a\,\underline{\underline{c'}}} \Vdash da_0 \dagger d_1$ i.e. $\Vdash d_1a_0$

3. $\overset{1}{ba_0} \dagger \overset{2}{cd'_0} \dagger \overset{3}{d_1b'_0}$; $\overset{1}{\underline{b}\,a} \dagger \overset{3}{\underline{d}\,\underline{\underline{b'}}} \dagger \overset{2}{c\,\underline{\underline{d'}}} \Vdash ac_0$

4. $\overset{1}{bc_0} \dagger \overset{2}{a_1b'_0} \dagger \overset{3}{c'd_0}$; $\overset{1}{\underline{b}\,\underline{c}} \dagger \overset{2}{a\,\underline{b'}} \dagger \overset{3}{\underline{\underline{c'}}d} \Vdash ad_0 \dagger a_1$ i.c $\Vdash a_1d_0$

Ex 110 ; Ans. 132.]

5. $\overset{1}{b'_1a_0} \dagger \overset{2}{bc_0} \dagger \overset{3}{a'd_0}$; $\overset{1}{\underline{b'}\underline{\underline{a}}} \dagger \overset{2}{\underline{\underline{b}}c} \dagger \overset{3}{\underline{\underline{a'}}d} \;\P\; cd_0$

6. $\overset{1}{a_1b_0} \dagger \overset{2}{b'c_0} \dagger \overset{3}{d_1a'_0}$; $\overset{1}{\underline{\underline{a}}\,\underline{b}} \dagger \overset{2}{\underline{\underline{b'}}c} \dagger \overset{3}{d\,\underline{\underline{a'}}} \;\P\; cd_0 \dagger d_1$ i.e. $\P\; d_1c_0$

7. $\overset{1}{db'_0} \dagger \overset{2}{b_1a'_0} \dagger \overset{3}{cd'_0}$; $\overset{1}{\underline{d}\,\underline{b'}} \dagger \overset{2}{\underline{\underline{b}}\,a'} \dagger \overset{3}{c\,\underline{\underline{d'}}} \;\P\; a'c_0$

8. $\overset{1}{b'd_0} \dagger \overset{2}{a'b_0} \dagger \overset{3}{c_1d'_0}$; $\overset{1}{\underline{b'}\underline{d}} \dagger \overset{2}{a'\underline{\underline{b}}} \dagger \overset{3}{c\,\underline{\underline{d'}}} \;\P\; a'c_0 \dagger c_1$ i.e. $\P\; c_1a'_0$

9. $\overset{1}{b'_1a'_0} \dagger \overset{2}{ad_0} \dagger \overset{3}{b_1c'_0}$; $\overset{1}{\underline{b'}\underline{\underline{a'}}} \dagger \overset{2}{\underline{\underline{a}}\,d} \dagger \overset{3}{\underline{\underline{b}}\,c'} \;\P\; dc'_0$

10. $\overset{1}{cd_0} \dagger \overset{2}{b_1c'_0} \dagger \overset{3}{ad'_0}$; $\overset{1}{\underline{c}\,\underline{d}} \dagger \overset{2}{b\,\underline{\underline{c'}}} \dagger \overset{3}{a\,\underline{\underline{d'}}} \;\P\; ba_0 \dagger b_1$ i.e. $\P\; b_1a_0$

11. $\overset{1}{bc_0} \dagger \overset{2}{d_1a'_0} \dagger \overset{3}{c'_1a_0}$; $\overset{1}{b\,\underline{c}} \dagger \overset{3}{\underline{\underline{c'}}\underline{a}} \dagger \overset{2}{d\underline{\underline{a'}}} \;\P\; bd_0 \dagger d_1$ i.e. $\P\; d_1b_0$

12. $\overset{1}{cb'_0} \dagger \overset{2}{c'_1d_0} \dagger \overset{3}{b_1a'_0}$; $\overset{1}{\underline{c}\,\underline{b'}} \dagger \overset{2}{\underline{\underline{c'}}d} \dagger \overset{3}{\underline{\underline{b}}\,a'} \;\P\; da'_0$

13. $\overset{1}{d_1e'_0} \dagger \overset{2}{c_1a'_0} \dagger \overset{3}{bd'_0} \dagger \overset{4}{e_1a_0}$; $\overset{1}{\underline{d}\,\underline{e'}} \dagger \overset{3}{b\,\underline{\underline{d'}}} \dagger \overset{4}{\underline{e}\,\underline{a}} \dagger \overset{2}{c\,\underline{\underline{a'}}} \;\P\; bc_0 \dagger c_1$
i.e. $\P\; c_1b_0$

14. $\overset{1}{c_1b'_0} \dagger \overset{2}{a_1e'_0} \dagger \overset{3}{d_1b_0} \dagger \overset{4}{a'_1c'_0}$; $\overset{1}{\underline{c}\,\underline{b'}} \dagger \overset{3}{d\,\underline{\underline{b}}} \dagger \overset{4}{\underline{a'}\underline{\underline{c'}}} \dagger \overset{2}{\underline{\underline{a}}\,e'} \;\P\; dc'_0 \dagger d_1$
i.e. $\P\; d_1c'_0$

15. $\overset{1}{b'd_0} \dagger \overset{2}{e_1c'_0} \dagger \overset{3}{b_1a'_0} \dagger \overset{4}{d'_1c_0}$; $\overset{1}{\underline{b'}\underline{d}} \dagger \overset{3}{\underline{\underline{b}}\,a'} \dagger \overset{4}{\underline{\underline{d'}}\underline{c}} \dagger \overset{2}{e\,\underline{\underline{c'}}} \;\P\; a'c_0 \dagger c_1$
i.e. $\P\; c_1a'_0$

16. $\overset{1}{a'c_0} \dagger \overset{2}{d_1c_0} \dagger \overset{3}{a_1b'_0} \dagger \overset{4}{c'_1d'_0}$; $\overset{1}{\underline{a'}\underline{c}} \dagger \overset{3}{\underline{\underline{a}}\,b'} \dagger \overset{4}{\underline{\underline{c'}}\underline{d'}} \dagger \overset{2}{\underline{\underline{d}}\,c} \;\P\; b'c_0$

17. $\overset{1}{d_1e'_0} \dagger \overset{2}{a_1c'_0} \dagger \overset{3}{bd'_0} \dagger \overset{4}{e_1c_0}$; $\overset{1}{\underline{d}\,\underline{e'}} \dagger \overset{3}{b\,\underline{\underline{d'}}} \dagger \overset{4}{\underline{e}\,\underline{c}} \dagger \overset{2}{a\,\underline{\underline{c'}}} \;\P\; ba_0 \dagger a_1$
i.e. $\P\; a_1b_0$

18. $\overset{1}{a_1b'_0} \dagger \overset{2}{d_1e'_0} \dagger \overset{3}{a'_1c_0} \dagger \overset{4}{be}$; $\overset{1}{\underline{a}\,\underline{b'}} \dagger \overset{3}{\underline{\underline{a'}}c} \dagger \overset{4}{\underline{\underline{b}}\,\underline{e}} \dagger \overset{2}{d\,\underline{\underline{e'}}} \;\P\; cd_0 \dagger d_1$ i.e. $\P\; d_1c_0$

19. $\overset{1}{bc_0} \dagger \overset{2}{c_1h'_0} \dagger \overset{3}{a_1b'_0} \dagger \overset{4}{dh_0} \dagger \overset{5}{c'_1e'_0}$; $\overset{1}{\underline{b}\,\underline{c}} \dagger \overset{3}{a\,\underline{\underline{b'}}} \dagger \overset{5}{\underline{c'}\underline{\underline{e'}}} \dagger \overset{2}{\underline{\underline{c}}\,\underline{h'}} \dagger \overset{4}{d\,\underline{h}}$
$\P\; ad_0 \dagger a_1$ i.e. $\P\; a_1d_0$

20. $\overset{1}{dh'_0} \dagger \overset{2}{ce_0} \dagger \overset{3}{h_1b'_0} \dagger \overset{4}{ad'_0} \dagger \overset{5}{be'_0}$; $\overset{1}{\underline{d}\,\underline{h'}} \dagger \overset{3}{\underline{\underline{h}}\,\underline{b'}} \dagger \overset{4}{a\,\underline{\underline{d'}}} \dagger \overset{5}{\underline{\underline{b}}\,\underline{e'}} \dagger \overset{2}{c\,\underline{\underline{e}}} \;\P\; ac_0$

21. $\overset{1}{b_1a'_0} \dagger \overset{2}{dh_0} \dagger \overset{3}{ce_0} \dagger \overset{4}{ah'_0} \dagger \overset{5}{c'_1b'_0}$; $\overset{1}{\underline{b}\,\underline{\underline{a'}}} \dagger \overset{4}{\underline{\underline{a}}\,\underline{h'}} \dagger \overset{2}{d\,\underline{\underline{h}}} \dagger \overset{5}{\underline{c'}\underline{\underline{b'}}} \dagger \overset{3}{\underline{\underline{e}}\,c} \;\P\; dc_0$

22. $\overset{1}{c_1d_0} \dagger \overset{2}{b'h'_0} \dagger \overset{3}{c'_1d'_0} \dagger \overset{4}{a_1e'_0} \dagger \overset{5}{ch}$; $\overset{1}{\underline{c}\,\underline{d}} \dagger \overset{3}{\underline{c}\,\underline{\underline{d'}}} \dagger \overset{4}{a\,\underline{\underline{e'}}} \dagger \overset{5}{\underline{c}\,\underline{h}} \dagger \overset{2}{b'\underline{\underline{h'}}}$
$\P\; ab'_0 \dagger a_1$ i.e. $\P\; a_1b_0$

[Ex. 110, 111 ; Ans. 132.

23. $\overset{1}{b'_1a_0} \dagger \overset{2}{dc'_0} \dagger \overset{3}{h_1b_0} \dagger \overset{4}{cc_0} \dagger \overset{5}{d'_1a'_0}$; $\overset{1}{\underline{b'}\underline{\underline{a}}} \dagger \overset{3}{h\,\underline{\underline{b}}} \dagger \overset{5}{\underline{d'}\underline{\underline{a'}}} \dagger \overset{2}{\underline{d}\,\underline{e'}} \dagger \overset{4}{c\,\underline{\underline{e}}}$
$\Vdash hc_0 \dagger h_1$ i.e. $\Vdash h_1c$

24. $\overset{1}{h'_1k_0} \dagger \overset{2}{b'a_0} \dagger \overset{3}{c_1d'_0} \dagger \overset{4}{e_1h_0} \dagger \overset{5}{dk'_0} \dagger \overset{6}{bc'_0}$;
$\overset{1}{\underline{h'}\underline{k}} \dagger \overset{4}{c\,\underline{\underline{h}}} \dagger \overset{5}{\underline{d}\,\underline{\underline{k'}}} \dagger \overset{3}{\underline{c}\,\underline{\underline{d'}}} \dagger \overset{6}{\underline{b}\,\underline{c'}} \dagger \overset{2}{\underline{\underline{b'}}a} \Vdash ca_0 \dagger e_1$ i.e. $\Vdash e_1a_0$

25. $\overset{1}{a_1d'_0} \dagger \overset{2}{k_1b'_0} \dagger \overset{3}{e_1h'_0} \dagger \overset{4}{a'b_0} \dagger \overset{5}{d_1c'_0} \dagger \overset{6}{h_1k'_0}$;
$\overset{1}{\underline{a}\,\underline{d'}} \dagger \overset{4}{\underline{\underline{a'}}\underline{b}} \dagger \overset{2}{\underline{k}\,\underline{\underline{b'}}} \dagger \overset{5}{\underline{\underline{d}}c'} \dagger \overset{6}{\underline{h}\,\underline{\underline{k'}}} \dagger \overset{3}{e\,\underline{\underline{h'}}} \Vdash c'e_0 \dagger e_1$ i.e. $\Vdash e_1c'_0$

26. $\overset{1}{a'_1h'_0} \dagger \overset{2}{d'k'_0} \dagger \overset{3}{e_1b_0} \dagger \overset{4}{hk_0} \dagger \overset{5}{a_1c_0} \dagger \overset{6}{b'd_0}$;
$\overset{1}{\underline{a'}\underline{h'}} \dagger \overset{4}{\underline{\underline{h}}\,\underline{k}} \dagger \overset{2}{\underline{d'}\underline{\underline{k'}}} \dagger \overset{5}{\underline{\underline{a}}c'} \dagger \overset{6}{\underline{b'}\underline{\underline{d}}} \dagger \overset{3}{e\underline{\underline{b}}} \Vdash c'e_0 \dagger e_1$ i.e. $\Vdash e_1c_0$

27. $\overset{1}{e_1d_0} \dagger \overset{2}{hb_0} \dagger \overset{3}{a'_1k'_0} \dagger \overset{4}{ce'_0} \dagger \overset{5}{b'_1d'_0} \dagger \overset{6}{ac'_0}$;
$\overset{1}{\underline{e}\,\underline{\underline{d}}} \dagger \overset{4}{\underline{c}\,\underline{\underline{e'}}} \dagger \overset{5}{\underline{b'}\underline{\underline{d'}}} \dagger \overset{2}{h\,\underline{\underline{b}}} \dagger \overset{6}{\underline{a}\,\underline{\underline{c'}}} \dagger \overset{3}{\underline{\underline{a'}}k'} \Vdash hk'_0$

28. $\overset{1}{a'k_0} \dagger \overset{2}{e_1b'_0} \dagger \overset{3}{hk'_0} \dagger \overset{4}{d'c_0} \dagger \overset{5}{ab_0} \dagger \overset{6}{c'_1h'_0}$;
$\overset{1}{\underline{\underline{a'}}\underline{k}} \dagger \overset{3}{\underline{h}\,\underline{\underline{k'}}} \dagger \overset{5}{\underline{\underline{a}}\,\underline{b}} \dagger \overset{2}{e\,\underline{\underline{b'}}} \dagger \overset{6}{\underline{c'}\underline{\underline{h'}}} \dagger \overset{4}{d'\underline{\underline{c}}} \Vdash ed'_0 \dagger e_1$ i.c. $\Vdash e_1d'_0$

29. $\overset{1}{ck_0} \dagger \overset{2}{b'm_0} \dagger \overset{3}{ac'_0} \dagger \overset{4}{h'_1e'_0} \dagger \overset{5}{d_1k'_0} \dagger \overset{6}{cb_0} \dagger \overset{7}{d'_1l'_0} \dagger \overset{8}{hm'_0}$;
$\overset{1}{\underline{e}\,\underline{k}} \dagger \overset{4}{\underline{h'}\underline{\underline{e'}}} \dagger \overset{5}{\underline{d}\,\underline{\underline{k'}}} \dagger \overset{7}{\underline{\underline{d'}}l'} \dagger \overset{8}{\underline{h}\,\underline{m'}} \dagger \overset{2}{\underline{b'}\underline{\underline{m}}} \dagger \overset{6}{\underline{c}\,\underline{\underline{b}}} \dagger \overset{3}{a\,\underline{\underline{c'}}} \Vdash l'a_0$

30. $\overset{1}{n_1m'_0} \dagger \overset{2}{a'_1e'_0} \dagger \overset{3}{c'l_0} \dagger \overset{4}{k_1r_0} \dagger \overset{5}{ah'_0} \dagger \overset{6}{dl'_0} \dagger \overset{7}{cn'_0} \dagger \overset{8}{e_1b'_0} \dagger \overset{9}{m_1r'_0} \dagger \overset{10}{h_1d'_1}$;
$\overset{1}{\underline{n}\,\underline{m'}} \dagger \overset{7}{\underline{c}\,\underline{\underline{n'}}} \dagger \overset{3}{\underline{\underline{c'}}l} \dagger \overset{6}{\underline{d}\,\underline{\underline{l'}}} \dagger \overset{9}{\underline{\underline{m}}\,\underline{r'}} \dagger \overset{4}{k\,\underline{\underline{r}}} \dagger \overset{10}{\underline{h}\,\underline{\underline{d'}}} \dagger \overset{5}{\underline{a}\,\underline{\underline{h'}}} \dagger \overset{2}{\underline{\underline{a'}}\underline{e'}} \dagger \overset{8}{\underline{\underline{e}}\,b'} \Vdash kb'_0 \dagger k_1$
i.e. $\Vdash k_1b'_0$

Solutions for § 9.

1.

$\overset{1}{b_1d_0} \dagger \overset{2}{ac_0} \dagger \overset{3}{d'_1c'_0}$; $\overset{1}{b\,\underline{d}} \dagger \overset{3}{\underline{\underline{d'}}\underline{c'}} \dagger \overset{2}{a\,\underline{\underline{c}}} \Vdash ba_0 \dagger b_1$, i.e. $\Vdash b_1a_0$

i.e. Babies cannot manage crocodiles.

2.

$\overset{1}{a_1b'_0} \dagger \overset{2}{d_1c'_0} \dagger \overset{3}{bc_0}$; $\overset{1}{a\,\underline{b'}} \dagger \overset{3}{\underline{\underline{b}}\,\underline{c}} \dagger \overset{2}{d\,\underline{\underline{c'}}} \Vdash ad_0 \dagger d_1$, i.e. $\Vdash d_1a_0$

i.e. *Your* presents to me are not made of tin.

Ex. 111, 112: Ans. 132.]

3.

$\overset{1}{da_0} \dagger \overset{2}{c_1b'_0} \dagger \overset{3}{a'b_0}$; $\overset{1}{d\underline{a}} \dagger \overset{3}{\underline{\underline{a}}'\underline{b}} \dagger \overset{2}{c\underline{\underline{b}}'} \P dc_0 \dagger c_1$, i.e. $\P c_1d_0$

i.e. All my potatoes in this dish are old ones.

4.

$\overset{1}{ba_0} \dagger \overset{2}{b'd_0} \dagger \overset{3}{c_1a'_0}$; $\overset{1}{\underline{b}\,\underline{a}} \dagger \overset{2}{\underline{\underline{b}}'d} \dagger \overset{3}{c\,\underline{\underline{a}}'} \P dc_0 \dagger c_1$, i.e. $\P c_1d_0$

i.e. My servants never say "shpoonj."

5.

$\overset{1}{ad_0} \dagger \overset{2}{cd'_0} \dagger \overset{3}{b_1a'_0}$; $\overset{1}{\underline{a}\,\underline{d}} \dagger \overset{2}{c\,\underline{\underline{d}}'} \dagger \overset{3}{b\,\underline{\underline{a}}'} \P cb_0 \dagger b_1$, i.e. $\P b_1c_0$

i.e. My poultry are not officers.

6.

$\overset{1}{c_1a'_0} \dagger \overset{2}{c'b_0} \dagger \overset{3}{da_0}$; $\overset{1}{\underline{c}\,\underline{a}'} \dagger \overset{2}{\underline{\underline{c}}'b} \dagger \overset{3}{d\,\underline{\underline{a}}} \P bd_0$

i.e. None of *your* sons are fit to serve on a jury.

7.

$\overset{1}{cb_0} \dagger \overset{2}{da_0} \dagger \overset{3}{b'_1a'_0}$; $\overset{1}{c\,\underline{b}} \dagger \overset{3}{\underline{\underline{b}}'\underline{a}'} \dagger \overset{2}{d\,\underline{\underline{a}}} \P cd_0$

i.e. No pencils of mine are sugarplums.

8.

$\overset{1}{cb'_0} \dagger \overset{2}{d_1a'_0} \dagger \overset{3}{ba_0}$; $\overset{1}{c\,\underline{b}'} \dagger \overset{3}{\underline{\underline{b}}\,\underline{a}} \dagger \overset{2}{d\,\underline{\underline{a}}'} \P cd_0 \dagger d_1$, i.e. $\P d_1c_0$

i.e. Jenkins is inexperienced.

9.

$\overset{1}{cd_0} \dagger \overset{2}{d'a_0} \dagger \overset{3}{c'b_0}$; $\overset{1}{\underline{c}\,\underline{d}} \dagger \overset{2}{\underline{\underline{d}}'a} \dagger \overset{3}{\underline{\underline{c}}'b} \P ab_0$.

i.e. No comet has a curly tail.

10.

$\overset{1}{d'c_0} \dagger \overset{2}{ba_0} \dagger \overset{3}{a'_1d_0}$; $\overset{1}{\underline{d}'c} \dagger \overset{3}{\underline{a}'\underline{\underline{d}}} \dagger \overset{2}{b\,\underline{\underline{a}}} \P cb_0$

i.e. No hedgehog takes in the *Times*.

11.

$\overset{1}{b_1a'_0} \dagger \overset{2}{c_1b'_0} \dagger \overset{3}{ad_0}$; $\overset{1}{\underline{b}\,\underline{a}'} \dagger \overset{2}{c\,\underline{\underline{b}}'} \dagger \overset{3}{\underline{\underline{a}}\,d} \P cd_0 \dagger c_1$, i.e. $\P c_1d_0$

i.e. This dish is unwholesome.

12.

$\overset{1}{b_1c'_0} \dagger \overset{2}{d'a_0} \dagger \overset{3}{a'c_0}$; $\overset{1}{b\,\underline{c}'} \dagger \overset{3}{\underline{a}'\underline{\underline{c}}} \dagger \overset{2}{d'\underline{\underline{a}}} \P bd'_0 \dagger b_1$, i.e. $\P b_1d'_0$

i.e. My gardener is very old.

13.

$\overset{1}{a_1d'_0} \dagger \overset{2}{bc_0} \dagger \overset{3}{c'_1d_0}$; $\overset{1}{a\,\underline{d}'} \dagger \overset{3}{\underline{c}'\underline{\underline{d}}} \dagger \overset{2}{b\,\underline{\underline{c}}} \P ab_0 \dagger a_1$, i.e. $\P a_1b_0$

i.e. All humming-birds are small.

[Ex. 112—114 : Ans. 132.

14.

$\overset{1}{c'b_0} \dagger \overset{2}{a_1d'_0} \dagger \overset{3}{ca'_0}$; $\overset{1}{\underline{c}'b} \dagger \overset{3}{\underline{\underline{c}}\,\underline{a}'} \dagger \overset{2}{\underline{\underline{a}}\,d'} \;\mathbb{P}\; bd'_0$

i.e. No one with a hooked nose ever fails to make money.

15.

$\overset{1}{b_1a'_0} \dagger \overset{2}{b'_1d_0} \dagger \overset{3}{ca_0}$; $\overset{1}{\underline{b}\,\underline{a}'} \dagger \overset{2}{\underline{\underline{b}}'d} \dagger \overset{3}{c\,\underline{\underline{a}}} \;\mathbb{P}\; dc_0$

i.e. No gray ducks in this village wear lace collars.

16.

$\overset{1}{d_1b'_0} \dagger \overset{2}{cd'_0} \dagger \overset{3}{ba_0}$; $\overset{1}{\underline{d}\,\underline{b}'} \dagger \overset{2}{c\,\underline{\underline{d}}'} \dagger \overset{3}{\underline{\underline{b}}\cdot a} \;\mathbb{P}\; ca_0$

i.e. No jug in this cupboard will hold water.

17.

$\overset{1}{b'_1d_0} \dagger \overset{2}{c_1d'_0} \dagger \overset{3}{ab_0}$; $\overset{1}{\underline{b}'\underline{d}} \dagger \overset{2}{c\,\underline{\underline{d}}'} \dagger \overset{3}{a\,\underline{\underline{b}}} \;\mathbb{P}\; ca_0 \dagger c_1$, i.e. $\mathbb{P}\; c_1a_0$

i.e. These apples were grown in the sun.

18.

$\overset{1}{d'_1b'_0} \dagger \overset{2}{c_1b_0} \dagger \overset{3}{c'a_0}$; $\overset{1}{d'\underline{b}'} \dagger \overset{2}{\underline{c}\,\underline{\underline{b}}} \dagger \overset{3}{\underline{\underline{c}}'a} \;\mathbb{P}\; d'a_0 \dagger d'_1$, i.e. $\mathbb{P}\; d'_1a_0$

i.e. Puppies, that will not lie still, never care to do worsted-work.

19.

$\overset{1}{bd'_0} \dagger \overset{2}{a_1c'_0} \dagger \overset{3}{a'd_0}$; $\overset{1}{b\,\underline{d}'} \dagger \overset{3}{\underline{a}'\underline{\underline{d}}} \dagger \overset{2}{\underline{\underline{a}}\,c'} \dagger \;\mathbb{P}\; bc'_0$

i.e. No name in this list is unmelodious.

20.

$\overset{1}{a_1b'_0} \dagger \overset{2}{dc_0} \dagger \overset{3}{a'_1d'_0}$; $\overset{1}{\underline{a}\,b'} \dagger \overset{3}{\underline{\underline{a}}'\underline{d}'} \dagger \overset{2}{\underline{\underline{d}}\,c} \;\mathbb{P}\; b'c_0$

i.e. No M.P. should ride in a donkey-race, unless he has perfect self-command.

21.

$\overset{1}{bd_0} \dagger \overset{2}{c'a_0} \dagger \overset{3}{b'c_0}$; $\overset{1}{\underline{b}\,d} \dagger \overset{3}{\underline{\underline{b}}'\underline{c}} \dagger \overset{2}{\underline{\underline{c}}'a} \;\mathbb{P}\; da_0$

i.e. No goods in this shop, that are still on sale, may be carried away.

22.

$\overset{1}{a'b_0} \dagger \overset{2}{cd_0} \dagger \overset{3}{d'a_0}$; $\overset{1}{\underline{a}'b} \dagger \overset{3}{\underline{d}'\underline{\underline{a}}} \dagger \overset{2}{c\,\underline{\underline{d}}} \;\mathbb{P}\; bc_0$

i.e. No acrobatic feat, which involves turning a quadruple somersault, is ever attempted in a circus.

23.

$\overset{1}{dc'_0} \dagger \overset{2}{a_1b'_0} \dagger \overset{3}{bc_0}$; $\overset{1}{d\,\underline{c}'} \dagger \overset{3}{\underline{b}\,\underline{\underline{c}}} \dagger \overset{2}{a\,\underline{\underline{b}}'} \;\mathbb{P}\; da_0 \dagger a_1$, i.e. $\mathbb{P}\; a_1d_0$

i.e. Guinea-pigs never really appreciate Beethoven.

Ex. 114, 115 ; Ans. 132, 133.]

24.

$\overset{1}{a_1 d'_0} \dagger \overset{2}{b'_1 c_0} \dagger \overset{3}{b a'_0}$; $\overset{1}{\underline{a}\, d'} \dagger \overset{3}{\underline{b}\,\underline{\underline{a}}'} \dagger \overset{2}{\underline{\underline{b}}' c}$ $\P$ $d'c_0$

i.e. No scentless flowers please me.

25.

$\overset{1}{c_1 d'_0} \dagger \overset{2}{b a'_0} \dagger \overset{3}{d_1 a_0}$; $\overset{1}{c\,\underline{d}'} \dagger \overset{3}{\underline{\underline{d}}\,\underline{a}} \dagger \overset{2}{b\,\underline{\underline{a}}'}$ $\P$ $cb_0 \dagger c_1$, i.e. $\P$ $c_1 b_0$

i.e. Showy talkers are not really well-informed.

26.

$\overset{1}{e a_0} \dagger \overset{2}{b_1 d'_0} \dagger \overset{3}{a'_1 c_0} \dagger \overset{4}{e' b'_0}$; $\overset{1}{\underline{e}\,\underline{a}} \dagger \overset{3}{\underline{\underline{a}}' c} \dagger \overset{4}{\underline{\underline{e}}'\underline{b}'} \dagger \overset{2}{\underline{\underline{b}}\, d'}$ $\P$ cd'_0

i.e. None but red-haired boys learn Greek in this school.

27.

$\overset{1}{b_1 d_0} \dagger \overset{2}{a c'_0} \dagger \overset{3}{e_1 d'_0} \dagger \overset{4}{c_1 b'_0}$; $\overset{1}{\underline{b}\,\underline{d}} \dagger \overset{3}{e\,\underline{\underline{d}}'} \dagger \overset{4}{\underline{c}\,\underline{\underline{b}}'} \dagger \overset{2}{a\,\underline{\underline{c}}'}$ $\P$ $ea_0 \dagger c_1$, i.e. $\P$ $c_1 a_0$

i.e. Wedding-cake always disagrees with me.

28.

$\overset{1}{a d_0} \dagger \overset{2}{c'_1 b'_0} \dagger \overset{3}{c_1 d'_0} \dagger \overset{4}{e_1 a'_0}$; $\overset{1}{\underline{a}\,\underline{d}} \dagger \overset{3}{c\,\underline{\underline{d}}'} \dagger \overset{4}{\underline{e}\,\underline{\underline{a}}'} \dagger \overset{2}{\underline{\underline{c}}' b'}$ $\P$ $cb'_0 \dagger c_1$, i.e. $\P$ $c_1 b'_0$

i.e. Discussions, that go on while Tomkins is in the chair, endanger the peacefulness of our Debating-Club.

29.

$\overset{1}{d_1 a_0} \dagger \overset{2}{e' c_0} \dagger \overset{3}{b_1 a'_0} \dagger \overset{4}{d' e_0}$; $\overset{1}{\underline{d}\,\underline{a}} \dagger \overset{3}{b\,\underline{\underline{a}}'} \dagger \overset{4}{\underline{\underline{d}}'\underline{e}} \dagger \overset{2}{\underline{\underline{e}}' c}$ $\P$ $bc_0 \dagger b_1$, i.e. $\P$ $b_1 c_0$

i.e. All the gluttons in my family are unhealthy.

30.

$\overset{1}{d_1 e_0} \dagger \overset{2}{c' a_0} \dagger \overset{3}{b_1 e'_0} \dagger \overset{4}{c_1 d'_0}$; $\overset{1}{\underline{d}\,\underline{e}} \dagger \overset{3}{b\,\underline{\underline{e}}'} \dagger \overset{4}{\underline{c}\,\underline{\underline{d}}'} \dagger \overset{2}{\underline{\underline{c}}' a}$ $\P$ $ba_0 \dagger b_1$, i.e. $\P$ $b_1 a_0$

i.e. An egg of the Great Auk is not to be had for a song.

31.

$\overset{1}{d' b_0} \dagger \overset{2}{a_1 c'_0} \dagger \overset{3}{c_1 e'_0} \dagger \overset{4}{a' d_0}$; $\overset{1}{\underline{d}' b} \dagger \overset{4}{\underline{a}'\underline{\underline{d}}} \dagger \overset{2}{\underline{\underline{a}}\,\underline{c}'} \dagger \overset{3}{\underline{\underline{c}}\, e'}$ $\P$ be'_0

i.e. No books sold here have gilt edges unless they are priced at 5s. and upwards.

32.

$\overset{1}{a'_1 c'_0} \dagger \overset{2}{d_1 b_0} \dagger \overset{3}{a_1 e'_0} \dagger \overset{4}{c_1 b'_0}$; $\overset{1}{\underline{a}'\underline{c}'} \dagger \overset{3}{\underline{\underline{a}}\, e'} \dagger \overset{4}{\underline{\underline{c}}\,\underline{b}'} \dagger \overset{2}{d\,\underline{\underline{b}}}$ $\P$ $e'd_0 \dagger d_1$, i.e. $\P$ $d_1 e'_0$

i.e. When you cut your finger, you will find Tincture of Calendula useful.

33.

$\overset{1}{d' b_0} \dagger \overset{2}{a_1 e'_0} \dagger \overset{3}{e c_0} \dagger \overset{4}{d_1 a'_0}$; $\overset{1}{\underline{d}' b} \dagger \overset{4}{\underline{\underline{d}}\,\underline{a}'} \dagger \overset{2}{\underline{\underline{a}}\,\underline{e}'} \dagger \overset{3}{\underline{\underline{e}}\, c}$ $\P$ bc_0

i.e. *I* have never come across a mermaid at sea.

[Ex. 116, 117 ; Ans. 133.

34.

$\overset{1}{c'_1b_0} \dagger \overset{2}{a_1c'_0} \dagger \overset{3}{d_1b'_0} \dagger \overset{4}{a'_1c_0}$; $\overset{1}{\underline{c}'\underline{b}} \dagger \overset{3}{d\,\underline{\underline{b}}'} \dagger \overset{4}{\underline{a}'\underline{\underline{c}}} \dagger \overset{2}{\underline{\underline{a}}\,e'} \Vdash de'_0 \dagger d_1$, i.e. $\Vdash d_1e'_0$

i.e. All the romances in this library are well-written.

35.

$\overset{1}{c'd_0} \dagger \overset{2}{c'a_0} \dagger \overset{3}{cb_0} \dagger \overset{4}{d'c_0}$; $\overset{1}{\underline{c}'\underline{d}} \dagger \overset{3}{\underline{\underline{c}}\,b} \dagger \overset{4}{\underline{\underline{d}}'\underline{c}} \dagger \overset{2}{\underline{\underline{c}}'a} \Vdash ba_0$

i.e. No bird in this aviary lives on mince-pies.

36.

$\overset{1}{d'_1c'_0} \dagger \overset{2}{c_1a'_0} \dagger \overset{3}{c_1b_0} \dagger \overset{4}{e'd_0}$; $\overset{1}{\underline{d}'\underline{c}'} \dagger \overset{3}{\underline{\underline{c}}\,b} \dagger \overset{4}{\underline{e}'\underline{\underline{d}}'} \dagger \overset{2}{\underline{\underline{e}}\,a'} \Vdash ba'_0$

i.e. No plum-pudding, that has not been boiled in a cloth, can be distinguished from soup.

37.

$\overset{1}{ce'_0} \dagger \overset{2}{b'a'_0} \dagger \overset{3}{h_1d'_0} \dagger \overset{4}{ac_0} \dagger \overset{5}{bd_0}$; $\overset{1}{c\,\underline{e}'} \dagger \overset{4}{\underline{a}\,\underline{\underline{e}}} \dagger \overset{2}{\underline{b}'\underline{\underline{a}}'} \dagger \overset{5}{\underline{\underline{b}}\,\underline{d}} \dagger \overset{3}{h\,\underline{\underline{d}}'} \Vdash ch_0 \dagger h_1$,

i.e. $\Vdash h_1c_0$

i.e. All *your* poems are uninteresting.

38.

$\overset{1}{b'_1a'_0} \dagger \overset{2}{db_0} \dagger \overset{3}{he'_0} \dagger \overset{4}{ec_0} \dagger \overset{5}{a_1h'_0}$; $\overset{1}{\underline{b}'\underline{a}'} \dagger \overset{2}{d\,\underline{\underline{b}}} \dagger \overset{5}{\underline{\underline{a}}\,\underline{h}'} \dagger \overset{3}{\underline{\underline{h}}\,\underline{e}'} \dagger \overset{4}{\underline{\underline{e}}\,c} \Vdash dc_0$

i.e. None of my peaches have been grown in a hothouse.

39.

$\overset{1}{c_1d_0} \dagger \overset{2}{h_1e'_0} \dagger \overset{3}{c'_1a'_0} \dagger \overset{4}{h'b_0} \dagger \overset{5}{e_1d'_0}$; $\overset{1}{\underline{c}'\underline{d}} \dagger \overset{3}{\underline{\underline{c}}'a'} \dagger \overset{5}{\underline{e}\,\underline{\underline{d}}'} \dagger \overset{2}{\underline{h}\,\underline{\underline{e}}'} \dagger \overset{4}{\underline{\underline{h}}'b} \Vdash a'b_0$

i.e. No pawnbroker is dishonest.

40.

$\overset{1}{ad'_0} \dagger \overset{2}{c'h_0} \dagger \overset{3}{c_1a'_0} \dagger \overset{4}{db_0} \dagger \overset{5}{e'c_0}$; $\overset{1}{\underline{a}\,\underline{d}'} \dagger \overset{3}{\underline{c}\,\underline{\underline{a}}'} \dagger \overset{4}{\underline{\underline{d}}\,b} \dagger \overset{5}{\underline{e}'\underline{\underline{c}}} \dagger \overset{2}{\underline{\underline{e}}'h} \Vdash bh_0$

i.e. No kitten with green eyes will play with a gorilla.

41.

$\overset{1}{c_1a'_0} \dagger \overset{2}{h'b_0} \dagger \overset{3}{ac_0} \dagger \overset{4}{d_1c'_0} \dagger \overset{5}{h_1c'_0}$; $\overset{1}{\underline{c}\,\underline{a}'} \dagger \overset{3}{\underline{\underline{a}}\,\underline{c}} \dagger \overset{4}{d\,\underline{\underline{c}}'} \dagger \overset{5}{\underline{h}\,\underline{\underline{c}}'} \dagger \overset{2}{\underline{\underline{h}}'b} \Vdash db_0 \dagger d_1$,

i.e. $\Vdash d_1b_0$

i.e. All *my* friends in this College dine at the lower table.

42.

$\overset{1}{ca_0} \dagger \overset{2}{h_1d'_0} \dagger \overset{3}{c'_1e'_0} \dagger \overset{4}{b'a'_0} \dagger \overset{5}{d_1e_0}$; $\overset{1}{\underline{c}\,\underline{a}} \dagger \overset{3}{\underline{\underline{c}}'\underline{e}'} \dagger \overset{4}{b'\underline{\underline{a}}'} \dagger \overset{5}{\underline{d}\,\underline{\underline{e}}} \dagger \overset{2}{h\,\underline{\underline{d}}'} \Vdash b'h_0 \dagger h_1$,

i.e. $\Vdash h_1b'_0$

i.e. My writing-desk is full of live scorpions.

43.

$\overset{1}{b_1e_0} \dagger \overset{2}{ah_0} \dagger \overset{3}{de_0} \dagger \overset{4}{e'_1a'_0} \dagger \overset{5}{be'_0}$; $\overset{1}{\underline{b}'\underline{e}} \dagger \overset{4}{\underline{\underline{e}}'\underline{a}'} \dagger \overset{2}{\underline{\underline{a}}\,h} \dagger \overset{5}{\underline{\underline{b}}\,\underline{e}'} \dagger \overset{3}{d\,\underline{\underline{e}}} \Vdash hd_0$

i.e. No Mandarin ever reads Hogg's poems.

Ex. 118, 119 ; Ans. 133.]

44.

$\overset{1}{c_1b'_0} \dagger \overset{2}{a'd_0} \dagger \overset{3}{c_1h'_0} \dagger \overset{4}{c'a_0} \dagger \overset{5}{d'h_0}$; $\overset{1}{\underline{c}\,b'} \dagger \overset{4}{\underline{\underline{c}}'\underline{\underline{a}}} \dagger \overset{2}{\underline{\underline{a}}'\underline{\underline{d}}} \dagger \overset{5}{\underline{\underline{d}}'\underline{h}} \dagger \overset{3}{c\,\underline{h}'} \;\P\; b'c_0 \dagger c_1$,
i.e. $\P\; c_1b'_0$

i.e. Shakespeare was clever.

45.

$\overset{1}{c'_1c'_0} \dagger \overset{2}{hb'_0} \dagger \overset{3}{d_1a_0} \dagger \overset{4}{c_1a'_0} \dagger \overset{5}{c_1b_0}$; $\overset{1}{\underline{c}'\underline{c}'} \dagger \overset{4}{\underline{\underline{c}}\,\underline{\underline{a}}'} \dagger \overset{3}{d\,\underline{\underline{a}}} \dagger \overset{5}{\underline{\underline{c}}\,\underline{b}} \dagger \overset{2}{h\,\underline{\underline{b}}'} \;\P\; dh_0 \dagger d_1$,
i.e. $\P\; d_1h_0$

i.e. Rainbows are not worth writing odes to.

46.

$\overset{1}{c'_1h'_0} \dagger \overset{2}{c_1a_0} \dagger \overset{3}{bd_0} \dagger \overset{4}{a'_1h_0} \dagger \overset{5}{d'c_0}$; $\overset{1}{\underline{c}'\underline{h}'} \dagger \overset{4}{\underline{\underline{a}}'\underline{\underline{h}}} \dagger \overset{2}{c\,\underline{\underline{a}}} \dagger \overset{5}{\underline{\underline{d}}'\underline{\underline{c}}} \dagger \overset{3}{b\,\underline{d}} \;\P\; cb_0 \dagger c_1$,
i.e. $\P\; c_1b_0$

i.e. These Sorites-examples are difficult.

47.

$\overset{1}{a'_1c'_0} \dagger \overset{2}{bk_0} \dagger \overset{3}{c'a_0} \dagger \overset{4}{ch'_0} \dagger \overset{5}{d_1b'_0} \dagger \overset{6}{k'h_0}$; $\overset{1}{\underline{\underline{a}}'\underline{c}'} \dagger \overset{3}{c'\,\underline{\underline{a}}} \dagger \overset{4}{\underline{\underline{c}}\,\underline{h}'} \dagger \overset{6}{\underline{\underline{k}}'\underline{\underline{h}}} \dagger \overset{2}{\underline{\underline{b}}\,\underline{k}} \dagger \overset{5}{d\,\underline{b}'}$
$\P\; c'd_0 \dagger d_1$, i.e. $\P\; d_1c'_0$

i.e. All my dreams come true.

48.

$\overset{1}{a'h_0} \dagger \overset{2}{c'k_0} \dagger \overset{3}{a_1d'_0} \dagger \overset{4}{e_1h'_0} \dagger \overset{5}{b_1k'_0} \dagger \overset{6}{c_1c'_0}$; $\overset{1}{\underline{\underline{a}}'\underline{h}} \dagger \overset{3}{\underline{\underline{a}}\,d'} \dagger \overset{4}{\underline{\underline{c}}\,\underline{h}'} \dagger \overset{6}{\underline{c}\,\underline{\underline{c}}'} \dagger \overset{2}{\underline{\underline{c}}'\underline{k}} \dagger \overset{5}{b\,\underline{k}'}$
$\P\; d'b_0 \dagger b_1$, i.e. $\P\; b_1d'_0$

i.e. All the English pictures here are painted in oils.

49.

$\overset{1}{k'_1e_0} \dagger \overset{2}{c_1h_0} \dagger \overset{3}{b_1a'_0} \dagger \overset{4}{kd_0} \dagger \overset{5}{h'a_0} \dagger \overset{6}{b'_1c'_0}$; $\overset{1}{\underline{\underline{k}}'\underline{e}} \dagger \overset{4}{\underline{k}\,d} \dagger \overset{6}{\underline{b}'\underline{\underline{c}}'} \dagger \overset{3}{\underline{\underline{b}}\,\underline{a}'} \dagger \overset{5}{\underline{h}'\underline{\underline{a}}} \dagger \overset{2}{c\,\underline{\underline{h}}}$
$\P\; dc_0 \dagger c_1$, i.e. $\P\; c_1d_0$

i.e. Donkeys are not easy to swallow.

50.

$\overset{1}{ab'_0} \dagger \overset{2}{h'd_0} \dagger \overset{3}{e_1c_0} \dagger \overset{4}{b_1d'_0} \dagger \overset{5}{a'k_0} \dagger \overset{6}{c_1h_0}$; $\overset{1}{\underline{\underline{a}}\,\underline{b}'} \dagger \overset{4}{\underline{\underline{b}}\,\underline{d}} \dagger \overset{2}{\underline{h}'\underline{\underline{d}}} \dagger \overset{5}{\underline{\underline{a}}'k} \dagger \overset{6}{\underline{c}'\underline{\underline{h}}} \dagger \overset{3}{e\,\underline{c}}$
$\P\; kc_0 \dagger c_1$, i.e. $\P\; c_1k_0$

i.e. Opium-eaters never wear white kid gloves.

51.

$\overset{1}{bc_0} \dagger \overset{2}{k_1a'_0} \dagger \overset{3}{ch_0} \dagger \overset{4}{d_1b'_0} \dagger \overset{5}{h'c'_0} \dagger \overset{6}{k'_1c'_0}$; $\overset{1}{\underline{b}\,\underline{c}} \dagger \overset{4}{d\,\underline{b}'} \dagger \overset{5}{\underline{h}'\underline{\underline{c}}'} \dagger \overset{3}{\underline{c}\,\underline{\underline{h}}} \dagger \overset{6}{\underline{\underline{k}}'\underline{\underline{c}}'} \dagger \overset{2}{\underline{k}\,a'}$
$\P\; da'_0 \dagger d_1$, i.e. $\P\; d_1a'_0$

i.e. A good husband always comes home for his tea.

52.

$\overset{1}{a'_1k'_0} \dagger \overset{2}{ch_0} \dagger \overset{3}{h'k'_0} \dagger \overset{4}{b_1d'_0} \dagger \overset{5}{ca_0} \dagger \overset{6}{d_1c'_0}$; $\overset{1}{\underline{\underline{a}}'\underline{k}'} \dagger \overset{3}{\underline{h}'\underline{\underline{k}}} \dagger \overset{2}{\underline{\underline{c}}\,\underline{\underline{h}}} \dagger \overset{6}{\underline{\underline{d}}\,\underline{\underline{c}}'} \dagger \overset{4}{b\,\underline{\underline{d}}'} \dagger \overset{5}{c\,\underline{\underline{a}}}$
$\P\; bc_0 \dagger b_1$, i.e. $\P\; b_1c_0$

i.e. Bathing-machines are never made of mother-of-pearl.

[Ex. 120, 122; Ans. 133.

53.

$\overset{1}{da'_0} \dagger \overset{2}{k_1b'_0} \dagger \overset{3}{c_1h_0} \dagger \overset{4}{d'_1k'_0} \dagger \overset{5}{e_1c'_0} \dagger \overset{6}{a_1h'_0}$;

$\overset{1}{\underline{d}\,\underline{a}'} \dagger \overset{4}{\underline{\underline{d}}'\underline{k}'} \dagger \overset{2}{\underline{\underline{k}}\,b'} \dagger \overset{6}{\underline{\underline{a}}\,\underline{h}'} \dagger \overset{3}{\underline{c}\,\underline{\underline{h}}} \dagger \overset{5}{e\,\underline{\underline{c}}'}$

$\P\ b'e_0 \dagger e_1$, i.e. $\P\ e_1b'_0$

i.e. Rainy days are always cloudy.

54.

$\overset{1}{kb'_0} \dagger \overset{2}{a'_1c'_0} \dagger \overset{3}{d'b_0} \dagger \overset{4}{k'_1h'_0} \dagger \overset{5}{ea_0} \dagger \overset{6}{d_1c_0}$;

$\overset{1}{\underline{k}\,\underline{b}'} \dagger \overset{3}{\underline{\underline{d}}'\underline{\underline{b}}} \dagger \overset{4}{\underline{\underline{k}}'h'} \dagger \overset{6}{\underline{\underline{d}}\,\underline{c}} \dagger \overset{2}{\underline{a}'\underline{\underline{c}}'} \dagger \overset{5}{e\,\underline{\underline{a}}}$

$\P\ h'e_0$

i.e. No heavy fish is unkind to children.

55.

$\overset{1}{k'_1b'_0} \dagger \overset{2}{eh'_0} \dagger \overset{3}{c'd_0} \dagger \overset{4}{hb_0} \dagger \overset{5}{ac_0} \dagger \overset{6}{kd'_0}$; $\overset{1}{\underline{k}'\underline{b}'} \dagger \overset{4}{\underline{h}\,\underline{\underline{b}}} \dagger \overset{2}{e\,\underline{\underline{h}}'} \dagger \overset{6}{\underline{\underline{k}}\,\underline{d}'} \dagger \overset{3}{\underline{c}'\underline{\underline{d}}'} \dagger \overset{5}{a\,\underline{\underline{c}}}\ \P\ ea_0$

i.e. No engine-driver lives on barley-sugar.

56.

$\overset{1}{h_1b'_0} \dagger \overset{2}{c_1d'_0} \dagger \overset{3}{k'a_0} \dagger \overset{4}{e_1h'_0} \dagger \overset{5}{b_1a'_0} \dagger \overset{6}{k_1c'_0}$;

$\overset{1}{\underline{h}\,\underline{b}'} \dagger \overset{4}{e\,\underline{h}'} \dagger \overset{5}{\underline{\underline{b}}\,\underline{a}'} \dagger \overset{3}{\underline{k}'\underline{\underline{a}}} \dagger \overset{6}{\underline{k}\,\underline{c}'} \dagger \overset{2}{\underline{\underline{c}}\,d'}$

$\P\ ed'_0 \dagger e_1$, i.e. $\P\ e_1d'_0$

i.e. All the animals in the yard gnaw bones.

57.

$\overset{1}{h'_1d'_0} \dagger \overset{2}{e_1c'_0} \dagger \overset{3}{k'a_0} \dagger \overset{4}{cb_0} \dagger \overset{5}{d_1l'_0} \dagger \overset{6}{e'h_0} \dagger \overset{7}{kl_0}$;

$\overset{1}{\underline{h}\,\underline{d}'} \dagger \overset{5}{\underline{\underline{d}}\,\underline{l}'} \dagger \overset{7}{\underline{k}\,\underline{\underline{l}}} \dagger \overset{3}{\underline{\underline{k}}'a} \dagger \overset{6}{\underline{e}'\underline{\underline{h}}} \dagger \overset{2}{\underline{\underline{e}}\,\underline{c}'} \dagger \overset{4}{\underline{\underline{c}}\,b}$

$\P\ ab_0$

i.e. No badger can guess a conundrum.

58.

$\overset{1}{b'h_0} \dagger \overset{2}{d'_1l'_0} \dagger \overset{3}{ca_0} \dagger \overset{4}{d_1k'_0} \dagger \overset{5}{h'_1e'_0} \dagger \overset{6}{me'_0} \dagger \overset{7}{a'b_0} \dagger \overset{8}{ek_0}$;

$\overset{1}{\underline{b}'\underline{h}} \dagger \overset{5}{\underline{\underline{h}}'\underline{e}'} \dagger \overset{7}{\underline{a}'\underline{\underline{b}}} \dagger \overset{3}{\underline{c}\,\underline{\underline{a}}} \dagger \overset{6}{m\,\underline{\underline{e}}'} \dagger \overset{8}{\underline{\underline{e}}\,\underline{k}} \dagger \overset{4}{\underline{d}\,\underline{\underline{k}}'} \dagger \overset{2}{\underline{\underline{d}}'l'}\ \P\ ml'_0$

i.e. No cheque of yours, received by me, is payable to order.

59.

$\overset{1}{c_1l'_0} \dagger \overset{2}{h'e_0} \dagger \overset{3}{kd_0} \dagger \overset{4}{mc'_0} \dagger \overset{5}{b'_1e'_0} \dagger \overset{6}{n_1a'_0} \dagger \overset{7}{l_1d'_0} \dagger \overset{8}{m'b_0} \dagger \overset{9}{ah_0}$;

$\overset{1}{\underline{c}\,\underline{l}'} \dagger \overset{4}{\underline{\underline{m}}\,\underline{\underline{c}}'} \dagger \overset{7}{\underline{\underline{l}}\,\underline{d}'} \dagger \overset{3}{k\,\underline{\underline{d}}} \dagger \overset{8}{\underline{\underline{m}}'\underline{b}} \dagger \overset{5}{\underline{\underline{b}}'\underline{e}'} \dagger \overset{2}{\underline{h}'\underline{\underline{e}}} \dagger \overset{9}{\underline{a}\,\underline{h}} \dagger \overset{6}{n\,\underline{\underline{a}}'}\ \P\ kn_0$

i.e. I cannot read any of Brown's letters.

60.

$\overset{1}{e_1c'_0} \dagger \overset{2}{l_1n'_0} \dagger \overset{3}{d_1a'_0} \dagger \overset{4}{m'b_0} \dagger \overset{5}{ck'_0} \dagger \overset{6}{e'r_0} \dagger \overset{7}{h_1n_0} \dagger \overset{8}{b'k_0} \dagger \overset{9}{r'_1d'_0} \dagger \overset{10}{m_1l'_0}$;

$\overset{1}{\underline{e}\,\underline{\underline{c}}'} \dagger \overset{5}{\underline{c}\,\underline{k}'} \dagger \overset{6}{\underline{\underline{e}}'\underline{r}} \dagger \overset{8}{\underline{b}'\underline{\underline{k}}} \dagger \overset{4}{\underline{\underline{m}}'\underline{\underline{b}}} \dagger \overset{9}{\underline{r}'\underline{d}'} \dagger \overset{3}{\underline{d}\,a'} \dagger \overset{10}{\underline{\underline{m}}\,\underline{l}'} \dagger \overset{2}{\underline{\underline{l}}\,\underline{n}'} \dagger \overset{7}{h\,\underline{\underline{n}}}\ \P\ a'h_0 \dagger h_1$, i.e. $\P\ h_1a'_0$

i.e. I always avoid a kangaroo.

NOTES.

(A) [See p. 80].

ONE of the favourite objections, brought against the Science of Logic by its detractors, is that a Syllogism has no real validity as an argument, since it involves the Fallacy of *Petitio Principii* (i.e. "Begging the Question", the essence of which is that the whole Conclusion is involved in *one* of the Premisses).

This formidable objection is refuted, with beautiful clearness and simplicity, by these three Diagrams, which show us that, in each of the three Figures, the Conclusion is really involved in the *two* Premisses taken together, each contributing its share.

Thus, in Fig. I., the Premiss xm_0 empties the *Inner* Cell of the N.W. Quarter, while the Premiss ym_0 empties its *Outer* Cell. Hence it needs the *two* Premisses to empty the *whole* of the N.W. Quarter, and thus to prove the Conclusion xy_0.

Again, in Fig. II., the Premiss xm_0 empties the Inner Cell of the N.W. Quarter. The Premiss ym_1 merely tells us that the Inner Portion of the W. Half is *occupied*, so that we may place a 'I' in it, *somewhere;* but, if this were the *whole* of our information, we should not know in *which* Cell to place it, so that it would have to 'sit on the fence': it is only when we learn, from the other Premiss, that the *upper* of these two Cells is *empty*, that we feel authorised to place the 'I' in the *lower* Cell, and thus to prove the Conclusion $x'y_1$.

Lastly, in Fig. III., the information, that *m exists*, merely authorises us to place a 'I' *somewhere* in the Inner Square——but it has large choice of fences to sit upon! It needs the Premiss xm_0 to drive it out of the N. Half of that Square; and it needs the Premiss ym_0 to drive it out of the W. Half. Hence it needs the *two* Premisses to drive it into the Inner Portion of the S.E. Quarter, and thus to prove the Conclusion $x'y'_1$.

APPENDIX,

ADDRESSED TO TEACHERS.

---

§ 1.

Introductory.

THERE are several matters, too hard to discuss with *Learners*, which nevertheless need to be explained to any *Teachers*, into whose hands this book may fall, in order that they may thoroughly understand what my Symbolic Method *is*, and in what respects it differs from the many other Methods already published.

These matters are as follows:—

The "Existential Import" of Propositions.
The use of "is-not" (or "are-not") as a Copula.
The theory "two Negative Premisses prove nothing."
Euler's Method of Diagrams.
Venn's Method of Diagrams.
My Method of Diagrams.
The Solution of a Syllogism by various Methods.
My Method of treating Syllogisms and Sorites.
Some account of Parts II, III.

§ 2.

The "Existential Import" of Propositions.

The writers, and editors, of the Logical text-books which run in the ordinary grooves——to whom I shall hereafter refer by the (I hope inoffensive) title "The Logicians"——take, on this subject, what seems to me to be a more humble position than is at all necessary. They speak of the Copula of a Proposition "with bated breath", almost as if it were a living, conscious Entity, capable of declaring for itself what it chose to mean, and that we, poor human creatures, had nothing to do but to ascertain *what* was its sovereign will and pleasure, and submit to it.

In opposition to this view, I maintain that any writer of a book is fully authorised in attaching any meaning he likes to any word or phrase he intends to use. If I find an author saying, at the beginning of his book, "Let it be understood that by the word '*black*' I shall always mean '*white*', and that by the word '*white*' I shall always mean '*black*'," I meekly accept his ruling, however injudicious I may think it.

And so, with regard to the question whether a Proposition is or is not to be understood as asserting the existence of its Subject, I maintain that every writer may adopt his own rule, provided of course that it is consistent with itself and with the accepted facts of Logic.

Let us consider certain views that may *logically* be held, and thus settle which of them may *conveniently* be held; after which I shall hold myself free to declare which of them *I* intend to hold.

The *kinds* of Proposition, to be considered, are those that begin with "some", with "no", and with "all". These are usually called Propositions "in *I*", "in *E*", and "in *A*".

First, then, a Proposition in *I* may be understood as asserting, or else as *not* asserting, the existence of its Subject. (By "existence" I mean of course whatever kind of existence suits its nature. The two Propositions, "*dreams* exist" and "*drums* exist", denote two totally different kinds of "existence". A *dream* is an aggregate of ideas, and exists only in the *mind of a dreamer*: whereas a *drum* is an aggregate of wood and parchment, and exists in the *hands of a drummer*.)

First, let us suppose that *I* "asserts" (i.e. "asserts the existence of its Subject").

Here, of course, we must regard a Proposition in *A* as making the *same* assertion, since it necessarily *contains* a Proposition in *I*.

We now have *I* and *A* "asserting". Does this leave us free to make what supposition we choose as to *E*? My answer is "No. We are tied down to the supposition that *E* does *not* assert." This can be proved as follows:—

If possible, let *E* "assert". Then (taking x, y, and z to represent Attributes) we see that, if the Proposition "No xy are z" be true, some things exist with the Attributes x and y: i.e. "Some x are y."

Also we know that, if the Proposition "Some *xy* are *z*" be true, the same result follows.

But these two Propositions are Contradictories, so that one or other of them *must* be true. Hence this result is *always* true: i.e. the Proposition "Some *x* are *y*" is *always* true!

Quod est absurdum. (See Note (A), p. 195).

We see, then, that the supposition "*I* asserts" necessarily leads to "*A* asserts, but *E* does not". And this is the *first* of the various views that may conceivably be held.

Next, let us suppose that *I* does *not* "assert." And, along with this, let us take the supposition that *E does* "assert."

Hence the Proposition "No *x* are *y*" means "Some *x* exist, and none of them are *y*": i.e. "*all* of them are *not*-y," which is a Proposition in *A*. We also know, of course, that the Proposition "All *x* are not-*y*" proves "No *x* are *y*." Now two Propositions, each of which proves the other, are *equivalent*. Hence every Proposition in *A* is equivalent to one in *E*, and therefore "*asserts*".

Hence our *second* conceivable view is "*E* and *A* assert, but *I* does not."

This view does not seem to involve any necessary contradiction with itself or with the accepted facts of Logic. But, when we come to *test* it, as applied to the actual *facts* of life, we shall find I think, that it fits in with them so badly that its adoption would be, to say the least of it, singularly inconvenient for ordinary folk.

Let me record a little dialogue I have just held with my friend Jones, who is trying to form a new Club, to be regulated on strictly *Logical* principles.

Author. "Well, Jones! Have you got your new Club started yet?"

Jones (*rubbing his hands*). "You'll be glad to hear that some of the Members (mind, I only say '*some*') are millionaires! Rolling in gold, my boy!"

Author. "That sounds well. And how many Members have entered?"

Jones (*staring*). "None at all. We haven't got it started yet. What makes you think we have?"

Author. "Why, I thought you said that some of the Members——"

Jones (*contemptuously*). "You don't seem to be aware that we're working on strictly *Logical* principles. A *Particular* Proposition does *not* assert the existence of its Subject. I merely meant to say that we've made a Rule not to admit *any* Members till we have at least *three* Candidates whose incomes are over ten thousand a year!"

Author. "Oh, *that's* what you meant, is it? Let's hear some more of your Rules."

Jones. "Another is, that no one, who has been convicted seven times of forgery, is admissible."

Author. "And here, again, I suppose you don't mean to assert there *are* any such convicts in existence?"

Jones. "Why, that's exactly what I *do* mean to assert! Don't you know that a Universal Negative *asserts* the existence of its Subject? *Of course* we didn't make that Rule till we had satisfied ourselves that there are several such convicts now living."

The Reader can now decide for himself how far this *second* conceivable view would fit in with the facts of life. He will, I think, agree with me that Jones' view, of the 'Existential Import' of Propositions, would lead to some inconvenience.

Thirdly, let us suppose that neither *I* nor *E* "asserts".

Now the supposition that the two Propositions, "Some x are y" and "No x are not-y", do *not* "assert", necessarily involves the supposition that "All x are y" does *not* "assert", since it would be absurd to suppose that they assert, when combined, more than they do when taken separately.

Hence the *third* (and last) of the conceivable views is that neither *I*, nor *E*, nor *A*, "asserts".

The advocates of this third view would interpret the Proposition "Some x are y" to mean "If there *were* any x in existence, some of them *would* be y"; and so with *E* and *A*.

It admits of proof that this view, as regards *A*, conflicts with the accepted facts of Logic.

Let us take the Syllogism *Darapti*, which is universally accepted as valid. Its form is

"All m are x;
All m are y.
∴ Some y are x".

This they would interpret as follows :—

"If there were any m in existence, all of them would be x;
If there were any m in existence, all of them would be y.
∴ If there were any y in existence, some of them would be x".

That this Conclusion does *not* follow has been so briefly and clearly explained by Mr. Keynes (in his "Formal Logic", dated 1894, pp. 356, 357), that I prefer to quote his words :—

"*Let no proposition imply the existence either of its subject or of its predicate.*

"Take, as an example, a syllogism in *Darapti* :—

'*All M is P,*
All M is S,
∴ *Some S is P.*'

"Taking S, M, P, as the minor, middle, and major terms respectively, the conclusion will imply that, if there is any S, there is some P. Will the premisses also imply this? If so, then the syllogism is valid; but not otherwise.

"The conclusion implies that if S exists P exists; but, consistently with the premisses, S may be existent while M and P are both non-existent. An implication is, therefore, contained in the conclusion, which is not justified by the premisses."

This seems to *me* entirely clear and convincing. Still, "to make sicker", I may as well throw the above (*soi-disant*) Syllogism into a concrete form, which will be within the grasp of even a *non*-logical Reader.

Let us suppose that a Boys' School has been set up, with the following system of Rules :—

"All boys in the First (the highest) Class are to do French, Greek, and Latin. All in the Second Class are to do Greek only. All in the Third Class are to do Latin only."

Suppose also that there *are* boys in the Third Class, and in the Second; but that no boy has yet risen into the First.

It is evident that there are no boys in the School doing French: still we know, by the Rules, what would happen if there *were* any.

We are authorised, then, by the *Data*, to assert the following two Propositions:—

> "If there were any boys doing French, all of them would be doing Greek;
> If there were any boys doing French, all of them would be doing Latin."

And the Conclusion, according to "The Logicians" would be

> "If there were any boys doing Latin, some of them would be doing Greek."

Here, then, we have two *true* Premisses and a *false* Conclusion (since we know that there *are* boys doing Latin, and that *none* of them are doing Greek). Hence the argument is *invalid*.

Similarly it may be shown that this "non-existential" interpretation destroys the validity of *Disamis, Datisi, Felapton*, and *Fresison*.

Some of "The Logicians" will, no doubt, be ready to reply "But we are not *Aldrichians!* Why should *we* be responsible for the validity of the Syllogisms of so antiquated an author as Aldrich?"

Very good. Then, for the *special* benefit of these "friends" of mine (with what ominous emphasis that name is sometimes used! "I must have a private interview with *you*, my young *friend*," says the bland Dr. Birch, "in my library, at 9 a.m. tomorrow. And you will please to be *punctual!*"), for their *special* benefit, I say, I will produce *another* charge against this "non-existential" interpretation.

It actually invalidates the ordinary Process of "Conversion", as applied to Propositions in '*I*'.

Every logician, Aldrichian or otherwise, accepts it as an established fact that "Some *x* are *y*" may be legitimately converted into "Some *y* are *x*."

But is it equally clear that the Proposition "If there *were* any *x*, some of them *would* be *y*" may be legitimately converted into "If there *were* any *y*, some of them would be *x*"? I trow not.

The example I have already used——of a Boys' School

with a non-existent First Class——will serve admirably to illustrate this new flaw in the theory of "The Logicians."

Let us suppose that there is yet *another* Rule in this School, viz. "In each Class, at the end of the Term, the head boy and the second boy shall receive prizes."

This Rule entirely authorises us to assert (in the sense in which "The Logicians" would use the words) "Some boys in the First Class will receive prizes", for this simply means (according to them) "If there *were* any boys in the First Class, some of them *would* receive prizes."

Now the Converse of this Proposition is, of course, "Some boys, who will receive prizes, are in the First Class", which means (according to "The Logicians") "If there *were* any boys about to receive prizes, some of them *would* be in the First Class" (which Class we know to be *empty*).

Of this Pair of Converse Propositions, the first is undoubtedly *true*: the second, *as* undoubtedly, *false*.

It is always sad to see a batsman knock down his own wicket: one pities him, as a man and a brother, but, as a *cricketer*, one can but pronounce him "Out!"

We see, then, that, among all the conceivable views we have here considered, there are only *two* which can *logically* be held, viz.

I and *A* "assert", but *E* does not.
E and *A* "assert", but *I* does not.

The *second* of these I have shown to involve great practical inconvenience.

The *first* is the one adopted in this book. (See p. 19.)

Some further remarks on this subject will be found in Note (B), at p. 196.

§ 3.

The use of "is-not" (or "are-not") as a Copula.

Is it better to say "John *is-not* in-the-house" or "John *is* not-in-the-house"? "Some of my acquaintances *are-not* men-I-should-like-to-be-seen-with" or "Some of my acquaintances *are* men-I-should-*not*-like-to-be-seen-with"? That is the sort of question we have now to discuss.

This is no question of Logical Right and Wrong: it is merely a matter of *taste*, since the two forms mean exactly the same thing. And here, again, "The Logicians" seem to me to take much too humble a position. When they are putting the final touches to the grouping of their Proposition, just before the curtain goes up, and when the Copula—— always a rather fussy 'heavy father', asks them "Am *I* to have the 'not', or will you tack it on to the Predicate?" they are much too ready to answer, like the subtle cab-driver, "Leave it to *you*, Sir!" The result seems to be, that the grasping Copula constantly gets a "not" that had better have been merged in the Predicate, and that Propositions are differentiated which had better have been recognised as precisely similar. Surely it is simpler to treat "Some men are Jews" and "Some men are Gentiles" as being, both of them, *affirmative* Propositions, instead of translating the latter into "Some men are-not Jews", and regarding it as a *negative* Proposition?

The fact is, "The Logicians" have somehow acquired a perfectly *morbid* dread of negative Attributes, which makes them shut their eyes, like frightened children, when they come across such terrible Propositions as "All not-x are y"; and thus they exclude from their system many very useful forms of Syllogisms.

Under the influence of this unreasoning terror, they plead that, in Dichotomy by Contradiction, the *negative* part is too large to deal with, so that it is better to regard each Thing as either included in, or excluded from, the *positive* part. I see no force in this plea: and the facts often go the other way. As a personal question, dear Reader, if *you* were to group your acquaintances into the two Classes, men that you *would* like to be seen with, and men that you would *not* like to be seen with, do you think the latter group would be so *very* much the larger of the two?

For the purposes of Symbolic Logic, it is so *much* the most convenient plan to regard the two sub-divisions, produced by Dichotomy, on the *same* footing, and to say, of any Thing, either that it "is" in the one, or that it "is" in the other, that I do not think any Reader of this book is likely to demur to my adopting that course.

§ 4.

The theory that "two Negative Premisses prove nothing".

This I consider to be *another* craze of "The Logicians", fully as morbid as their dread of a negative Attribute.

It is, perhaps, best refuted by the method of *Instantia Contraria.*

Take the following Pairs of Premisses:—

"None of my boys are conceited;
None of my girls are greedy".

"None of my boys are clever;
None but a clever boy could solve this problem".

"None of my boys are learned;
Some of my boys are not choristers".

(This last Proposition is, in *my* system, an *affirmative* one, since *I* should read it "are not-choristers"; but, in dealing with "The Logicians," I may fairly treat it as a *negative* one, since *they* would read it "are-not choristers".)

If you, dear Reader, declare, after full consideration of these Pairs of Premisses, that you cannot deduce a Conclusion from *any* of them——why, all I can say is that, like the Duke in *Patience*, you "will have to be contented with our heart-felt sympathy"! [See Note (C), p. 196.]

§ 5.

Euler's Method of Diagrams.

Diagrams seem to have been used, at first, to represent *Propositions* only. In Euler's well-known Circles, each was supposed to contain a Class, and the Diagram consisted of two Circles, which exhibited the relations, as to inclusion and exclusion, existing between the two Classes.

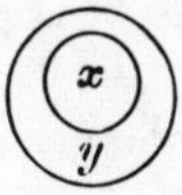

Thus, the Diagram, here given, exhibits the two Classes, whose respective Attributes are x and y, as so related to each other that the following Propositions are all simultaneously true:—"All x are y", "No x are not-y", "Some x are y", "Some y are not-x", "Some not-y are not-x", and, of course, the Converses of the last four.

x
y

Similarly, with this Diagram, the following Propositions are true :—" All *y* are *x* ", " No *y* are not-*x* ", " Some *y* are *x* ", " Some *x* are not-*y* ", " Some not-*x* are not-*y* ", and, of course, the Converses of the last four.

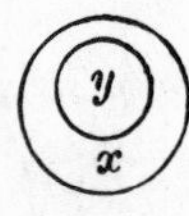

Similarly, with this Diagram, the following are true :—" All *x* are not-*y* ", " All *y* are not-*x* ", " No *x* are *y* ", " Some *x* are not-*y* ", " Some *y* are not-*x* ", " Some not-*x* are not-*y* ", and the Converses of the last four.

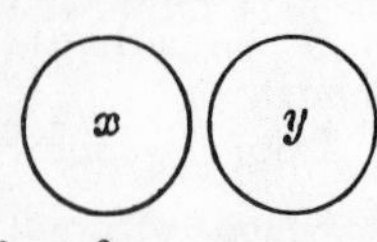

Similarly, with this Diagram, the following are true :—" Some *x* are *y* ", " Some *x* are not-*y* ", " Some not-*x* are *y* ", " Some not-*x* are not-*y* ", and, of course, their four Converses.

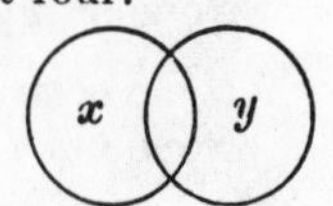

Note that *all* Euler's Diagrams assert " Some not-*x* are not-*y*." Apparently it never occurred to him that it might *sometimes* fail to be true!

Now, to represent " All *x* are *y* ", the *first* of these Diagrams would suffice. Similarly, to represent " No *x* are *y* ", the *third* would suffice. But to represent any *Particular* Proposition, at least *three* Diagrams would be needed (in order to include all the possible cases), and, for " Some not-*x* are not-*y* ", all the *four*.

§ 6.

Venn's Method of Diagrams.

Let us represent " not-*x* " by " *x'* ".

Mr. Venn's Method of Diagrams is a great advance on the above Method.

He uses the last of the above Diagrams to represent *any* desired relation between *x* and *y*, by simply shading a Compartment known to be *empty*, and placing a + in one known to be *occupied*.

Thus, he would represent the three Propositions " Some *x* ar *y* ", " No *x* are *y* ", and " All *x* are *y* ", as follows :—

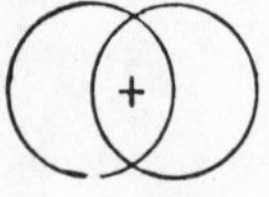

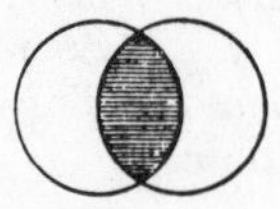

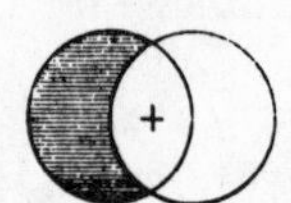

It will be seen that, of the *four* Classes, whose peculiar Sets of Attributes are xy, xy', $x'y$, and $x'y'$, only *three* are here provided with closed Compartments, while the *fourth* is allowed the rest of the Infinite Plane to range about in!

This arrangement would involve us in very serious trouble, if we ever attempted to represent "No x' are y'." Mr. Venn *once* (at p. 281) encounters this awful task; but evades it, in a quite masterly fashion, by the simple foot-note "We have not troubled to shade the outside of this diagram"!

To represent *two* Propositions (containing a common Term) *together*, a *three*-letter Diagram is needed. This is the one used by Mr. Venn.

Here, again, we have only *seven* closed Compartments, to accommodate the *eight* Classes whose peculiar Sets of Attributes are xym, xym', &c.

"With four terms in request," Mr. Venn says, "the most simple and symmetrical diagram seems to me that produced by making four ellipses intersect one another in the desired manner". This, however, provides only *fifteen* closed compartments.

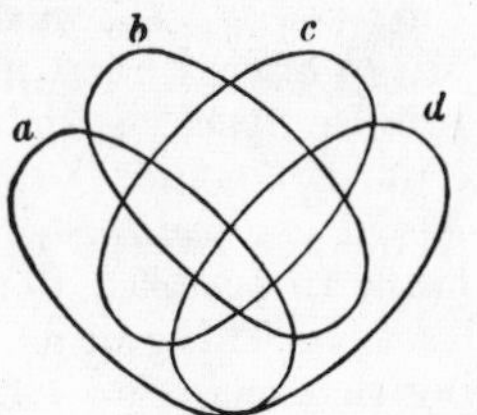

For *five* letters, "the simplest diagram I can suggest," Mr. Venn says, "is one like this (the small ellipse in the centre is to be regarded as a portion of the *outside* of *c*; i.e. its four component portions are inside *b* and *d* but are no part of *c*). It must be admitted that such a diagram is not quite so simple to draw as one might wish it to be; but then consider what the alternative is if one undertakes to deal with five terms and all their combinations—nothing short of the disagreeable task of writing out, or in some way putting before us, all the 32 combinations involved."

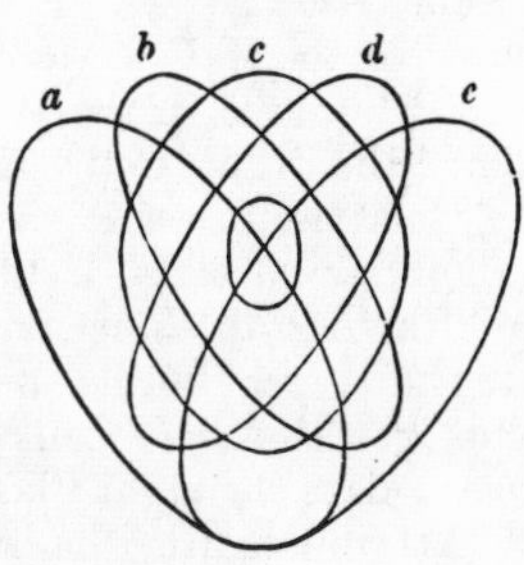

This Diagram gives us 31 closed compartments.

For *six* letters, Mr. Venn suggests that we might use *two* Diagrams, like the above, one for the f-part, and the other for the not-f-part, of all the other combinations. "This", he says, "would give the desired 64 subdivisions." This, however, would only give 62 closed Compartments, and *one* infinite area, which the two Classes, $a'b'c'd'e'f$ and $a'b'c'd'e'f'$, would have to share between them.

Beyond *six* letters Mr. Venn does not go.

§ 7.

My Method of Diagrams.

My Method of Diagrams *resembles* Mr. Venn's, in having separate Compartments assigned to the various Classes, and in marking these Compartments as *occupied* or as *empty*; but it *differs* from his Method, in assigning a *closed* area to the *Universe of Discourse*, so that the Class which, under Mr. Venn's liberal sway, has been ranging at will through Infinite Space, is suddenly dismayed to find itself "cabin'd, cribb'd, confined", in a limited Cell like any other Class! Also I use *rectilinear*, instead of *curvilinear*, Figures; and I mark an *occupied* Cell with a 'I' (meaning that there is at least *one* Thing in it), and an *empty* Cell with a 'O' (meaning that there is *no* Thing in it).

For *two* letters, I use this Diagram, in which the North Half is assigned to 'x', the South to 'not-x' (or 'x''), the West to y, and the East to y'. Thus the N.W. Cell contains the xy-Class, the N.E. Cell the xy'-Class, and so on.

For *three* letters, I subdivide these four Cells, by drawing an *Inner* Square, which I assign to m, the *Outer* Border being assigned to m'. I thus get the *eight* Cells that are needed to accommodate the eight Classes, whose peculiar Sets of Attributes are xym, xym', &c.

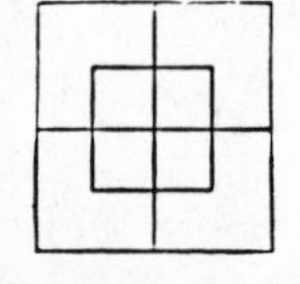

This last Diagram is the most complex that I use in the *Elementary* Part of my 'Symbolic Logic.' But I may as well take this opportunity of describing the more complex ones which will appear in Part II.

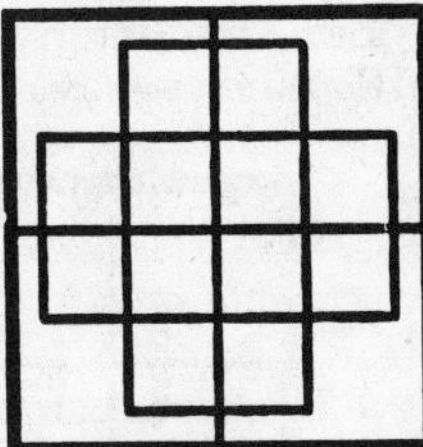

For *four* letters (which I call *a*, *b*, *c*, *d*) I use this Diagram; assigning the North Half to *a* (and of course the *rest* of the Diagram to *a′*), the West Half to *b*, the Horizontal Oblong to *c*, and the Upright Oblong to *d*. We have now got 16 Cells.

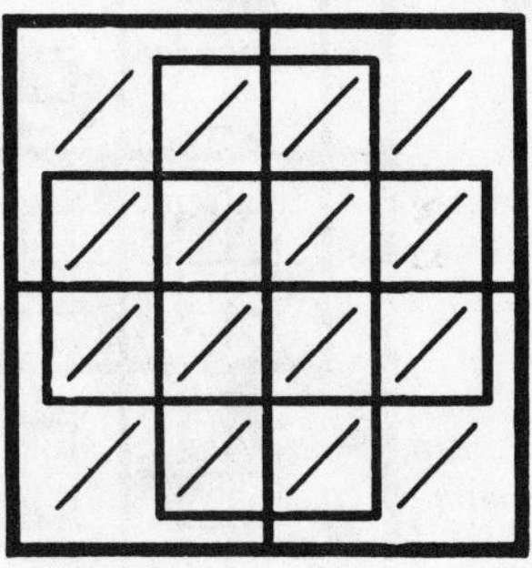

For *five* letters (adding *e*) I subdivide the 16 Cells of the previous Diagram by *oblique* partitions, assigning all the *upper* portions to *e*, and all the *lower* portions to *e′*. Here, I admit, we lose the advantage of having the *e*-Class all *together*, "in a ring-fence", like the other 4 Classes. Still, it is very easy to find; and the operation, of erasing it, is nearly as easy as that of erasing any other Class. We have now got 32 Cells.

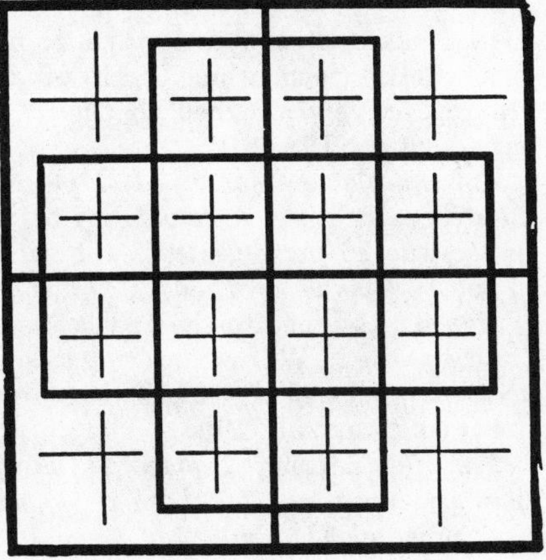

For *six* letters (adding *h*, as I avoid *tailed* letters) I substitute upright crosses for the oblique partitions, assigning the 4 portions, into which each of the 16 Cells is thus divided, to the four Classes *eh*, *eh′*, *e′h*, *e′h′*. We have now got 64 Cells.

For *seven* letters (adding *k*) I add, to each upright cross, a little inner square. All these 16 little squares are assigned to

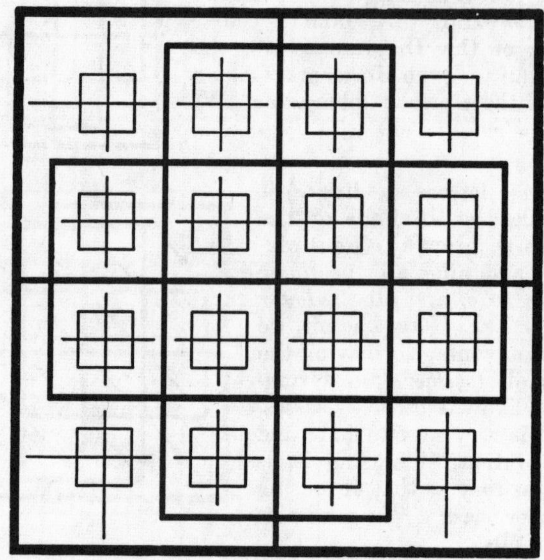

the *k*-Class, and all outside them to the *k'*-Class; so that the 8 little Cells (into which each of the 16 Cells is divided) are respectively assigned to the 8 Classes *ehk*, *ehk'*, &c. We have now got 128 Cells.

For *eight* letters (adding *l*) I place, in each of the 16 Cells, a *lattice*, which is a reduced copy of the whole Diagram; and, just as the 16 large Cells of the whole Diagram are assigned to the 16 Classes *abcd*, *abcd'*, &c., so the 16 little Cells of each lattice are assigned to the 16 Classes *ehkl*, *ehkl'*, &c. Thus, the lattice in the N.W. corner serves to accommodate the 16 Classes *abc'd'ehkl*, *abc'd'eh'kl'*, &c. This Octoliteral Diagram (see next page) contains 256 Cells.

For *nine* letters, I place 2 Octoliteral Diagrams side by side, assigning one of them to *m*, and the other to *m'*. We have now got 512 Cells.

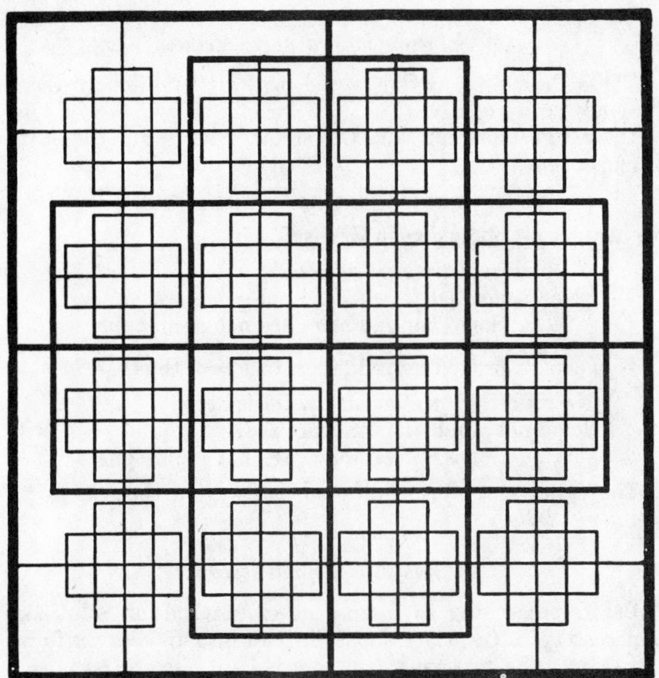

Finally, for *ten* letters, I arrange 4 Octoliteral Diagrams, like the above, in a square, assigning them to the 4 Classes *mn*, *mn′*, *m′n*, *m′n′*. We have now got 1024 Cells.

§ 8.

Solution of a Syllogism by various Methods.

The best way, I think, to exhibit the differences between these various Methods of solving Syllogisms, will be to take a concrete example, and solve it by each Method in turn. Let let us take, as our example, No. 29 (see p. 102).

"No philosophers are conceited;
Some conceited persons are not gamblers.
∴ Some persons, who are not gamblers, are not philosophers."

(1) *Solution by ordinary Method.*

These Premisses, as they stand, will give no Conclusion, as they are both negative.

If by 'Permutation' or 'Obversion', we write the Minor Premiss thus,

'Some conceited persons are not-gamblers,'

we can get a Conclusion in *Fresison*, viz.

"No philosophers are conceited;
Some conceited persons are not-gamblers.
∴ Some not-gamblers are not philosophers"

This can be proved by reduction to *Ferio*, thus:—

"No conceited persons are philosophers:
Some not-gamblers are conceited.
∴ Some not-gamblers are not philosophers".

The validity of *Ferio* follows directly from the Axiom '*De Omni et Nullo*'.

(2) *Symbolic Representation.*

Before proceeding to discuss other Methods of Solution, it is necessary to translate our Syllogism into an *abstract* form.

Let us take "persons" as our 'Universe of Discourse'; and let x = "philosophers", m = "conceited", and y = "gamblers."

Then the Syllogism may be written thus:—

"No x are m;
Some m are y'.
∴ Some y' are x'."

(3) *Solution by Euler's Method of Diagrams.*

The Major Premiss requires only *one* Diagram, viz.

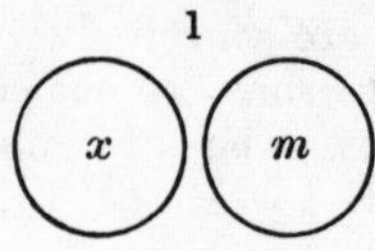

The Minor requires *three*, viz.

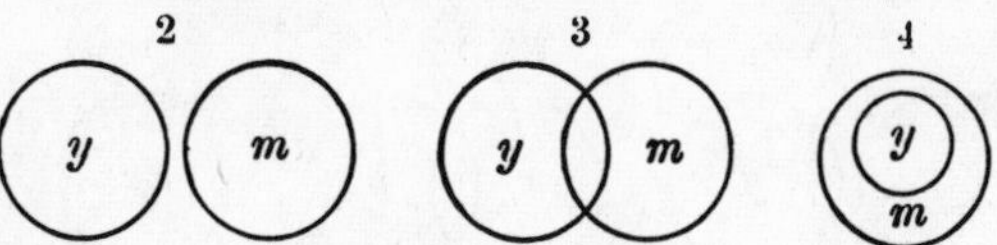

The combination of Major and Minor, in every possible way, requires *nine*, viz.

Figs. 1 and 2 give

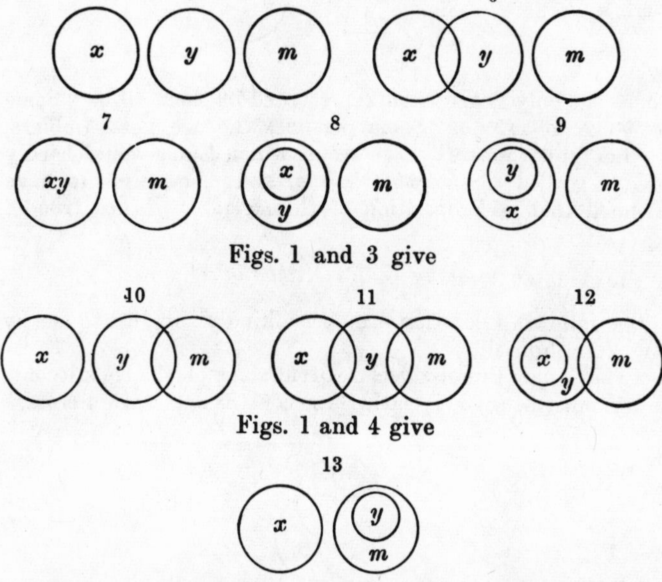

From this group (Figs. 5 to 13) we have, by disregarding m, to find the relation of x and y. On examination we find that Figs. 5, 10, 13 express the relation of entire mutual exclusion; that Figs. 6, 11 express partial inclusion and partial exclusion; that Fig. 7 expresses coincidence; that Figs. 8, 12 express entire inclusion of x in y; and that Fig. 9 expresses entire inclusion of y in x.

We thus get five Biliteral Diagrams for x and y, viz.

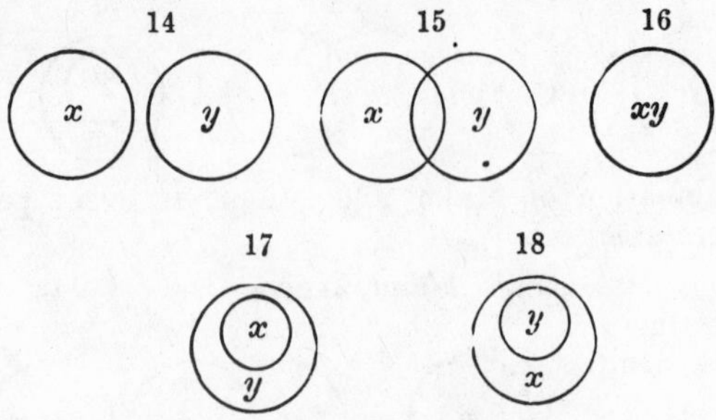

where the only Proposition, represented by them all, is "Some not-y are not-x," i.e. "Some persons, who are not gamblers, are not philosophers"——a result which Euler would hardly have regarded as a *valuable* one, since he seems to have assumed that a Proposition of this form is *always* true!

(4) *Solution by Venn's Method of Diagrams.*

The following Solution has been kindly supplied to me by Mr. Venn himself.

"The Minor Premiss declares that some of the constituents in my' must be saved: mark these constituents with a cross.

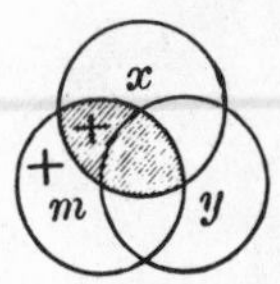

The Major declares that all xm must be destroyed; erase it.

Then, as some my' is to be saved, it must clearly be $my'x'$. That is, there must exist $my'x'$; or, eliminating m, $y'x'$. In common phraseology,

Some y' are x'', or, 'Some not-gamblers are not-philosophers.'"

(5) *Solution by my Method of Diagrams.*

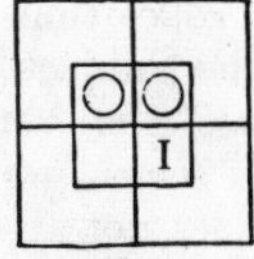

The first Premiss asserts that no *xm* exist: so we mark the *xm*-Compartment as empty, by placing a 'O' in each of its Cells.

The second asserts that some *my′* exist: so we mark the *my′*-Compartment as occupied, by placing a 'I' in its only available Cell.

The only information, that this gives us as to *x* and *y*, is that the *x′y′*-Compartment is *occupied*, i.e. that some *x′y′* exist.

Hence "Some *x′* are *y′*": i.e. "Some persons, who are not philosophers, are not gamblers".

(6) *Solution by my Method of Subscripts.*

$$xm_0 \dagger my'_1 \;\text{⁋}\; x'y'_1$$

i. e. "Some persons, who are not philosophers, are not gamblers."

§ 9.

My Method of treating Syllogisms and Sorites.

Of all the strange things, that are to be met with in the ordinary text-books of Formal Logic, perhaps the strangest is the violent contrast one finds to exist between their ways of dealing with these two subjects. While they have elaborately discussed no less than *nineteen* different forms of *Syllogisms*——each with its own special and exasperating Rules, while the whole constitute an almost useless machine, for practical purposes, many of the Conclusions being incomplete, and many quite legitimate forms being ignored——they have limited *Sorites* to *two* forms only, of childish simplicity; and these they have dignified with special *names*, apparently under the impression that no other possible forms existed!

As to *Syllogisms*, I find that their nineteen forms, with about a score of others which they have ignored, can all be arranged under *three* forms, each with a very simple Rule of its own; and the only question the Reader has to settle, in working any one of the 101 Examples given at p. 101 of this book, is "Does it belong to Fig. I. II., or III.?"

As to *Sorites*, the only two forms, recognised by the text-books, are the *Aristotelian*, whose Premisses are a series of Propositions in *A*, so arranged that the Predicate of each is the Subject of the next, and the *Goclenian*, whose Premisses are the very same series, written backwards. Goclenius, it seems, was the first who noticed the startling fact that it does not affect the force of a Syllogism to invert the order of its Premisses, and who applied this discovery to a Sorites. If we assume (as surely we may?) that he is the *same* man as that transcendent genius who first noticed that 4 times 5 is the same thing as 5 times 4, we may apply to him what somebody (Edmund Yates, I think it was) has said of Tupper, viz., "here is a man who, beyond all others of his generation, has been favoured with Glimpses of the Obvious!"

These puerile——not to say infantine——forms of a Sorites I have, in this book, ignored from the very first, and have not only admitted freely Propositions in *E*, but have purposely stated the Premisses in random order, leaving to the Reader the useful task of arranging them, for himself, in an order which can be worked as a series of regular Syllogisms. In doing this, he can begin with *any one* of them he likes.

I have tabulated, for curiosity, the various orders in which the Premisses of the Aristotelian Sorites

1. All *a* are *b*;
2. All *b* are *c*;
3. All *c* are *d*;
4. All *d* are *e*;
5. All *e* are *h*.

∴ All *a* are *h*.

may be syllogistically arranged, and I find there are no less than *sixteen* such orders, viz., 12345, 21345, 23145, 23415, 23451, 32145, 32415, 32451, 34215, 34251, 34521, 43215, 43251, 43521, 45321, 54321. Of these the *first* and the *last* have been dignified with names; but the other *fourteen*——first enumerated by an obscure Writer on Logic, towards the end of the Nineteenth Century——remain without a name!

---

§ 10.

Some account of Parts II, III.

In Part II. will be found some of the matters mentioned in this Appendix, viz., the "Existential Import" of Propositions, the use of a *negative* Copula, and the theory that "two negative Premisses prove nothing." I shall also extend the range of Syllogisms, by introducing Propositions containing *alternatives* (such as "Not-all *x* are *y*"), Propositions containing 3 or more Terms (such as "All *ab* are *c*", which, taken along with "Some *bc'* are *d*", would prove "Some *d* are *a'*"), &c. I shall also discuss Sorites containing Entities, and the *very* puzzling subjects of Hypotheticals and Dilemmas. I hope, in the course of Part II., to go over all the ground usually traversed in the text-books used in our Schools and Universities, and to enable my Readers to solve Problems of the same kind as, and far harder than, those that are at present set in their Examinations.

In Part III. I hope to deal with many curious and out-of-the-way subjects, some of which are not even alluded to in any of the treatises I have met with. In this Part will be found such matters as the Analysis of Propositions into their Elements (let the Reader, who has never gone into this branch of the subject, try to make out for himself what *additional* Proposition would be needed to convert "Some *a* are *b*" into "Some *a* are *bc*"), the treatment of Numerical and Geometrical Problems, the construction of Problems, and the solution of Syllogisms and Sorites containing Propositions more complex than any that I have used in Part II.

I will conclude with eight Problems, as a taste of what is coming in Part II. I shall be very glad to receive, from any Reader, who thinks he has solved any one of them (more especially if he has done so *without* using any Method of Symbols), what he conceives to be its complete Conclusion.

It may be well to explain what I mean by the *complete* Conclusion of a Syllogism or a Sorites. I distinguish their Terms as being of two kinds——those which *can* be eliminated (e.g. the Middle Term of a Syllogism), which I call the "Eliminands," and those which *cannot*, which I call the "Retinends"; and I do not call the Conclusion *complete*, unless it states *all* the relations, among the Retinends only, which can be deduced from the Premisses.

1.

All the boys, in a certain School, sit together in one large room every evening. They are of no less than *five* nationalities ——English, Scotch, Welsh, Irish, and German. One of the Monitors (who is a great reader of Wilkie Collins' novels) is very observant, and takes MS. notes of almost everything that happens, with the view of being a good sensational witness, in case any conspiracy to commit a murder should be on foot. The following are some of his notes:—

(1) Whenever some of the English boys are singing "Rule Britannia", and some not, some of the Monitors are wide-awake;
(2) Whenever some of the Scotch are dancing reels, and some of the Irish fighting, some of the Welsh are eating toasted cheese;
(3) Whenever all the Germans are playing chess, some of the Eleven are *not* oiling their bats;
(4) Whenever some of the Monitors are asleep, and some not, some of the Irish are fighting;
(5) Whenever some of the Germans are playing chess, and none of the Scotch are dancing reels, some of the Welsh are *not* eating toasted cheese;
(6) Whenever some of the Scotch are *not* dancing reels, and some of the Irish *not* fighting, some of the Germans are playing chess;
(7) Whenever some of the Monitors are awake, and some of the Welsh are eating toasted cheese, none of the Scotch are dancing reels;
(8) Whenever some of the Germans are *not* playing chess, and some of the Welsh are *not* eating toasted cheese, none of the Irish are fighting;

(9) Whenever all the English are singing "Rule Britannia," and some of the Scotch are *not* dancing reels, none of the Germans are playing chess;

(10) Whenever some of the English are singing "Rule Britannia", and some of the Monitors are asleep, some of the Irish are *not* fighting;

(11) Whenever some of the Monitors are awake, and some of the Eleven are *not* oiling their bats, some of the Scotch are dancing reels;

(12) Whenever some of the English are singing "Rule Britannia", and some of the Scotch are *not* dancing reels, * * * *

Here the MS. breaks off suddenly. The Problem is to complete the sentence, if possible.

[N.B. In solving this Problem, it is necessary to remember that the Proposition "All x are y" is a *Double* Proposition, and is equivalent to "Some x are y, and none are y'." See p. 17.]

2.

(1) A logician, who eats pork-chops for supper, will probably lose money;

(2) A gambler, whose appetite is not ravenous, will probably lose money;

(3) A man who is depressed, having lost money and being likely to lose more, always rises at 5 a.m.;

(4) A man, who neither gambles nor eats pork-chops for supper, is sure to have a ravenous appetite;

(5) A lively man, who goes to bed before 4 a.m., had better take to cab-driving;

(6) A man with a ravenous appetite, who has not lost money and does not rise at 5 a.m., always eats pork-chops for supper;

(7) A logician, who is in danger of losing money, had better take to cab-driving;

(8) An earnest gambler, who is depressed though he has not lost money, is in no danger of losing any;

(9) A man, who does not gamble, and whose appetite is not ravenous, is always lively;

(10) A lively logician, who is really in earnest, is in no danger of losing money;
(11) A man with a ravenous appetite has no need to take to cab-driving, if he is really in earnest;
(12) A gambler, who is depressed though in no danger of losing money, sits up till 4 a.m.
(13) A man, who has lost money and does not eat pork-chops for supper, had better take to cab-driving, unless he gets up at 5 a.m.
(14) A gambler, who goes to bed before 4 a.m., need not take to cab-driving, unless he has a ravenous appetite;
(15) A man with a ravenous appetite, who is depressed though in no danger of losing money, is a gambler.

Univ. "men"; a = earnest; b = eating pork-chops for supper; c = gamblers; d = getting up at 5; e = having lost money; h = having a ravenous appetite; k = likely to lose money; l = lively; m = logicians; n = men who had better take to cab-driving; r = sitting up till 4.

[N.B. In this Problem, clauses, beginning with "though", are intended to be treated as *essential* parts of the Propositions in which they occur, just as if they had begun with "and".]

3.

(1) When the day is fine, I tell Froggy "You're quite the dandy, old chap!";
(2) Whenever I let Froggy forget that £10 he owes me, and he begins to strut about like a peacock, his mother declares "He shall *not* go out a-wooing!";
(3) Now that Froggy's hair is out of curl, he has put away his gorgeous waistcoat;
(4) Whenever I go out on the roof to enjoy a quiet cigar, I'm sure to discover that my purse is empty;
(5) When my tailor calls with his little bill, and I remind Froggy of that £10 he owes me, he does *not* grin like a hyæna;

(6) When it is very hot, the thermometer is high;

(7) When the day is fine, and I'm not in the humour for a cigar, and Froggy is grinning like a hyæna, I never venture to hint that he's quite the dandy;

(8) When my tailor calls with his little bill and finds me with an empty purse, I remind Froggy of that £10 he owes me;

(9) My railway-shares are going up like anything!

(10) When my purse is empty, and when, noticing that Froggy has got his gorgeous waistcoat on, I venture to remind him of that £10 he owes me, things are apt to get rather warm;

(11) Now that it looks like rain, and Froggy is grinning like a hyæna, I can do without my cigar;

(12) When the thermometer is high, you need not trouble yourself to take an umbrella;

(13) When Froggy has his gorgeous waistcoat on, but is *not* strutting about like a peacock, I betake myself to a quiet cigar;

(14) When I tell Froggy that he's quite the dandy, he grins like a hyæna;

(15) When my purse is tolerably full, and Froggy's hair is one mass of curls, and when he is *not* strutting about like a peacock, I go out on the roof;

(16) When my railway-shares are going up, and when it is chilly and looks like rain, I have a quiet cigar;

(17) When Froggy's mother lets him go a-wooing, he seems nearly mad with joy, and puts on a waistcoat that is gorgeous beyond words;

(18) When it is going to rain, and I am having a quiet cigar, and Froggy is *not* intending to go a-wooing, you had better take an umbrella;

(19) When my railway-shares are going up, and Froggy seems nearly mad with joy, *that* is the time my tailor always chooses for calling with his little bill;

(20) When the day is cool and the thermometer low, and I say nothing to Froggy about his being quite the dandy, and there's not the ghost of a grin on his face, I haven't the heart for my cigar!

4.

(1) Any one, fit to be an M.P., who is not always speaking, is a public benefactor;

(2) Clear-headed people, who express themselves well, have had a good education;

(3) A woman, who deserves praise, is one who can keep a secret;

(4) People, who benefit the public, but do not use their influence for good purposes, are not fit to go into Parliament;

(5) People, who are worth their weight in gold and who deserve praise, are always unassuming;

(6) Public benefactors, who use their influence for good objects, deserve praise;

(7) People, who are unpopular and not worth their weight in gold, never can keep a secret;

(8) People, who can talk for ever and are fit to be Members of Parliament, deserve praise;

(9) Any one, who can keep a secret and who is unassuming, is a never-to-be-forgotten public benefactor;

(10) A woman, who benefits the public, is always popular;

(11) People, who are worth their weight in gold, who never leave off talking, and whom it is impossible to forget, are just the people whose photographs are in all the shop-windows;

(12) An ill-educated woman, who is not clear-headed, is not fit to go into Parliament;

(13) Any one, who can keep a secret and is not for ever talking, is sure to be unpopular;

(14) A clear-headed person, who has influence and uses it for good objects, is a public benefactor;

(15) A public benefactor, who is unassuming, is not the sort of person whose photograph is in every shop-window;

(16) People, who can keep a secret and who use their influence for good purposes, are worth their weight in gold;

(17) A person, who has no power of expression and who cannot influence others, is certainly not a *woman;*

(18) People, who are popular and worthy of praise, either are public benefactors or else are unassuming.

Univ. "persons"; *a* = able to keep a secret; *b* = clear-headed; *c* = constantly talking; *d* = deserving praise; *e* = exhibited in shop-windows; *h* = expressing oneself well; *k* = fit to be an M.P.; *l* = influential; *m* = never-to-be-forgotten; *n* = popular; *r* = public benefactors; *s* = unassuming; *t* = using one's influence for good objects; *v* = well-educated; *w* = women; *z* = worth one's weight in gold.

15.

Six friends, and their six wives, are staying in the same hotel; and they all walk out daily, in parties of various size and composition. To ensure variety in these daily walks, they have agreed to observe the following Rules:—

(1) If Acres is with (i.e. is in the same party with) his wife, and Barry with his, and Eden with Mrs. Hall, Cole must be with Mrs. Dix;

(2) If Acres is with his wife, and Hall with his, and Barry with Mrs. Cole, Dix must *not* be with Mrs. Eden;

(3) If Cole and Dix and their wives are all in the same party, and Acres *not* with Mrs. Barry, Eden must *not* be with Mrs. Hall;

(4) If Acres is with his wife, and Dix with his, and Barry *not* with Mrs. Cole, Eden must be with Mrs. Hall;

(5) If Eden is with his wife, and Hall with his, and Cole with Mrs. Dix, Acres must *not* be with Mrs. Barry;

(6) If Barry and Cole and their wives are all in the same party, and Eden *not* with Mrs. Hall, Dix must be with Mrs. Eden.

The Problem is to prove that there must be, every day, at least *one* married couple who are not in the same party.

6.

After the six friends, named in Problem 5, had returned from their tour, three of them, Barry, Cole, and Dix, agreed, with two other friends of theirs, Lang and Mill, that the five should meet, every day, at a certain *table-d'hôte.* Remembering how much amusement they had derived from their code of rules for walking-parties, they devised the following rules, to be observed whenever beef appeared on the table:—

(1) If Barry takes salt, then either Cole or Lang takes *one* only of the two condiments, salt and mustard: if he takes mustard, then either Dix takes neither condiment, or Mill takes both.

(2) If Cole takes salt, then either Barry takes only *one* condiment, or Mill takes neither: if he takes mustard, then either Dix or Lang takes both.

(3) If Dix takes salt, then either Barry takes neither condiment or Cole takes both: if he takes mustard, then either Lang or Mill takes neither.

(4) If Lang takes salt, then either Barry or Dix takes only *one* condiment: if he takes mustard, then either Cole or Mill takes neither.

(5) If Mill takes salt, then either Barry or Lang takes both condiments: if he takes mustard, then either Cole or Dix takes only *one.*

The Problem is to discover whether these rules are *compatible;* and, if so, what arrangements are possible.

[N.B. In this Problem, it is assumed that the phrase "if Barry takes salt" allows of *two* possible cases, viz. (1) "he takes salt *only*"; (2) "he takes *both* condiments". And so with all similar phrases.

It is also assumed that the phrase "either Cole or Lang takes *one* only of the two condiments" allows of *three* possible cases, viz. (1) "Cole takes *one* only, Lang takes both or neither"; (2) "Cole takes both or neither, Lang takes *one* only"; (3) "Cole takes *one* only, Lang takes *one* only". And so with all similar phrases.

It is also assumed that every rule is to be understood as implying the words "and *vice versâ.*" Thus the first rule would imply the addition "and, if either Cole or Lang takes only *one* condiment, then Barry takes salt."]

7.

(1) Brothers, who are much admired, are apt to be self-conscious;

(2) When two men of the same height are on opposite sides in Politics, if one of them has his admirers, so also has the other;

(3) Brothers, who avoid general Society, look well when walking together;

(4) Whenever you find two men, who differ in Politics and in their views of Society, and who are not both of them ugly, you may be sure that they look well when walking together;

(5) Ugly men, who look well when walking together, are not both of them free from self-consciousness;

(6) Brothers, who differ in Politics, and are not both of them handsome, never give themselves airs;

(7) John declines to go into Society, but never gives himself airs;

(8) Brothers, who are apt to be self-conscious, though not *both* of them handsome, usually dislike Society;

(9) Men of the same height, who do not give themselves airs, are free from self-consciousness;

(10) Men, who agree on questions of Art, though they differ in Politics, and who are not both of them ugly, are always admired;

(11) Men, who hold opposite views about Art and are not admired, always give themselves airs;

(12) Brothers of the same height always differ in Politics;

(13) Two handsome men, who are neither both of them admired nor both of them self-conscious, are no doubt of different heights;

(14) Brothers, who are self-conscious, and do not both of them like Society, never look well when walking together.

[N.B. See Note at end of Problem 2.]

[TURN OVER.

8.

(1) A man can always master his father;
(2) An inferior of a man's uncle owes that man money;
(3) The father of an enemy of a friend of a man owes that man nothing;
(4) A man is always persecuted by his son's creditors;
(5) An inferior of the master of a man's son is senior to that man;
(6) A grandson of a man's junior is not his nephew;
(7) A servant of an inferior of a friend of a man's enemy is never persecuted by that man;
(8) A friend of a superior of the master of a man's victim is that man's enemy;
(9) An enemy of a persecutor of a servant of a man's father is that man's friend.

The Problem is to deduce some fact about great-grandsons.

[N.B. In this Problem, it is assumed that all the men, here referred to, live in the same town, and that every pair of them are either "friends" or "enemies," that every pair are related as "senior and junior", "superior and inferior", and that certain pairs are related as "creditor and debtor", "father and son", "master and servant", "persecutor and victim", "uncle and nephew".]

9.

"Jack Sprat could eat no fat:
His wife could eat no lean:
And so, between them both,
They licked the platter clean."

Solve this as a Sorites-Problem, taking lines 3 and 4 as the Conclusion to be proved. It is permitted to use, as Premisses, not only all that is here *asserted*, but also all that we may reasonably understand to be *implied*.

———

NOTES TO APPENDIX.

(A) [See p. 167, line 6.]

It may, perhaps, occur to the Reader, who has studied Formal Logic, that the argument, here applied to the Propositions *I* and *E*, will apply equally well to the Propositions *I* and *A* (since, in the ordinary text-books, the Propositions "All *xy* are *z*" and "Some *xy* are not *z*" are regarded as Contradictories). Hence it may appear to him that the argument might have been put as follows :—

"We now have *I* and *A* 'asserting.' Hence, if the Proposition 'All *xy* are *z*' be true, some things exist with the Attributes *x* and *y* : i.e. 'Some *x* are *y*.'

"Also we know that, if the Proposition 'Some *xy* are not-*z*' be true, the same result follows.

"But these two Propositions are Contradictories, so that one or other of them *must* be true. Hence this result is *always* true: i.e. the Proposition 'Some *x* are *y*' is *always* true !

"*Quod est absurdum.* Hence *I cannot* assert."

This matter will be discussed in Part II ; but I may as well give here what seems to me to be an irresistible proof that this view (that *A* and *I* are Contradictories), though adopted in the ordinary text-books, is untenable. The proof is as follows :—

With regard to the relationship existing between the Class '*xy*' and the two Classes '*z*' and 'not-*z*', there are *four* conceivable states of things, viz.

(1)	Some *xy*	are *z*,	and some	are not-*z* ;
(2)	,,	,,	none	,,
(3)	No *xy*	,,	some	,,
(4)	,,	,,	none	,,

Of these four, No. (2) is equivalent to "All *xy* are *z*", No. (3) is equivalent to "All *xy* are not-*z*", and No. (4) is equivalent to "No *xy* exist."

Now it is quite undeniable that, of these *four* states of things, each is, *a priori, possible*, some *one must* be true, and the other three *must* be false.

Hence the Contradictory to (2) is "Either (1) or (3) or (4) is true." Now the assertion "Either (1) or (3) is true" is equivalent to "Some *xy* are not-*z*"; and the assertion "(4) is true" is equivalent to "No *xy* exist." Hence the Contradictory to "All *xy* are *z*" may be expressed as the Alternative Proposition "Either some *xy* are not-*z*, or no *xy* exist," but *not* as the Categorical Proposition "Some *y* are not-*z*."

(B) [See p. 171, at end of Section 2.]

There are yet *other* views current among "The Logicians", as to the "Existential Import" of Propositions, which have not been mentioned in this Section.

One is, that the Proposition "Some x are y" is to be interpreted, neither as "Some x *exist* and are y", nor yet as "If there *were* any x in existence, some of them *would* be y", but merely as "Some x *can be y;* i.e. the Attributes x and y are *compatible*". On *this* theory, there would be nothing offensive in my telling my friend Jones "Some of your brothers are swindlers"; since, if he indignantly retorted "What do you *mean* by such insulting language, you scoundrel?", I should calmly reply "I merely mean that the thing is *conceivable*——that some of your brothers *might possibly* be swindlers". But it may well be doubted whether such an explanation would *entirely* appease the wrath of Jones!

Another view is, that the Proposition "All x are y" *sometimes* implies the actual *existence* of x, and *sometimes* does *not* imply it; and that we cannot tell, without having it in *concrete* form, *which* interpretation we are to give to it. *This* view is, I think, strongly supported by common usage; and it will be fully discussed in Part II: but the difficulties, which it introduces, seem to me too formidable to be even alluded to in Part I, which I am trying to make, as far as possible, easily intelligible to mere *beginners*.

(C) [See p. 173, § 4.]

The three Conclusions are

"No conceited child of mine is greedy";
"None of my boys could solve this problem
"Some unlearned boys are not choristers."

INDEX.

---

§ 1.

Tables.

§ 2.

Words &c. explained.

THE END.

THE GAME OF LOGIC

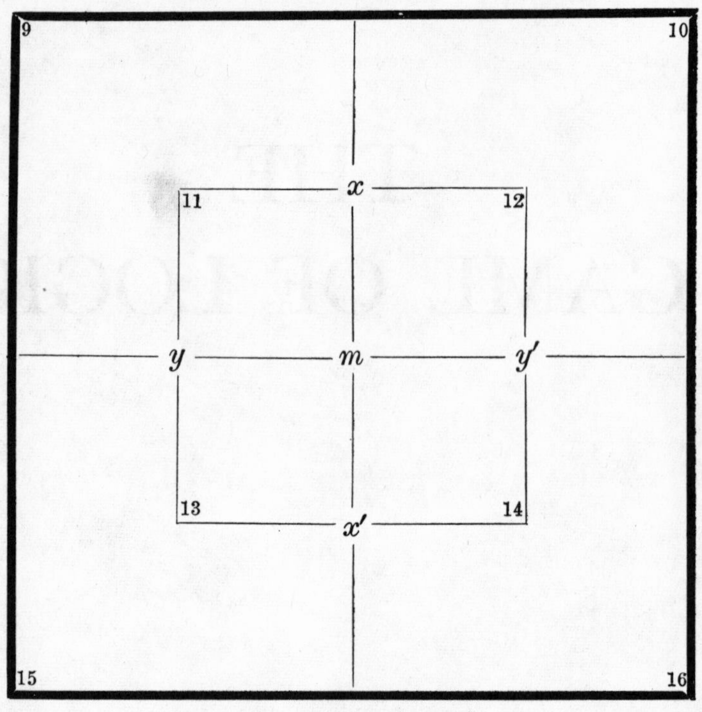

COLOURS FOR
COUNTERS.

See, the Sun is overhead,
Shining on us, FULL and
RED!
Now the Sun is gone away,
And the EMPTY sky is
GREY!

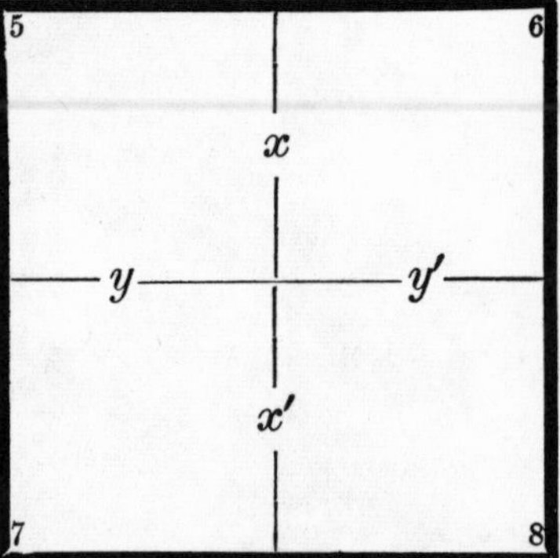

THE GAME OF LOGIC

By Lewis Carroll

To my Child-Friend.

I charm in vain; for never again,
All keenly as my glance I bend,
    Will Memory, goddess coy,
    Embody for my joy
Departed days, nor let me gaze
    On thee, my Fairy Friend!

Yet could thy face, in mystic grace,
A moment smile on me, 'twould send
    Far-darting rays of light
    From Heaven athwart the night,
By which to read in very deed
    Thy spirit, sweetest Friend!

So may the stream of Life's long dream
Flow gently onward to its end,
    With many a floweret gay,
    Adown its willowy way:
May no sigh vex, no care perplex,
    My loving little Friend!

NOTA BENE.

With each copy of this Book is given an Envelope, containing a Diagram (similar to the frontispiece) on card, and nine Counters, four red and five grey.

The Envelope, &c. can be had separately, at *3d.* each.

The Author will be very grateful for suggestions, especially from beginners in Logic, of any alterations, or further explanations, that may seem desirable. Letters should be addressed to him at "29, Bedford Street, Covent Garden, London."

The material contained in the envelope referred to above is reproduced in its entirety on the inside back cover of the Dover edition.

PREFACE

"There foam'd rebellious Logic, gagg'd and bound."

THIS Game requires nine Counters—four of one colour and five of another: say four red and five grey.

Besides the nine Counters, it also requires one Player, *at least*. I am not aware of any Game that can be played with *less* than this number: while there are several that require *more:* take Cricket, for instance, which requires twenty-two. How much easier it is, when you want to play a Game, to find *one* Player than twenty-two. At the same time, though one Player is enough, a good deal more amusement may be got by two working at it together, and correcting each other's mistakes.

A second advantage, possessed by this Game, is that, besides being an endless source of amusement (the number of arguments, that may be worked by it, being infinite), it will give the Players a little instruction as well. But is there any great harm in *that*, so long as you get plenty of amusement?

CONTENTS.

CHAPTER I.

NEW LAMPS FOR OLD.

"Light come, light go."

---

§ 1. *Propositions.*

"Some new Cakes are nice."
"No new Cakes are nice."
"All new Cakes are nice."

There are three '*Propositions*' for you——the only three kinds we are going to use in this Game: and the first thing to be done is to learn how to express them on the Board.

Let us begin with

"Some new Cakes are nice."

But, before doing so, a remark has to be made——one that is rather important, and by no means easy to understand all in a moment: so please to read this *very* carefully.

The world contains many *Things* (such as "Buns", "Babies", "Beetles", "Battledores", &c.); and these Things possess many *Attributes* (such as "baked", "beautiful", "black", "broken", &c.: in fact, whatever can be "attributed to", that is "said to belong to", any Thing, is an Attribute). Whenever we wish to mention a Thing, we use a *Substantive*: when we wish to mention an Attribute, we use an *Adjective*. People have asked the question "Can a Thing exist without any Attributes belonging to it?" It is a very puzzling question, and I'm not going to try to answer it: let us turn up our noses, and treat it with contemptuous silence, as if it really wasn't worth noticing. But, if they put it the other way, and ask "Can an Attribute exist without any Thing for it to belong to?", we may say at once "No: no more than a Baby could go a railway-journey with no one to take care of it!" You never saw "beautiful" floating about in the air, or littered about on the floor, without any Thing to *be* beautiful, now did you?

And now what am I driving at, in all this long rigmarole? It is this. You may put "is" or "are" between the names of two *Things* (for example, "some Pigs are fat Animals"), or between the names of two *Attributes* (for example, "pink is light-red"), and in each case it will make good sense. But, if you put "is" or "are" between the name of a *Thing* and the name of an *Attribute* (for example, "some Pigs are pink"), you do *not* make good sense (for how can a Thing *be* an Attribute?) unless you have an understanding with the person to whom you are speaking. And the simplest understanding would, I think, be this——that the Substantive shall be supposed to be repeated at the end of the sentence, so that the sentence, if written out in full, would be "some Pigs are pink (Pigs)". And now the word "are" makes quite good sense.

Thus, in order to make good sense of the Proposition "some new Cakes are nice", we must suppose it to be written out in full, in the form "some new Cakes are nice (Cakes)". Now this contains two '*Terms*'——"new Cakes" being one of them, and "nice (Cakes)" the other. "New Cakes," being the one we are talking about, is called the '*Subject*' of the Proposition, and "nice (Cakes)" the '*Predicate*'. Also this Proposition is said to be a '*Particular*' one, since it does not speak of the *whole* of its Subject, but only of a *part* of it. The other two kinds are said to be '*Universal*', because they speak of the *whole* of their Subjects——the one denying niceness, and the other asserting it, of the *whole* class of "new Cakes". Lastly, if you would like to have a definition of the word '*Proposition*' itself, you may take this:—"a sentence stating that some, or none, or all, of the Things belonging to a certain class, called its 'Subject', are also Things belonging to a certain other class, called its 'Predicate'".

You will find these seven words —— *Proposition, Attribute, Term, Subject, Predicate, Particular, Universal* ——charmingly useful, if any friend should happen to ask if you have ever studied Logic. Mind you bring all seven words into your answer, and your friend will go away deeply impressed——'a sadder and a wiser man'.

Now please to look at the smaller Diagram on the Board, and suppose it to be a cupboard, intended for all the Cakes in the world (it would have to be a good large one, of course). And let us suppose all the new ones to be put into the upper half (marked 'x'), and all the rest (that is, the *not*-new ones) into the lower half (marked 'x''). Thus the lower half would contain *elderly* Cakes, *aged* Cakes, *ante-diluvian* Cakes——if there are any: I haven't seen many, myself——and so on. Let us also suppose all the nice Cakes to be put into the left-hand half (marked 'y'), and all the rest (that is, the not-nice ones) into the right-hand half (marked 'y''). At present, then, we must understand x to mean "new", x' "not-new", y "nice", and y' "not-nice."

And now what kind of Cakes would you expect to find in compartment No. 5?

It is part of the upper half, you see; so that, if it has any Cakes in it, they must be *new*: and it is part of the left-hand half; so that they must be *nice.* Hence if there are any Cakes in this compartment, they must have the double '*Attribute*' "new and nice": or, if we use letters, they must be "x y."

Observe that the letters x, y are written on two of the edges of this compartment. This you will find a very convenient rule for knowing what Attributes belong to the Things in any compartment. Take No. 7, for instance. If there are any Cakes there, they must be "x' y", that is, they must be "not-new and nice."

Now let us make another agreement——that a red counter in a compartment shall mean that it is '*occupied*', that is, that there are *some* Cakes in it. (The word 'some,' in Logic, means 'one or more': so that a single Cake in a compartment would be quite enough reason for saying "there are *some* Cakes here"). Also let us agree that a grey counter in a compartment shall mean that it is '*empty*', that is, that there are *no* Cakes in it. In the following Diagrams, I shall put '1' (meaning 'one or more') where you are to put a *red* counter, and '0' (meaning 'none') where you are to put a *grey* one.

As the Subject of our Proposition is to be "new Cakes", we are only concerned, at present, with the *upper* half of the cupboard, where all the Cakes have the attribute x, that is, "new."

Now, fixing our attention on this upper half, suppose we found it marked like this,

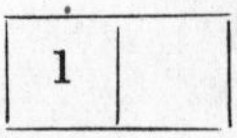

1	

that is, with a red counter in No. 5. What would this tell us, with regard to the class of "new Cakes"?

Would it not tell us that there are *some* of them in the $x\ y$-compartment? That is, that some of them (besides having the Attribute x, which belongs to both compartments) have the Attribute y (that is, "nice"). This we might express by saying "some x-Cakes are y-(Cakes)", or, putting words instead of letters,

"Some new Cakes are nice (Cakes)",

or, in a shorter form,

"Some new Cakes are nice".

At last we have found out how to represent the first Proposition of this Section. If you have not *clearly* understood all I have said, go no further, but read it over and over again, till you *do* understand it. After that is once mastered, you will find all the rest quite easy.

It will save a little trouble, in doing the other Propositions, if we agree to leave out the word "Cakes" altogether. I find it convenient to call the whole class of Things, for which the cupboard is intended, the '*Universe.*' Thus we might have begun this business by saying "Let us take a Universe of Cakes." (Sounds nice, doesn't it?)

Of course any other Things would have done just as well as Cakes. We might make Propositions about "a Universe of Lizards", or even "a Universe of Hornets". (Wouldn't *that* be a charming Universe to live in?)

So far, then, we have learned that

1	

means "some x and y," i. e. "some new are nice."

I think you will see, without further explanation, that

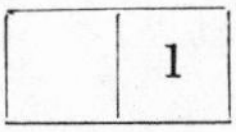

	1

means "some x are y'," i. e. "some new are not-nice."

Now let us put a *grey* counter into No. 5, and ask ourselves the meaning of

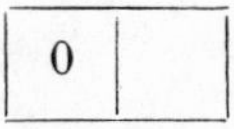

0	

This tells us that the x y-compartment is *empty*, which we may express by "no x are y", or, "no new Cakes are nice". This is the second of the three Propositions at the head of this Section.

In the same way,

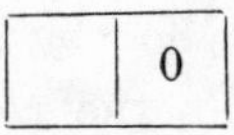

	0

would mean "no x are y'," or, "no new Cakes are not-nice."

What would you make of this, I wonder?

1	1

I hope you will not have much trouble in making out that this represents a *double* Proposition: namely, "some x are y, *and* some are y'," i. e. "some new are nice, *and* some are not-nice."

The following is a little harder, perhaps:—

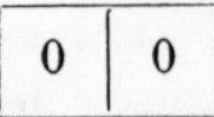

This means "no x are y, *and* none are y'," i. e. "no new are nice, *and* none are not-nice": which leads to the rather curious result that "no new exist," i.e. "no Cakes are new." This is because "nice" and "not-nice" make what we call an '*exhaustive*' division of the class "new Cakes": i. e. between them, they *exhaust* the whole class, so that all the new Cakes, that exist, must be found in one or the other of them.

And now suppose you had to represent, with counters, the contradictory to "no Cakes are new", which would be "some Cakes are new", or, putting letters for words, "some Cakes are x", how would you do it?

This will puzzle you a little, I expect. Evidently you must put a red counter *somewhere* in the x-half of the cupboard, since you know there are *some* new Cakes. But you must not put it into the *left-hand* compartment, since you do not know them to be *nice*: nor may you put it into the *right-hand* one, since you do not know them to be *not-nice*.

What, then, are you to do? I think the best way out of the difficulty is to place the red counter *on the division-line* between the xy-compartment and the xy'-compartment. This I shall represent (as *I* always put '1' where *you* are to put a red counter) by the diagram

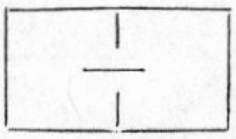

Our ingenious American cousins have invented a phrase to express the position of a man who wants to join one or other of two parties——such as their two parties 'Democrats' and 'Republicans'——but ca'n't make up his mind *which*. Such a man is said to be "sitting on the fence." Now that is exactly the position of the red counter you have just placed on the division-line. He likes the look of No. 5, and he likes the look of No. 6, and he doesn't know *which* to jump down into. So there he sits astride, silly fellow, dangling his legs, one on each side of the fence!

Now I am going to give you a much harder one to make out. What does this mean?

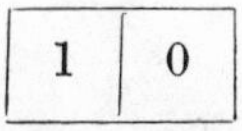

1	0

This is clearly a *double* Proposition. It tells us, not only that "some x are y," but also that "no x are *not* y." Hence the result is "*all* x are y," i. e. "all new Cakes are nice", which is the last of the three Propositions at the head of this Section.

We see, then, that the Universal Proposition

"All new Cakes are nice"

consists of *two* Propositions taken together, namely,

"Some new Cakes are nice,"

and "No new Cakes are not-nice."

In the same way

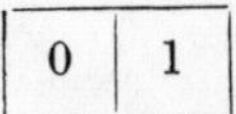

would mean "all x are y'", that is,

"All new Cakes are not-nice."

Now what would you make of such a Proposition as "The Cake you have given me is nice"? Is it Particular, or Universal?

"Particular, of course," you readily reply. "One single Cake is hardly worth calling 'some,' even."

No, my dear impulsive Reader, it is 'Universal'. Remember that, few as they are (and I grant you they couldn't well be fewer), they are (or rather 'it is') *all* that you have given me! Thus, if (leaving 'red' out of the question) I divide my Universe of Cakes into two classes——the Cakes you have given me (to which I assign the upper half of the cupboard), and those you *haven't* given me (which are to go below)—— I find the lower half fairly full, and the upper one as nearly as possible empty. And then, when I am told to put an upright division into each half, keeping the *nice* Cakes to the left, and the *not-nice* ones to the right, I begin by carefully collecting *all* the Cakes you have given me (saying to myself, from time to time, "Generous creature! How shall I ever repay such kindness?"), and piling them up in the left-hand compartment. *And it doesn't take long to do it!*

Here is another Universal Proposition for you. "Barzillai Beckalegg is an honest man." That means "*All* the Barzillai Beckaleggs, that I am now considering, are honest men." (You think I invented that name, now don't you? But I didn't. It's on a carrier's cart, somewhere down in Cornwall.)

This kind of Universal Proposition (where the Subject is a single Thing) is called an '*Individual*' Proposition.

Now let us take "*nice* Cakes" as the Subject of our Proposition: that is, let us fix our thoughts on the *left-hand* half of the cupboard, where all the Cakes have the attribute y, that is, "nice."

Suppose we find it marked like this:—
What would that tell us?

1

I hope that it is not necessary, after explaining the *horizontal* oblong so fully, to spend much time over the *upright* one. I hope you will see, for yourself, that this means "some y are x", that is,

"Some nice Cakes are new."

"But," you will say, "we have had this case before. You put a red counter into No. 5, and you told us it meant 'some new Cakes are nice'; and *now* you tell us that it means 'some *nice* Cakes are *new*'! Can it mean *both*?"

The question is a very thoughtful one, and does you *great* credit, dear Reader! It *does* mean both. If you choose to take x (that is, "new Cakes") as your Subject, and to regard No. 5 as part of a *horizontal* oblong, you may read it "some x are y", that is, "some new Cakes are nice": but, if you choose to take y (that is, "nice Cakes") as your Subject, and to regard No. 5 as part of an *upright* oblong, *then* you may read it "some y are x", that is, "some nice Cakes are new". They are merely two different ways of expressing the very same truth.

Without more words, I will simply set down the other ways in which this upright oblong might be marked, adding the meaning in each case. By comparing them with the various cases of the horizontal oblong, you will, I hope, be able to understand them clearly.

You will find it a good plan to examine yourself on this table, by covering up first one column and then the other, and 'dodging about', as the children say.

Also you will do well to write out for yourself two other tables——one for the *lower* half of the cupboard, and the other for its *right-hand* half.

And now I think we have said all we need to say about the smaller Diagram, and may go on to the larger one.

Symbols.	Meanings.
 — 1	Some y are x'; i. e. Some nice are not-new.
0 — 	No y are x; i. e. No nice are new. [Observe that this is merely another way of expressing " No new are nice."]
 — 0	No y are x'; i. e. No nice are not-new.
1 — 1	Some y are x, and some are x'; i. e. Some nice are new, and some are not-new.
0 — 0	No y are x, and none are x'; i. e. No y exist; i. e. No Cakes are nice.
1 — 0	All y are x; i. e. All nice are new.
0 — 1	All y are x'; i. e. All nice are not-new.

This may be taken to be a cupboard divided in the same way as the last, but *also* divided into two portions, for the Attribute m. Let us give to m the meaning "wholesome": and let us suppose that all *wholesome* Cakes are placed *inside* the central Square, and all the *unwholesome* ones *outside* it, that is, in one or other of the four queer-shaped *outer* compartments.

We see that, just as, in the smaller Diagram, the Cakes in each compartment had *two* Attributes, so, here, the Cakes in each compartment have *three* Attributes: and, just as the letters, representing the *two* Attributes, were written on the *edges* of the compartment, so, here, they are written at the *corners*. (Observe that m' is supposed to be written at each of the four outer corners.) So that we can tell in a moment, by looking at a compartment, what three Attributes belong to the Things in it. For instance, take No. 12. Here we find x, y', m, at the corners: so we know that the Cakes in it, if there are any, have the triple Attribute, '$xy'm$', that is, "new, not-nice, and wholesome." Again, take No. 16. Here we find, at the corners, x', y', m': so the Cakes in it are "not-new, not-nice, and unwholesome." (Remarkably untempting Cakes!)

It would take far too long to go through all the Propositions, containing x and y, x and m, and y and m, which can be represented on this diagram (there are ninety-six altogether, so I am sure you will excuse me!)

and I must content myself with doing two or three, as specimens. You will do well to work out a lot more for yourself.

Taking the upper half by itself, so that our Subject is "new Cakes", how are we to represent "no new Cakes are wholesome"?

This is, writing letters for words, "no x are m." Now this tells us that none of the Cakes, belonging to the upper half of the cupboard, are to be found *inside* the central Square: that is, the two compartments, No. 11 and No. 12, are *empty*. And this, of course, is represented by

And now how are we to represent the contradictory Proposition "*some* x are m"? This is a difficulty I have already considered. I think the best way is to place a red counter *on the division-line* between No. 11 and No. 12, and to understand this to mean that *one* of the two compartments is 'occupied,' but that we do not at present know *which*. This I shall represent thus:—

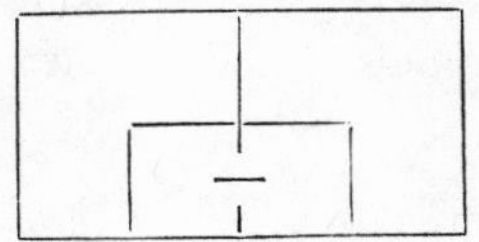

Now let us express "all x are m."

This consists, we know, of *two* Propositions,

"Some x are m,"

and "No x are m'."

Let us express the negative part first. This tells us that none of the Cakes, belonging to the upper half of the cupboard, are to be found *outside* the central Square: that is, the two compartments, No. 9 and No. 10, are *empty*. This, of course, is represented by

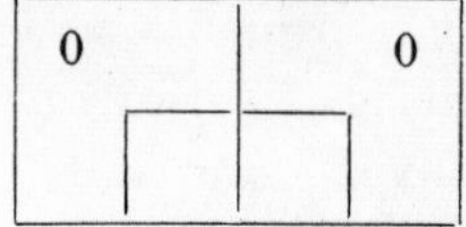

But we have yet to represent "Some x are m." This tells us that there are *some* Cakes in the oblong consisting of No. 11 and No. 12: so we place our red counter, as in the previous example, on the division-line between No. 11 and No. 12, and the result is

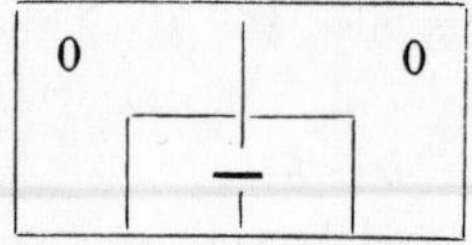

Now let us try one or two interpretations.

What are we to make of this, with regard to x and y?

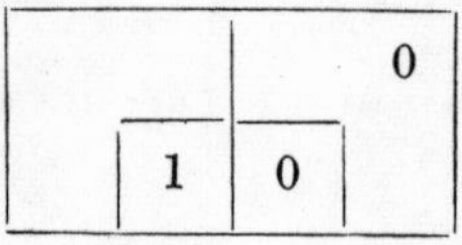

0

1 0

This tells us, with regard to the xy'-Square, that it is wholly 'empty', since *both* compartments are so marked. With regard to the xy-Square, it tells us that it is 'occupied'. True, it is only *one* compartment of it that is so marked; but that is quite enough, whether the other be 'occupied' or 'empty', to settle the fact that there is *something* in the Square.

If, then, we transfer our marks to the smaller Diagram, so as to get rid of the m-subdivisions, we have a right to mark it

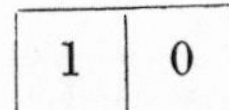

which means, you know, "all x are y."

The result would have been exactly the same, if the given oblong had been marked thus:—

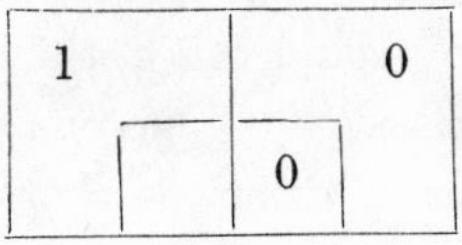

Once more: how shall we interpret this, with regard to x and y?

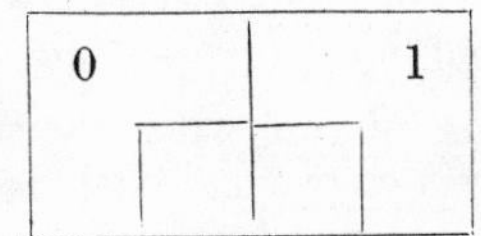

This tells us, as to the xy-Square, that *one* of its compartments is 'empty'. But this information is quite useless, as there is no mark in the *other* compartment. If the other compartment happened to be 'empty' too, the Square would be 'empty': and, if it happened to be 'occupied', the Square would be 'occupied'. So, as we do not know *which* is the case, we can say nothing about *this* Square.

The other Square, the $x\,y'$-Square, we know (as in the previous example) to be 'occupied'.

If, then, we transfer our marks to the smaller Diagram, we get merely this :—

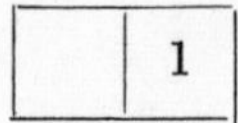

which means, you know, "some x are y'."

These principles may be applied to all the other oblongs. For instance, to represent "all y' are m'" we should mark the *right-hand upright oblong* (the one that has the attribute y') thus :—

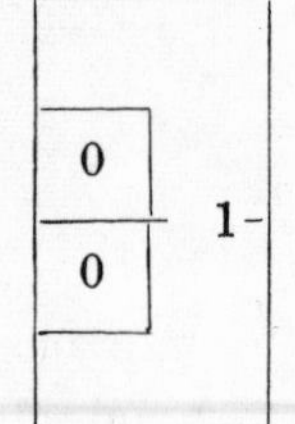

and, if we were told to interpret the lower half of the cupboard, marked as follows, with regard to x and y, we should transfer it to the smaller Diagram thus,

1	0

and read it "all x' are y."

Two more remarks about Propositions need to be made.

One is that, in every Proposition beginning with "some" or "all", the *actual existence* of the 'Subject' is asserted. If, for instance, I say "all misers are selfish," I mean that misers *actually exist*. If I wished to avoid making this assertion, and merely to state the *law* that miserliness necessarily involves selfishness, I should say "no misers are unselfish" which does not assert that any misers exist at all, but merely that, if any *did* exist, they *would* be selfish.

The other is that, when a Proposition begins with "some" or "no", and contains more than two Attributes, these Attributes may be re-arranged, and shifted from one Term to the other, *ad libitum*. For example, "some *abc* are *def*" may be re-arranged as "some *bf* are *acde*," each being equivalent to "some Things are *abcdef*". Again "No wise old men are rash and reckless gamblers" may be re-arranged as "No rash old gamblers are wise and reckless," each being equivalent to "No men are wise old rash reckless gamblers."

§ 2. *Syllogisms.*

Now suppose we divide our Universe of Things in three ways, with regard to three different Attributes. Out of these three Attributes, we may make up three different couples (for instance, if they were *a*, *b*, *c*, we might make up the three couples *ab*, *ac*, *bc*). Also suppose we have two Propositions given us, containing two of these three couples, and that from them we can prove a third Proposition containing the third couple. (For example, if we divide our Universe for *m*, *x*, and *y*; and if we have the two Propositions given us, "no *m* are *x'*" and "all *m'* are *y*", containing the two couples *mx* and *my*, it might be possible to prove from them a third Proposition, containing *x* and *y*.)

In such a case we call the given Propositions '*the Premisses*', the third one '*the Conclusion*' and the whole set '*a Syllogism*'.

Evidently, *one* of the Attributes must occur in both Premisses; or else one must occur in *one* Premiss, and its *contradictory* in the other.

In the first case (when, for example, the Premisses are "some m are x" and "no m are y'") the Term, which occurs twice, is called '*the Middle Term*', because it serves as a sort of link between the other two Terms.

In the second case (when, for example, the Premisses are "no m are x'" and "all m' are y") the two Terms, which contain these contradictory Attributes, may be called '*the Middle Terms*'.

Thus, in the first case, the class of "m-Things" is the Middle Term; and, in the second case, the two classes of "m-Things" and "m'-Things" are the Middle Terms.

The Attribute, which occurs in the Middle Term or Terms, disappears in the Conclusion, and is said to be "eliminated", which literally means "turned out of doors".

Now let us try to draw a Conclusion from the two Premisses—

"Some new Cakes are unwholesome;
No nice Cakes are unwholesome."

In order to express them with counters, we need to divide Cakes in *three* different ways, with regard to newness, to niceness, and to wholesomeness. For this we must use the larger Diagram, making x mean "new", y "nice", and m "wholesome". (Everything *inside* the central Square is supposed to have the attribute *m*, and everything *outside* it the attribute *m′*, i.e. "not-*m*".)

You had better adopt the rule to make *m* mean the Attribute which occurs in the *Middle* Term or Terms. (I have chosen *m* as the symbol, because 'middle' begins with 'm'.)

Now, in representing the two Premisses, I prefer to begin with the *negative* one (the one beginning with "no"), because *grey* counters can always be placed with *certainty*, and will then help to fix the position of the red counters, which are sometimes a little uncertain where they will be most welcome.

Let us express, then, "no nice Cakes are unwholesome (Cakes)", i.e. "no *y*-Cakes are *m′*-(Cakes)". This tells us that none of the Cakes belonging to the *y*-half of the cupboard are in its *m′*-compartments (i.e. the ones *outside* the central Square). Hence the two compartments, No. 9 and No. 15, are both '*empty*'; and we must place a grey counter in *each* of them, thus:—

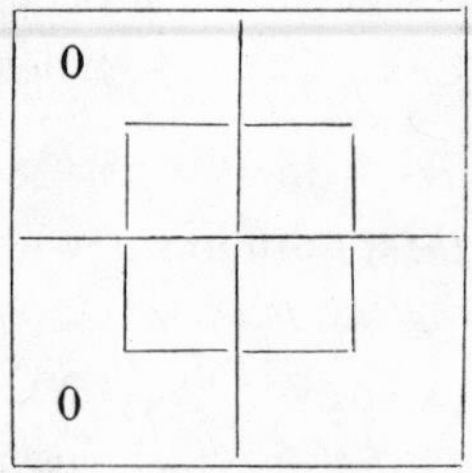

We have now to express the other Premiss, namely, "some new Cakes are unwholesome (Cakes)", i.e. "some x-Cakes are m'-(Cakes)". This tells us that some of the Cakes in the x-half of the cupboard are in its m'-compartments. Hence *one* of the two compartments, No. 9 and No. 10, is 'occupied': and, as we are not told in *which* of these two compartments to place the red counter, the usual rule would be to lay it on the division-line between them: but, in this case, the other Premiss has settled the matter for us, by declaring No. 9 to be *empty*. Hence the red counter has no choice, and *must* go into No. 10, thus:—

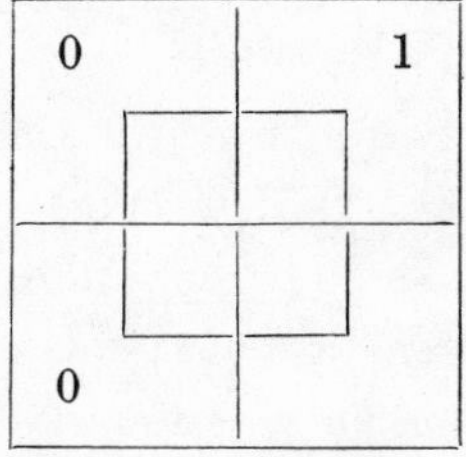

And now what counters will this information enable us to place in the *smaller* Diagram, so as to get some Proposition involving x and y only, leaving out m? Let us take its four compartments, one by one.

First, No. 5. All we know about *this* is that its *outer* portion is empty: but we know nothing about its *inner* portion. Thus the Square *may* be empty, or it *may* have something in it. Who can tell? So we dare not place *any* counter in this Square.

Secondly, what of No. 6? Here we are a little better off. We know that there is *something* in it, for there is a red counter in its outer portion. It is true we do not know whether its inner portion is empty or occupied: but what does *that* matter? One solitary Cake, in one corner of the Square, is quite sufficient excuse for saying "*this Square is occupied*", and for marking it with a red counter.

As to No. 7, we are in the same condition as with No. 5——we find it *partly* 'empty', but we do not know whether the other part is empty or occupied: so we dare not mark this Square.

And as to No. 8, we have simply no information *at all*.

The result is

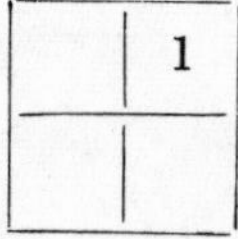

Our 'Conclusion', then, must be got out of the rather meagre piece of information that there is a red counter in the xy'-Square. Hence our Conclusion is "some x are y'", i.e. "some new Cakes are not-nice (Cakes)": or, if you prefer to take y' as your Subject, "some not-nice Cakes are new (Cakes)"; but the other looks neatest.

We will now write out the whole Syllogism, putting the symbol ∴ for "therefore", and omitting "Cakes", for the sake of brevity, at the end of each Proposition.

"Some new Cakes are unwholesome ;
No nice Cakes are unwholesome.
∴ Some new Cakes are not-nice."

And you have now worked out, successfully, your first '*Syllogism*'. Permit me to congratulate you, and to express the hope that it is but the beginning of a long and glorious series of similar victories!

We will work out one other Syllogism——a rather harder one than the last——and then, I think, you may be safely left to play the Game by yourself, or (better) with any friend whom you can find, that is able and willing to take a share in the sport.

Let us see what we can make of the two Premisses—

"All Dragons are uncanny ;
All Scotchmen are canny."

Remember, I don't guarantee the Premisses to be *facts*. In the first place, I never even saw a Dragon: and, in the second place, it isn't of the slightest consequence to us, as *Logicians*, whether our Premisses are true or false: all *we* have to do is to make out whether they *lead logically to the Conclusion*, so that, if *they* were true, *it* would be true also.

You see, we must give up the "Cakes" now, or our cupboards will be of no use to us. We must take, as our 'Universe', some class of things which will include Dragons and Scotchmen: shall we say 'Animals'? And, as "canny" is evidently the Attribute belonging to the 'Middle Terms', we will let m stand for "canny", x for "Dragons", and y for "Scotchmen". So that our two Premisses are, in full,

"All Dragon-Animals are uncanny (Animals);
All Scotchman-Animals are canny (Animals)."

And these may be expressed, using letters for words, thus:—

"All x are m';
All y are m."

The first Premiss consists, as you already know, of two parts:—

"Some x are m',"
and "No x are m."

And the second also consists of two parts:—

"Some y are m,"
and "No y are m'."

Let us take the negative portions first.

We have, then, to mark, on the larger Diagram, first, "no x are m", and secondly, "no y are m'". I think you will see, without further explanation, that the two results, separately, are

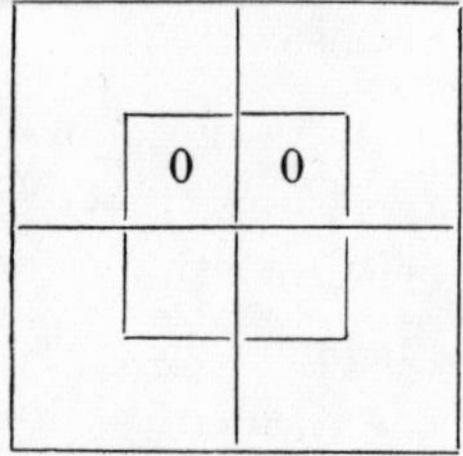

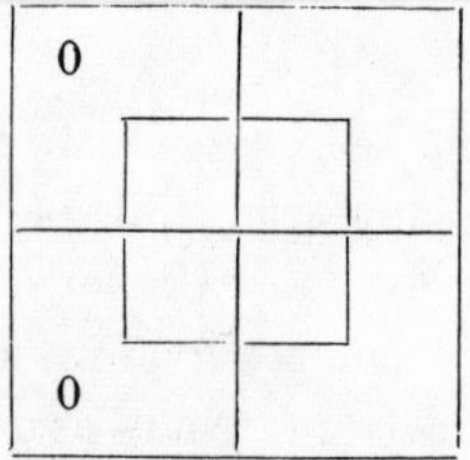

and that these two, when combined, give us

0	
0	0
0	

We have now to mark the two positive portions, "some x are m'" and "some y are m".

The only two compartments, available for Things which are xm', are No. 9 and No. 10. Of these, No. 9 is already marked as 'empty'; so our red counter *must* go into No. 10.

Similarly, the only two, available for ym, are No. 11 and No. 13. Of these, No. 11 is already marked as 'empty'; so our red counter *must* go into No. 13.

The final result is

0	1
0	0
1	
0	

And now how much of this information can usefully be transferred to the smaller Diagram?

Let us take its four compartments, one by one.

As to No. 5? This, we see, is wholly 'empty'. (So mark it with a grey counter.)

As to No. 6? This, we see, is 'occupied'. (So mark it with a red counter.)

As to No. 7? Ditto, ditto.

As to No. 8? No information.

The smaller Diagram is now pretty liberally marked:—

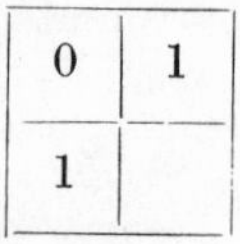

0	1
1	

And now what Conclusion can we read off from this? Well, it is impossible to pack such abundant information into *one* Proposition: we shall have to indulge in *two*, this time.

First, by taking x as Subject, we get "all x are y'", that is,

"All Dragons are not-Scotchmen":

secondly, by taking y as Subject, we get "all y are x'", that is,

"All Scotchmen are not-Dragons".

Let us now write out, all together, our two Premisses and our brace of Conclusions.

"All Dragons are uncanny;
All Scotchmen are canny.

∴ All Dragons are not-Scotchmen;
All Scotchmen are not-Dragons."

Let me mention, in conclusion, that you may perhaps meet with logical treatises in which it is not assumed that any Thing *exists* at all, but "some x are y" is understood to mean "the Attributes x, y are *compatible*, so that a Thing can have both at once", and "no x are y" to mean "the Attributes x, y are *incompatible*, so that nothing can have both at once".

In such treatises, Propositions have quite different meanings from what they have in our 'Game of Logic', and it will be well to understand exactly what the difference is.

First take "some x are y". Here *we* understand "are" to mean "are, as an actual *fact*"——which of course implies that some x-Things *exist*. But *they* (the writers of these other treatises) only understand "are" to mean "*can* be", which does not at all imply that any *exist*. So they mean *less* than we do: our meaning includes theirs (for of course "some x *are* y" includes "some x *can be* y"), but theirs does *not* include ours. For example, "some Welsh hippopotami are heavy" would be *true*, according to these writers (since the

Attributes "Welsh" and "heavy" are quite *compatible* in a hippopotamus), but it would be *false* in our Game (since there are no Welsh hippopotami to *be* heavy).

Secondly, take "no x are y". Here *we* only understand "are" to mean "are, as an actual *fact*"——which does not at all imply that no x *can* be y. But *they* understand the Proposition to mean, not only that none *are* y, but that none *can possibly* be y. So they mean *more* than we do: their meaning includes ours (for of course "no x *can* be y" includes "no x *are* y"), but ours does *not* include theirs. For example, "no Policemen are eight feet high" would be *true* in our Game (since, as an actual fact, no such splendid specimens are ever found), but it would be *false*, according to these writers (since the Attributes "belonging to the Police Force" and "eight feet high" are quite *compatible*: there is nothing to *prevent* a Policeman from growing to that height, if sufficiently rubbed with Rowland's Macassar Oil——which is said to make *hair* grow, when rubbed on hair, and so of course will make a *Policeman* grow, when rubbed on a Policeman).

Thirdly, take "all x are y", which consists of the two partial Propositions "some x are y" and "no x are y'". Here, of course, the treatises mean *less* than we do in the *first* part, and *more* than we do in the *second*. But the two operations don't balance each other——

any more than you can console a man, for having knocked down one of his chimneys, by giving him an extra door-step.

If you meet with Syllogisms of this kind, you may work them, quite easily, by the system I have given you: you have only to make 'are' mean 'are *capable* of being', and all will go smoothly. For "some x are y" will become "some x are capable of being y", that is, "the Attributes x, y are *compatible*". And "no x are y" will become "no x are capable of being y", that is, "the Attributes x, y are *incompatible*". And, of course, "all x are y" will become "some x are capable of being y, and none are capable of being y'", that is, "the Attributes x, y are *compatible*, and the Attributes x, y' are *incompatible*." In using the Diagrams for this system, you must understand a red counter to mean "there may *possibly* be something in this compartment," and a grey one to mean "there cannot *possibly* be anything in this compartment."

§ 3. *Fallacies.*

And so you think, do you, that the chief use of Logic, in real life, is to deduce Conclusions from workable Premisses, and to satisfy yourself that the Conclusions, deduced by other people, are correct? I only wish it were! Society would be much less liable to panics and other delusions, and *political* life, especially, would be a totally different thing, if even a majority of the arguments, that are scattered broadcast over the world, were correct! But it is all the other way, I fear. For *one* workable Pair of Premisses (I mean a Pair that lead to a logical Conclusion) that you meet with in reading your newspaper or magazine, you will probably find *five* that lead to no Conclusion at all: and, even when the Premisses *are* workable, for *one* instance, where the writer draws a correct Conclusion, there are probably *ten* where he draws an incorrect one.

In the first case, you may say "the *Premisses* are fallacious": in the second, "the *Conclusion* is fallacious."

The chief use you will find, in such Logical skill as this Game may teach you, will be in detecting '*Fallacies*' of these two kinds.

The first kind of Fallacy——'Fallacious Premisses'——you will detect when, after marking them on the larger Diagram, you try to transfer the marks to the smaller. You will take its four compartments, one by one, and ask, for each in turn, "What mark can I place *here*?"; and in *every* one the answer will be "No information!", showing that there is *no Conclusion at all.* For instance,

"All soldiers are brave;
Some Englishmen are brave. }
∴ Some Englishmen are soldiers."

looks uncommonly *like* a Syllogism, and might easily take in a less experienced Logician. But *you* are not to be caught by such a trick! You would simply set out the Premisses, and would then calmly remark "Fallacious *Premisses*!": you wouldn't condescend to ask what *Conclusion* the writer professed to draw——knowing that, *whatever* it is, it *must* be wrong. You would be just as safe as that wise mother was, who said "Mary, just go up to the nursery, and see what Baby's doing, *and tell him not to do it*!"

The other kind of Fallacy——'Fallacious Conclusion'——you will not detect till you have marked *both* Diagrams, and have read off the correct Conclusion, and have compared it with the Conclusion which the writer has drawn.

But mind, you mustn't say "*Fallacious* Conclusion," simply because it is not *identical* with the correct one: it may be a *part* of the correct Conclusion, and so be quite correct, *as far as it goes.* In this case you would merely remark, with a pitying smile, "*Defective* Conclusion!" Suppose, for example, you were to meet with this Syllogism:—

"All unselfish people are generous;
No misers are generous.
∴ No misers are unselfish."

the Premisses of which might be thus expressed in letters:—

"All x' are m;
No y are m."

Here the correct Conclusion would be "All x' are y'" (that is, "All unselfish people are not misers"), while the Conclusion, drawn by the writer, is "No y are x'," (which is the same as "No x' are y," and so is *part* of "All x' are y'.") Here you would simply say "*Defective* Conclusion!" The same thing would happen, if you were in a confectioner's shop, and if a little boy were to come in, put down twopence, and march off triumphantly with a single penny-bun. You would shake your head mournfully, and would remark "Defective Conclusion! Poor little chap!" And perhaps you would ask the young lady behind the counter whether she would let *you* eat the bun, which the little boy had paid for and left behind him: and perhaps *she* would reply "Sha'n't!"

But if, in the above example, the writer had drawn the Conclusion "All misers are selfish" (that is, "All y are x"), this would be going *beyond* his legitimate rights (since it would assert the *existence* of y, which is not contained in the Premisses), and you would very properly say "Fallacious Conclusion!"

Now, when you read other treatises on Logic, you will meet with various kinds of (so-called) 'Fallacies', which are by no means *always* so. For example, if you were to put before one of these Logicians the Pair of Premisses

"No honest men cheat;
No dishonest men are trustworthy."

and were to ask him what Conclusion followed, he would probably say "None at all! Your Premisses offend against *two* distinct Rules, and are as fallacious as they can well be!" Then suppose you were bold enough to say "The Conclusion is 'No men who cheat are trustworthy'," I fear your Logical friend would turn away hastily——perhaps angry, perhaps only scornful: in any case, the result would be unpleasant. *I advise you not to try the experiment!*

"But why is this?" you will say. "Do you mean to tell us that all these Logicians are wrong?" Far from it, dear Reader! From *their* point of view, they are perfectly right. But they do not include, in their system, anything like *all* the possible forms of Syllogisms.

They have a sort of nervous dread of Attributes beginning with a negative particle. For example, such Propositions as "All not-x are y," "No x are not-y," are quite outside their system. And thus, having (from sheer nervousness) excluded a quantity of very useful forms, they have made rules which, though quite applicable to the few forms which they allow of, are no use at all when you consider all possible forms.

Let us not quarrel with them, dear Reader! There is room enough in the world for both of us. Let us quietly take our broader system: and, if they choose to shut their eyes to all these useful forms, and to say "They are not Syllogisms at all!" we can but stand aside, and let them Rush upon their Fate! There is scarcely anything of yours, upon which it is so dangerous to Rush, as your Fate. You may Rush upon your Potato-beds, or your Strawberry-beds, without doing much harm: you may even Rush upon your Balcony (unless it is a new house, built by contract, and with no clerk of the works) and may survive the foolhardy enterprise: but if you once Rush upon your *Fate*—why, you must take the consequences!

CHAPTER II.

CROSS QUESTIONS.

"The Man in the Wilderness asked of me
'How many strawberries grow in the sea?'"

---

§ 1. *Elementary.*

1. What is an 'Attribute'? Give examples.

2. When is it good sense to put "is" or "are" between two names? Give examples.

3. When is it *not* good sense? Give examples.

4. When it is *not* good sense, what is the simplest agreement to make, in order to make good sense?

5. Explain 'Proposition', 'Term', 'Subject', and 'Predicate'. Give examples.

6. What are 'Particular' and 'Universal' Propositions? Give examples.

7. Give a rule for knowing, when we look at the smaller Diagram, what Attributes belong to the things in each compartment.

8. What does "some" mean in Logic?
[See pp. 55, 6]

9. In what sense do we use the word 'Universe' in this Game?

10. What is a 'Double' Proposition? Give examples.

11. When is a class of Things said to be 'exhaustively' divided? Give examples.

12. Explain the phrase "sitting on the fence."

13. What two partial Propositions make up, when taken together, "all x are y"?

14. What are 'Individual' Propositions? Give examples.

15. What kinds of Propositions imply, in this Game, the *existence* of their Subjects?

16. When a Proposition contains more than two Attributes, these Attributes may in some cases be re-arranged, and shifted from one Term to the other. In what cases may this be done? Give examples.

Break up each of the following into two *partial* Propositions:

17. All tigers are fierce.

18. All hard-boiled eggs are unwholesome.

19. I am happy.

20. John is not at home.

[See pp. 56, 7]

21. Give a rule for knowing, when we look at the larger Diagram, what Attributes belong to the Things contained in each compartment.

22. Explain 'Premisses', 'Conclusion', and 'Syllogism'. Give examples.

23. Explain the phrases 'Middle Term' and 'Middle Terms'.

24. In marking a pair of Premisses on the larger Diagram, why is it best to mark *negative* Propositions before *affirmative* ones?

25. Why is it of no consequence to us, as Logicians, whether the Premisses are true or false?

26. How can we work Syllogisms in which we are told that "some x are y" is to be understood to mean "the Attributes x, y are *compatible*", and "no x are y" to mean "the Attributes x, y are *incompatible*"?

27. What are the two kinds of 'Fallacies'?

28. How may we detect 'Fallacious Premisses'?

29. How may we detect a 'Fallacious Conclusion'?

30. Sometimes the Conclusion, offered to us, is not identical with the correct Conclusion, and yet cannot be fairly called 'Fallacious'. When does this happen? And what name may we give to such a Conclusion?

[See pp. 57—59]

§ 2. *Half of Smaller Diagram.*
Propositions to be represented.

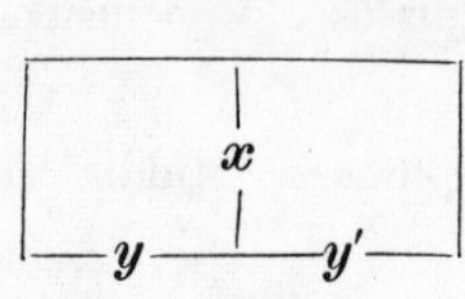

---

1. Some x are not-y.
2. All x are not-y.
3. Some x are y, and some are not-y.
4. No x exist.
5. Some x exist.
6. No x are not-y.
7. Some x are not-y, and some x exist.

Taking x = "judges"; y = "just";

8. No judges are just.
9. Some judges are unjust.
10. All judges are just.

Taking x = "plums"; y = "wholesome";

11. Some plums are wholesome.
12. There are no wholesome plums.
13. Plums are some of them wholesome, and some not.
14. All plums are unwholesome.

[See pp. 59, 60]

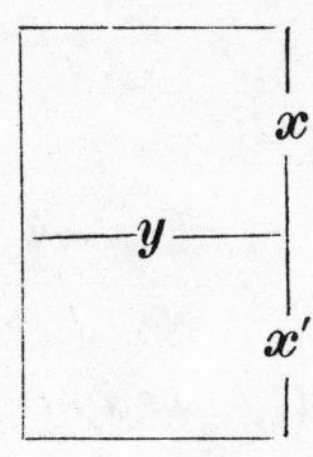

Taking y = "diligent students"; x = "successful";

15. No diligent students are unsuccessful.
16. All diligent students are successful.
17. No students are diligent.
18. There are some diligent, but unsuccessful, students.
19. Some students are diligent.

[See pp. 60, 1]

§ 3. *Half of Smaller Diagram.*
Symbols to be interpreted.

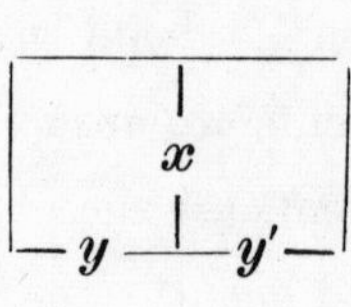

No.	y	y′		No.	y	y′
1.		0		2.	0	0
3.				4.	0	1

Taking x = "good riddles"; y = "hard";

No.	y	y′		No.	y	y′
5.	1			6.	1	0
7.	0	0		8.	0	

[See pp. 61, 2]

Taking x = "lobsters"; y = "selfish";

9.

	1

10.

0	

11.

0	1

12.

1	1

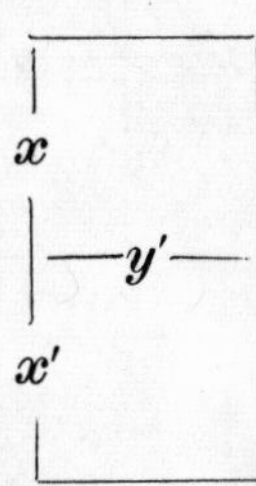

Taking y = "healthy people"; x = "happy";

13.

0
1

14.

– 1 –

15.

1
1

16.

0
0

[See p. 62]

§ 4. *Smaller Diagram.*
Propositions to be represented.

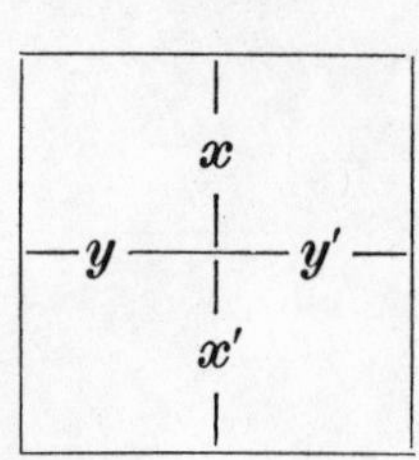

1. All y are x.
2. Some y are not-x.
3. No not-x are not-y.
4. Some x are not-y.
5. Some not-y are x.
6. No not-x are y.
7. Some not-x are not-y.
8. All not-x are not-y.
9. Some not-y exist.
10. No not-x exist.
11. Some y are x, and some are not-x.
12. All x are y, and all not-y are not-x.

[See pp. 62, 3]

Taking "nations" as Universe; x = "civilised"; y = "warlike";

13. No uncivilised nation is warlike.

14. All unwarlike nations are uncivilised.

15. Some nations are unwarlike.

16. All warlike nations are civilised, and all civilised nations are warlike.

17. No nation is uncivilised.

Taking "crocodiles" as Universe; x = "hungry"; and y = "amiable";

18. All hungry crocodiles are unamiable.

19. No crocodiles are amiable when hungry.

20. Some crocodiles, when not hungry, are amiable; but some are not.

21. No crocodiles are amiable, and some are hungry.

22. All crocodiles, when not hungry, are amiable; and all unamiable crocodiles are hungry.

23. Some hungry crocodiles are amiable, and some that are not hungry are unamiable.

[See pp. 63, 4]

§ 5. *Smaller Diagram.* *Symbols to be interpreted.*

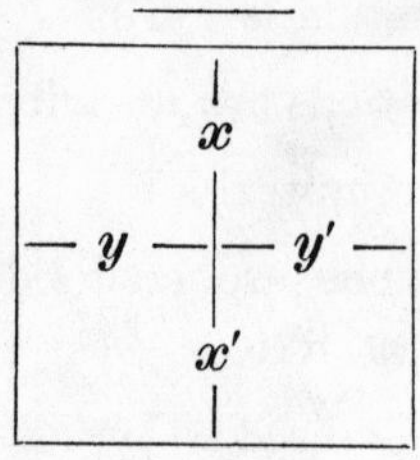

1.

1	

2.

	0

3.

	1
	0

4.

0	0

Taking "houses" as Universe; x = "built of brick"; and y = "two-storied"; interpret

5.

0	
0	

6.

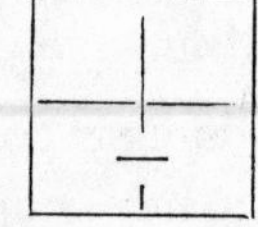

7.

	0

8.

0	1

[See p. 65]

Taking "boys" as Universe; x = "fat"; and y = "active"; interpret

9. 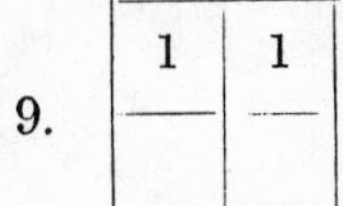

10.

	0
	1

11.

0	1
	0

12.

1	
0	1

Taking "cats" as Universe; x = "green-eyed"; and y = "good-tempered"; interpret

13.

0	0
	0

14.

	1
1	

15.

1	
	0

16.

0	1
1	0

[See pp. 65, 6]

§ 6. *Larger Diagram.*
Propositions to be represented.

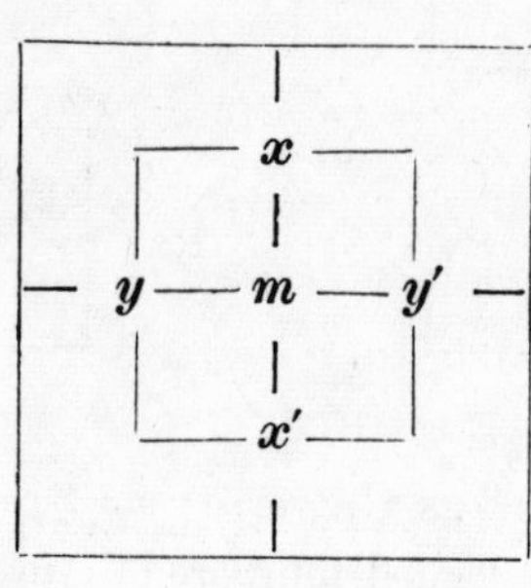

1. No x are m.
2. Some y are m'.
3. All m are x'.
4. No m' are y'.
5. No m are x; All y are m.
6. Some x are m; No y are m.
7. All m are x'; No m are y.
8. No x' are m; No y' are m'.

[See pp. 67, 8]

Taking "rabbits" as Universe; m = "greedy"; x = "old"; and y = "black"; represent

9. No old rabbits are greedy.

10. Some not-greedy rabbits are black.

11. All white rabbits are free from greediness.

12. All greedy rabbits are young.

13. No old rabbits are greedy;
All black rabbits are greedy.

14. All rabbits, that are not greedy, are black;
No old rabbits are free from greediness.

Taking "birds" as Universe; m = "that sing loud"; x = "well-fed"; and y = "happy"; represent

15. All well-fed birds sing loud;
No birds, that sing loud, are unhappy.

16. All birds, that do not sing loud, are unhappy;
No well-fed birds fail to sing loud.

Taking "persons" as Universe; m = "in the house"; x = "John"; and y = "having a tooth-ache"; represent

17. John is in the house;
Everybody in the house is suffering from tooth-ache.

18. There is no one in the house but John;
Nobody, out of the house, has a tooth-ache.

[See pp. 68—70]

Taking "persons" as Universe; m="I"; x="that has taken a walk"; y="that feels better"; represent

19. I have been out for a walk;
I feel much better.

Choosing your own 'Universe' &c., represent

20. I sent him to bring me a kitten;
He brought me a kettle by mistake.

[See pp. 70, 1]

§ 7. *Both Diagrams to be employed.*

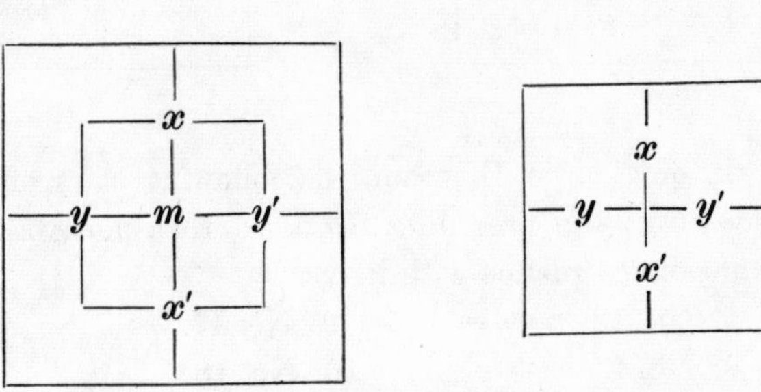

N.B. In each Question, a small Diagram should be drawn, for x and y only, and marked in accordance with the given large Diagram: and then as many Propositions as possible, for x and y, should be read off from this small Diagram.

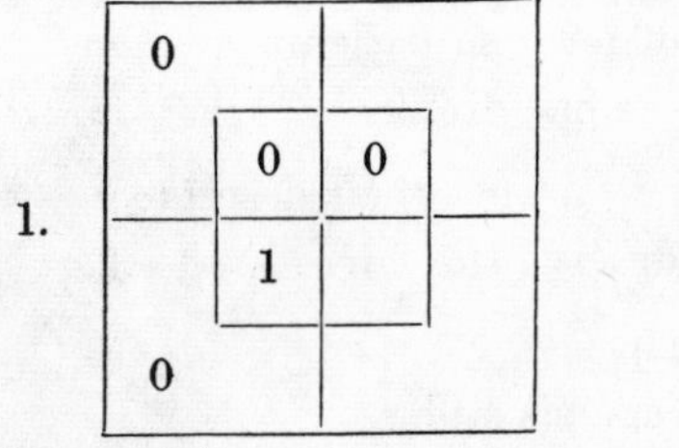

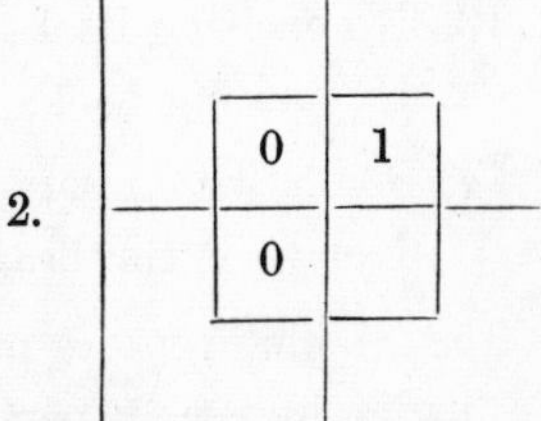

[See p. 72]

3. 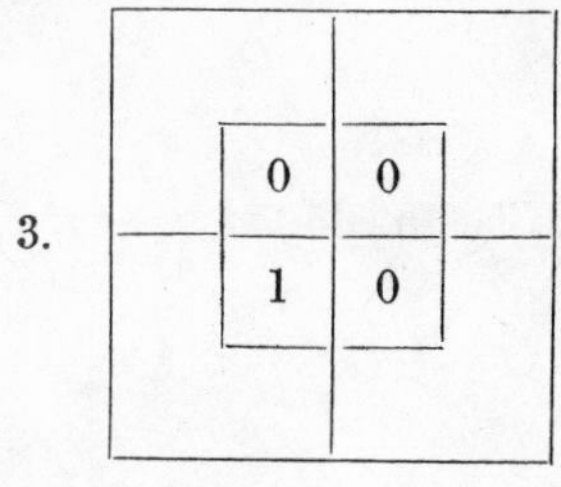

4. 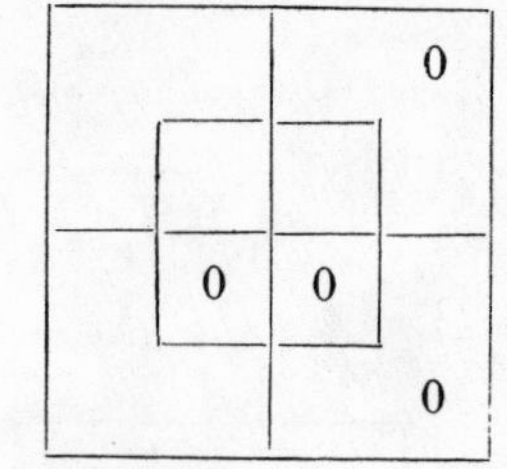

Mark, on a large Diagram, the following pairs of Propositions from the preceding Section: then mark a small Diagram in accordance with it, &c.

5. No. 13. [see p. 49]
6. No. 14.
7. No. 15.
8. No. 16.
9. No. 17.
10. No. 18.
11. No. 19. [see p. 50]
12. No. 20.

Mark, on a large Diagram, the following Pairs of Propositions: then mark a small Diagram, &c. These are, in fact, Pairs of *Premisses* for Syllogisms: and the results, read off from the small Diagram, are the *Conclusions.*

13. No exciting books suit feverish patients;
Unexciting books make one drowsy.

14. Some, who deserve the fair, get their deserts;
None but the brave deserve the fair.

15. No children are patient;
No impatient person can sit still.

[See pp. 72—5]

16. All pigs are fat;
No skeletons are fat.

17. No monkeys are soldiers;
All monkeys are mischievous.

18. None of my cousins are just;
No judges are unjust.

19. Some days are rainy;
Rainy days are tiresome.

20. All medicine is nasty;
Senna is a medicine.

21. Some Jews are rich;
All Patagonians are Gentiles.

22. All teetotalers like sugar;
No nightingale drinks wine.

23. No muffins are wholesome;
All buns are unwholesome.

24. No fat creatures run well;
Some greyhounds run well.

25. All soldiers march;
Some youths are not soldiers.

26. Sugar is sweet;
Salt is not sweet.

27. Some eggs are hard-boiled;
No eggs are uncrackable.

28. There are no Jews in the house;
There are no Gentiles in the garden.

[See pp. 75—82]

29. All battles are noisy;
What makes no noise may escape notice.

30. No Jews are mad;
All Rabbis are Jews.

31. There are no fish that cannot swim;
Some skates are fish.

32. All passionate people are unreasonable;
Some orators are passionate.

[See pp. 82—84]

CHAPTER III.

CROOKED ANSWERS.

"I answered him, as I thought good,
'As many as red-herrings grow in the wood'."

---

§ 1. *Elementary.*

1. Whatever can be "attributed to", that is "said to belong to", a Thing, is called an 'Attribute'. For example, "baked", which can (frequently) be attributed to "Buns", and "beautiful", which can (seldom) be attributed to "Babies".

2. When they are the Names of two Things (for example, "these Pigs are fat Animals"), or of two Attributes (for example, "pink is light red").

3. When one is the Name of a Thing, and the other the Name of an Attribute (for example, "these Pigs are pink"), since a Thing cannot actually *be* an Attribute.

4. That the Substantive shall be supposed to be repeated at the end of the sentence (for example, "these Pigs are pink (Pigs)").

5. A 'Proposition' is a sentence stating that some, or none, or all, of the Things belonging to a certain class,

[See p. 37]

called the 'Subject', are also Things belonging to a certain other class, called the 'Predicate'. For example, "some new Cakes are not nice", that is (written in full) "some new Cakes are not nice Cakes"; where the class "new Cakes" is the Subject, and the class "not-nice Cakes" is the Predicate.

6. A Proposition, stating that *some* of the Things belonging to its Subject are so-and-so, is called 'Particular'. For example, "some new Cakes are nice", "some new Cakes are not nice."

A Proposition, stating that *none* of the Things belonging to its Subject, or that *all* of them, are so-and-so, is called 'Universal'. For example, "no new Cakes are nice", "all new Cakes are not nice".

7. The Things in each compartment possess *two* Attributes, whose symbols will be found written on two of the *edges* of that compartment.

8. "One or more."

9. As a name of the class of Things to which the whole Diagram is assigned.

10. A Proposition containing two statements. For example, "some new Cakes are nice and some are not-nice."

11. When the whole class, thus divided, is "exhausted" among the sets into which it is divided, there being no member of it which does not belong to some one of them. For example, the class "new Cakes" is "exhaustively"

[See pp. 37, 8]

divided into "nice" and "not-nice" since *every* new Cake must be one or the other.

12. When a man cannot make up his mind which of two parties he will join, he is said to be "sitting on the fence"——not being able to decide on which side he will jump down.

13. "Some x are y" and "no x are y'".

14. A Proposition, whose Subject is a single Thing, is called 'Individual'. For example, "I am happy", "John is not at home". These are Universal Propositions, being the same as "all the I's that exist are happy", "*all* the Johns, that I am now considering, are not at home".

15. Propositions beginning with "some" or "all".

16. When they begin with "some" or "no". For example, "some *abc* are *def*" may be re-arranged as "some *bf* are *acde*", each being equivalent to "some *abcdef* exist".

17. Some tigers are fierce,
No tigers are not-fierce.

18. Some hard-boiled eggs are unwholesome,
No hard-boiled eggs are wholesome.

19. Some I's are happy,
No I's are unhappy.

20. Some Johns are not at home,
No Johns are at home.

21. The Things, in each compartment of the larger Diagram, possess *three* Attributes, whose symbols will be

[See pp. 38, 9]

found written at three of the *corners* of the compartment (except in the case of m', which is not actually inserted in the Diagram, but is *supposed* to stand at each of its four outer corners).

22. If the Universe of Things be divided with regard to three different Attributes; and if two Propositions be given, containing two different couples of these Attributes; and if from these we can prove a third Proposition, containing the two Attributes that have not yet occurred together; the given Propositions are called 'the Premisses', the third one 'the Conclusion', and the whole set 'a Syllogism'. For example, the Premisses might be "no m are x'" and "all m' are y"; and it might be possible to prove from them a Conclusion containing x and y.

23. If an Attribute occurs in both Premisses, the Term containing it is called 'the Middle Term'. For example, if the Premisses are "some m are x" and "no m are y'", the class of "m-Things" is 'the Middle Term.'

If an Attribute occurs in one Premiss, and its contradictory in the other, the Terms containing them may be called 'the Middle Terms'. For example, if the Premisses are "no m are x'" and "all m' are y", the two classes of "m-Things" and "m'-Things" may be called 'the Middle Terms'.

24. Because they can be marked with *certainty*: whereas *affirmative* Propositions (that is, those that begin with "some" or "all") sometimes require us to place a red counter 'sitting on a fence'.

[See p. 39]

25. Because the only question we are concerned with is whether the Conclusion *follows logically* from the Premisses, so that, if *they* were true, *it* also would be true.

26. By understanding a red counter to mean "this compartment *can* be occupied", and a grey one to mean "this compartment *cannot* be occupied" or "this compartment *must* be empty".

27. 'Fallacious Premisses' and 'Fallacious Conclusion'.

28. By finding, when we try to transfer marks from the larger Diagram to the smaller, that there is 'no information' for any of its four compartments.

29. By finding the correct Conclusion, and then observing that the Conclusion, offered to us, is neither identical with it nor a part of it.

30. When the offered Conclusion is *part* of the correct Conclusion. In this case, we may call it a 'Defective Conclusion'.

§ 2. *Half of Smaller Diagram. Propositions represented.*

1.

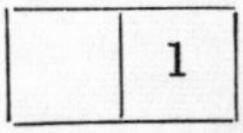

	1

2.

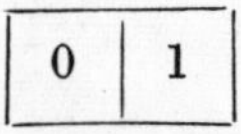

0	1

3.

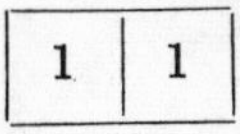

1	1

4.

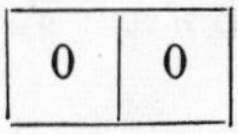

0	0

[See pp. 39, 40]

5. | — | 6. | | 0 |

7. | | 1 | It might be thought that the proper Diagram would be | —1 |, in order to express "some x exist": but this is really contained in "some x are y'." To put a red counter on the division-line would only tell us "*one of the two* compartments is occupied", which we know already, in knowing that *one* is occupied.

8. No x are y. i. e. | 0 | |

9. Some x are y'. i. e. | | 1 |

10. All x are y. i. e. | 1 | 0 |

11. Some x are y. i. e. | 1 | |

12. No x are y. i. e. | 0 | |

13. Some x are y, and some are y'. i. e. | 1 | 1 |

14. All x are y'. i. e. | 0 | 1 |

15. No y are x'. i. e. | — / 0 |

[See pp. 40, 1]

16. All y are x. i. e.

1
0

17. No y exist. i. e.

0
0

18. Some y are x'. i. e.

1

19. Some y exist. i. e.

– 1 –

§ 3. *Half of Smaller Diagram. Symbols interpreted.*

1. No x are y'.
2. No x exist.
3. Some x exist.
4. All x are y'.
5. Some x are y. i. e. Some good riddles are hard.
6. All x are y. i. e. All good riddles are hard.
7. No x exist. i. e. No riddles are good.

[See pp. 41, 2]

8. No x are y. i. e. No good riddles are hard.

9. Some x are y'. i. e. Some lobsters are unselfish.

10. No x are y. i. e. No lobsters are selfish.

11. All x are y'. i. e. All lobsters are unselfish.

12. Some x are y, and some are y'. i. e. Some lobsters are selfish, and some are unselfish.

13. All y' are x'. i. e. All invalids are unhappy.

14. Some y' exist. i. e. Some people are unhealthy.

15. Some y' are x, and some are x'. i. e. Some invalids are happy, and some are unhappy.

16. No y' exist. i. e. Nobody is unhealthy.

§ 4. *Smaller Diagram. Propositions represented.*

1.

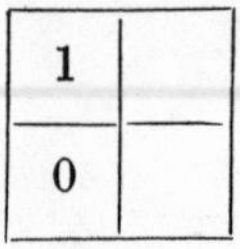

1	
0	

2.

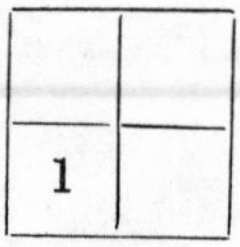

1	

3.

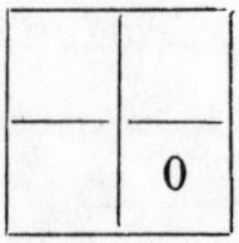

	0

4.

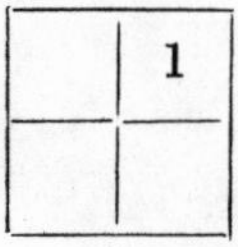

	1

[See pp. 42—4]

5. 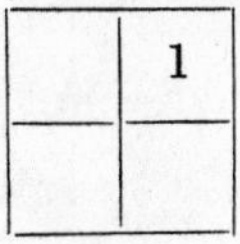 1

6. 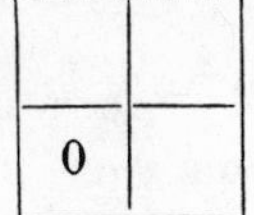

7. 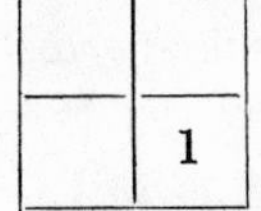

8. 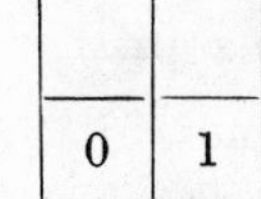

9. 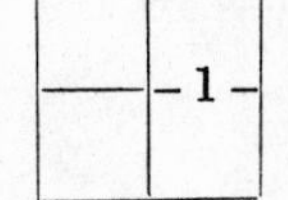

10. 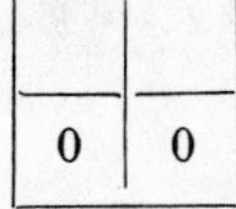

11. 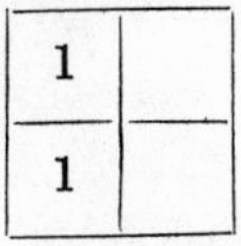 1 1

12. 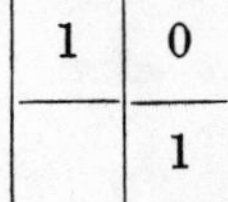

13. No x' are y. i. e. 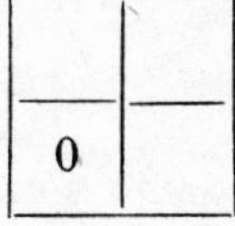

14. All y' are x'. i. e. 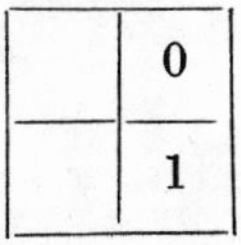 0 1

15. Some y' exist. i. e. 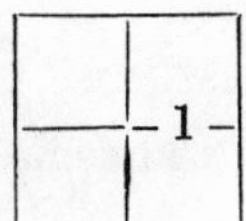

[See pp. 44, 5]

16. All y are x, and all x are y. i. e.

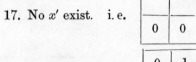

1	0
0	

17. No x' exist. i. e.

0	0

18. All x are y'. i. e.

0	1

19. No x are y. i. e.

0	

20. Some x' are y, and some are y'. i. e.

1	1

21. No y exist, and some x exist. i. e.

0	1
0	

22. All x' are y, and all y' are x. i. e.

	1
1	0

23. Some x are y, and some x' are y'. i. e.

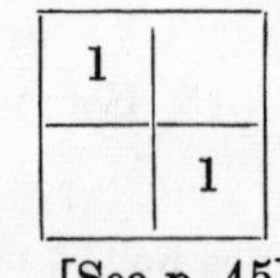

[See p. 45]

§ 5. *Smaller Diagram.* *Symbols interpreted.*

---

1. Some y are not-x,
   or, Some not-x are y.
2. No not-x are not-y,
   or, No not-y are not-x.
3. No not-y are x.
4. No not-x exist. i. e. No Things are not-x.
5. No y exist. i. e. No houses are two-storied.
6. Some x' exist. i. e. Some houses are not built of brick.
7. No x are y'. Or, no y' are x. i. e. No houses, built of brick, are other than two-storied. Or, no houses, that are not two-storied, are built of brick.
8. All x' are y'. i. e. All houses, that are not built of brick, are not two-storied.
9. Some x are y, and some are y'. i. e. Some fat boys are active, and some are not.
10. All y' are x'. i. e. All lazy boys are thin.
11. All x are y', and all y' are x. i. e. All fat boys are lazy, and all lazy ones are fat.

[See pp. 46, 7]

12. All y are x, and all x' are y. i. e. All active boys are fat, and all thin ones are lazy.

13. No x exist, and no y' exist. i. e. No cats have green eyes, and none have bad tempers.

14. Some x are y', and some x' are y. Or, some y are x', and some y' are x. i. e. Some green-eyed cats are bad-tempered, and some, that have not green eyes, are good-tempered. Or, some good-tempered cats have not green eyes, and some bad-tempered ones have green eyes.

15. Some x are y, and no x' are y'. Or, some y are x, and no y' are x'. i. e. Some green-eyed cats are good-tempered, and none, that are not green-eyed, are bad-tempered. Or, some good-tempered cats have green eyes, and none, that are bad-tempered, have not green eyes.

16. All x are y', and all x' are y. Or, all y are x', and all y' are x. i. e. All green-eyed cats are bad-tempered, and all, that have not green eyes, are good-tempered. Or, all good-tempered ones have eyes that are not green, and all bad-tempered ones have green eyes.

[See p. 47]

§ 6. *Larger Diagram. Propositions represented.*

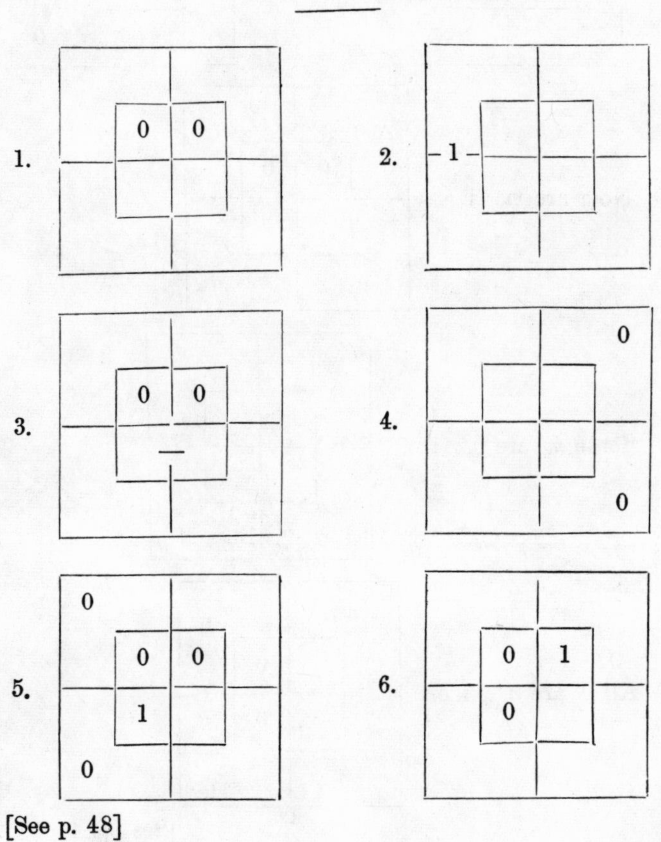

[See p. 48]

7 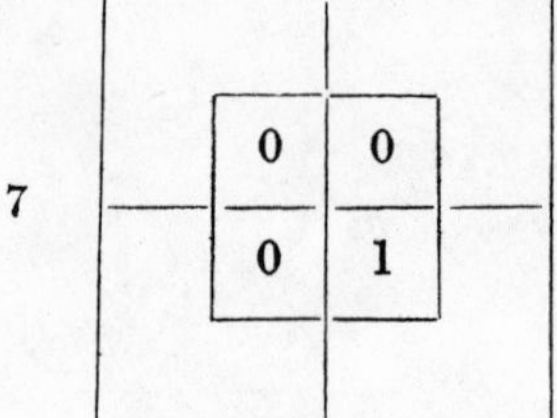

8. 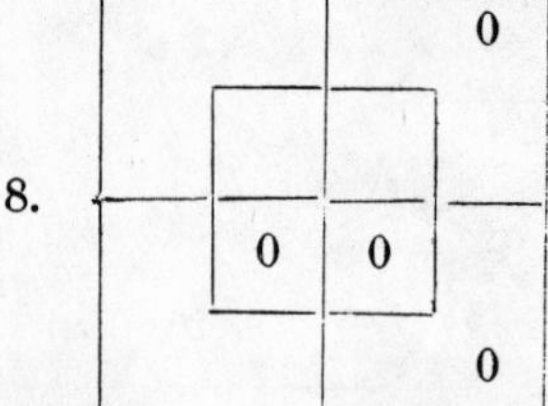

9. No x are m. i. e. 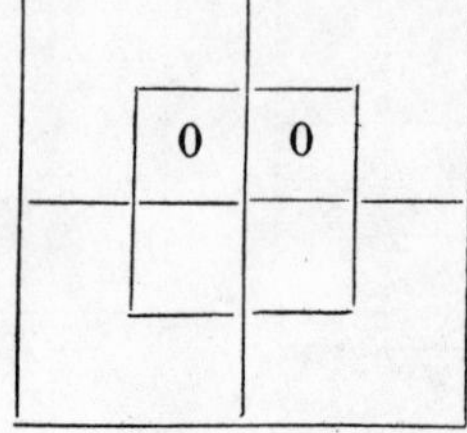

10. Some m' are y. i. e. 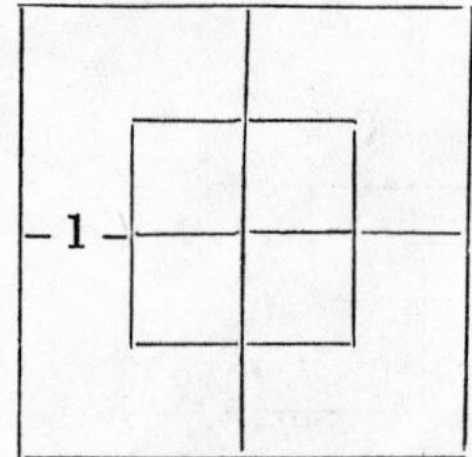

11. All y' are m'. i. e. 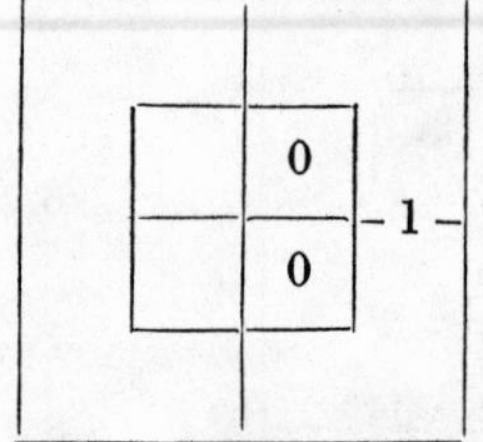

[See pp. 48, 9]

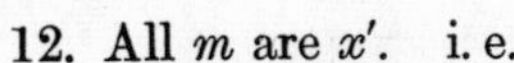

12. All m are x'. i. e.

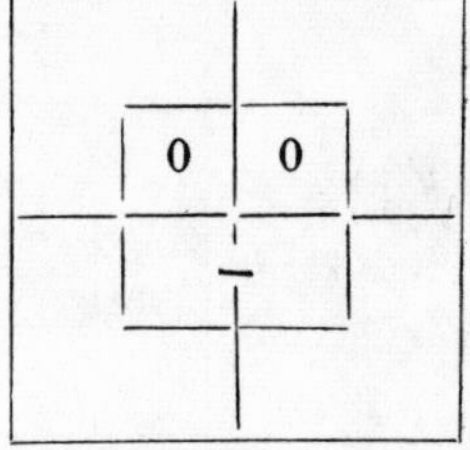

13. No x are m; All y are m. } i. e.

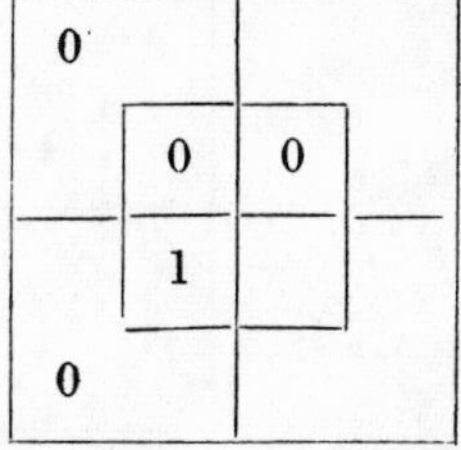

14. All m' are y; No x are m'. } i. e.

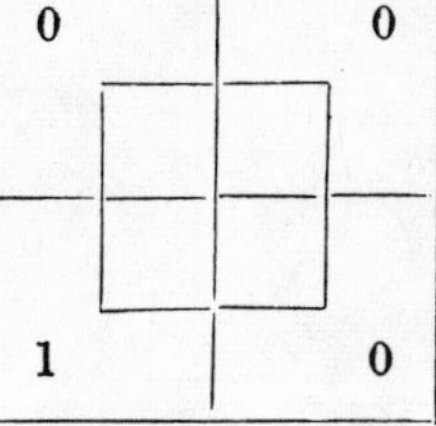

15. All x are m; No m are y'. } i. e.

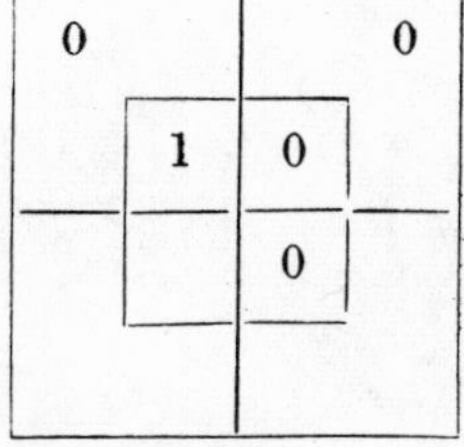

[See p. 49]

16. All m' are y'; No x are m'. } i. e.

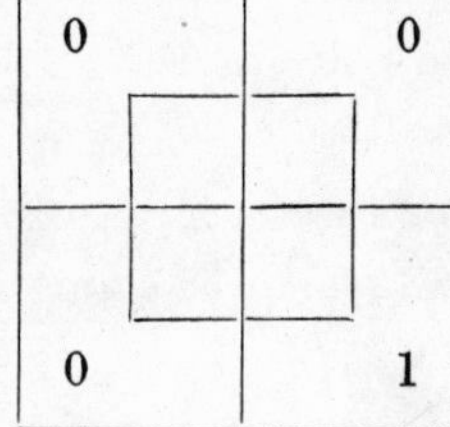

17. All x are m; All m are y. } i. e.

[See remarks on No. 7, p. 60.]

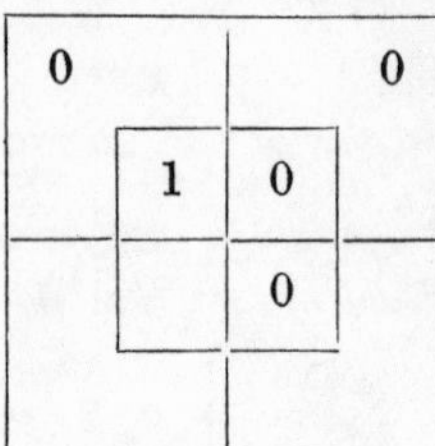

18. No x' are m; No m' are y. } i. e.

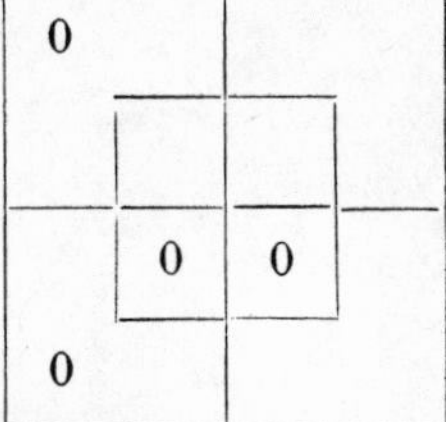

19. All m are x; All m are y. } i. e.

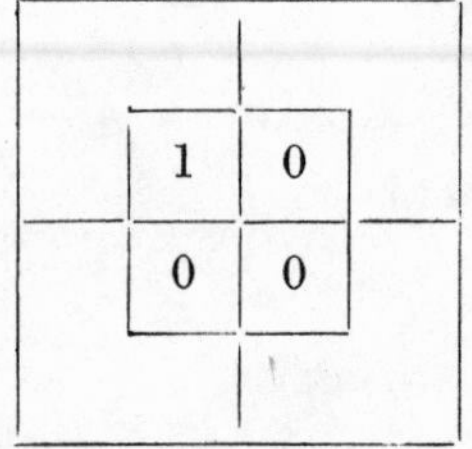

[See pp. 49, 50]

20. We had better take "persons" as Universe. We may choose "myself" as 'Middle Term', in which case the Premisses will take the form

I am a-person-who-sent-him-to-bring-a-kitten;
I am a-person-to-whom-he-brought-a-kettle-by-mistake.

Or we may choose "he" as 'Middle Term', in which case the Premisses will take the form

He is a-person-whom-I-sent-to-bring-me-a-kitten;
He is a-person-who-brought-me-a-kettle-by-mistake.

The latter form seems best, as the interest of the anecdote clearly depends on *his* stupidity——not on what happened to *me*. Let us then make m = "he"; x = "persons whom I sent, &c."; and y = "persons who brought, &c."

Hence, All m are x; All m are y. and the required Diagram is

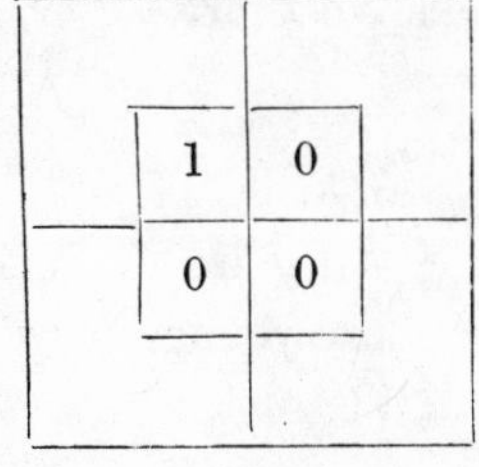

[See p. 50]

§ 7. *Both Diagrams employed.*

---

1. 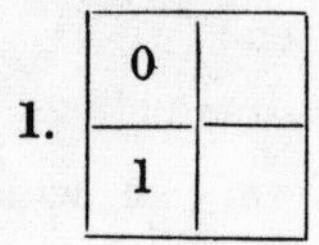

i. e. All y are x'.

2. 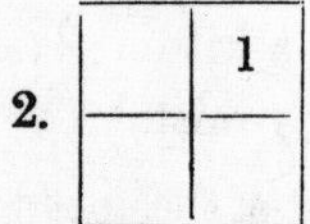

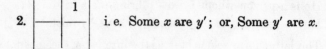

i. e. Some x are y'; or, Some y' are x.

3. 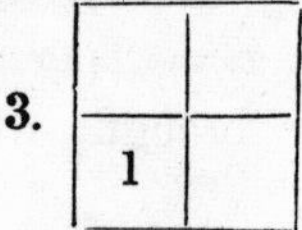

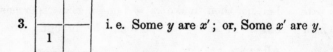

i. e. Some y are x'; or, Some x' are y.

4. 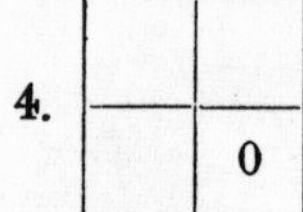

i. e. No x' are y'; or, No y' are x'.

5. 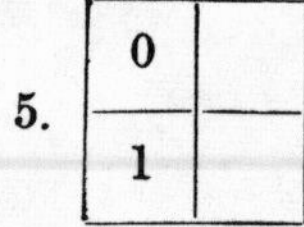

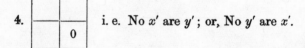

i. e. All y are x'. i. e. All black rabbits are young.

6. 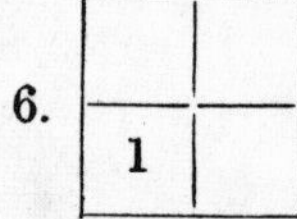

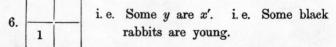

i. e. Some y are x'. i. e. Some black rabbits are young.

[See pp. 51, 2]

7. i.e. All x are y. i.e. All well-fed birds are happy.

8. 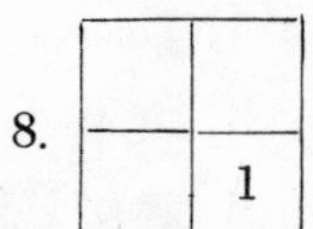

i.e. Some x' are y'. i.e. Some birds, that are not well-fed, are unhappy; or, Some unhappy birds are not well-fed.

9. 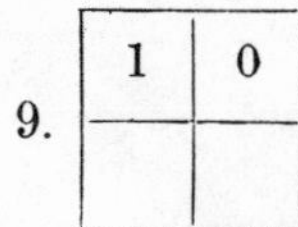

i.e. All x are y. i.e. John has got a tooth-ache.

10. 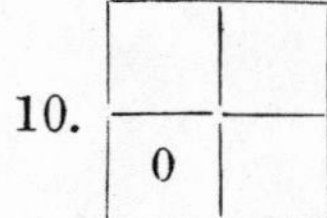

i.e. No x' are y. i.e. No one, but John, has got a tooth-ache.

11. 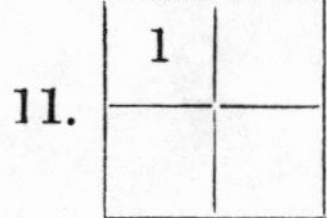

i.e. Some x are y. i.e. Some one, who has taken a walk, feels better.

12. 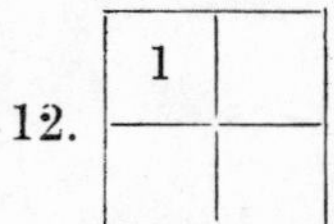

i.e. Some x are y. i.e. Some one, whom I sent to bring me a kitten, brought me a kettle by mistake.

[See p. 52]

13.

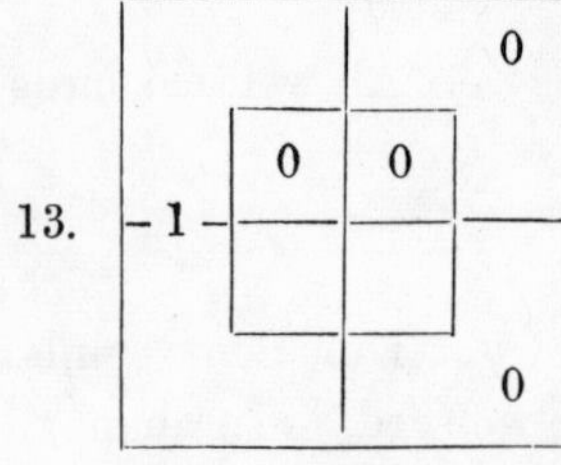

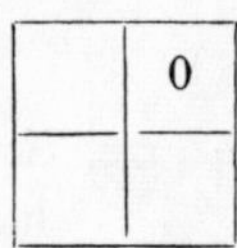

Let "books" be Universe ; m = "exciting",
x = "that suit feverish patients" ; y = "that make one drowsy".

No m are x ;
All m' are y. } ∴ No y' are x.

i. e. No books suit feverish patients, except such as make one drowsy.

14.

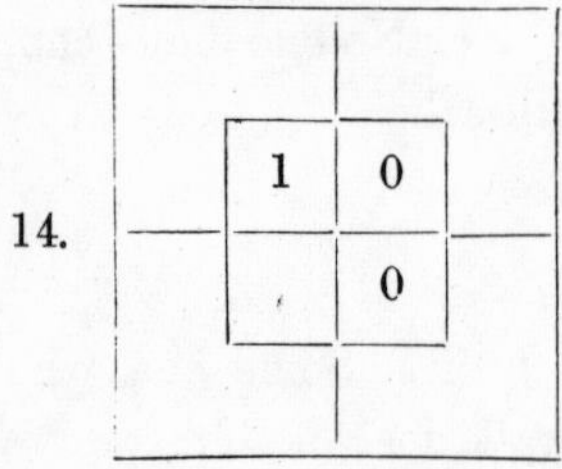

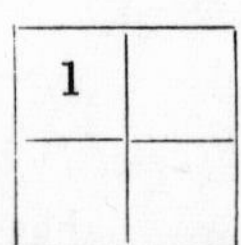

Let "persons" be Universe ; m = "that deserve the fair" :
x = "that get their deserts" ; y = "brave".

Some m are x ;
No y' are m. } ∴ Some y are x.

i. e. Some brave persons get their deserts.

[See p. 52]

15. 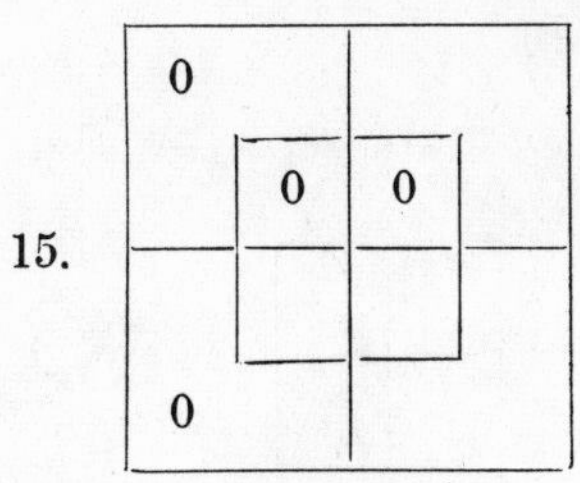

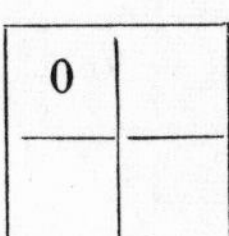

Let "persons" be Universe; m = "patient";
x = "children"; y = "that can sit still".

No x are m;
No m' are y. } ∴ No x are y.

i. e. No children can sit still.

16. 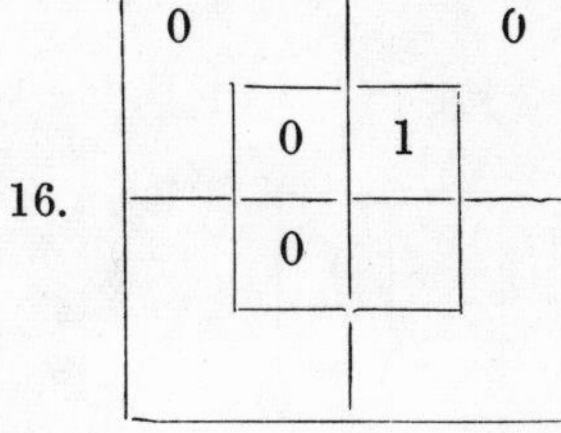

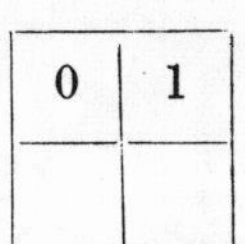

Let "things" be Universe; m = "fat"; x = "pigs";
y = "skeletons".

All x are m;
No y are m. } ∴ All x are y'.

i. e. All pigs are not-skeletons.

[See pp. 52, 3]

17. 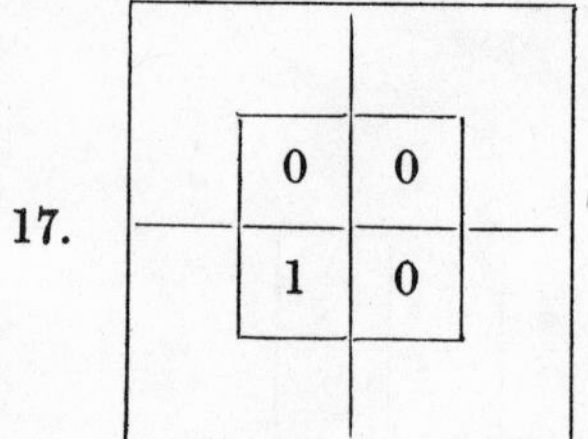

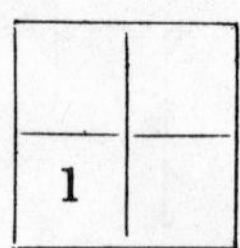

Let "creatures" be Universe; m = "monkeys";
x = "soldiers"; y = "mischievous".

$$\left.\begin{array}{l}\text{No } m \text{ are } x;\\ \text{All } m \text{ are } y.\end{array}\right\} \therefore \text{ Some } y \text{ are } x'.$$

i. e. Some mischievous creatures are not soldiers.

18. 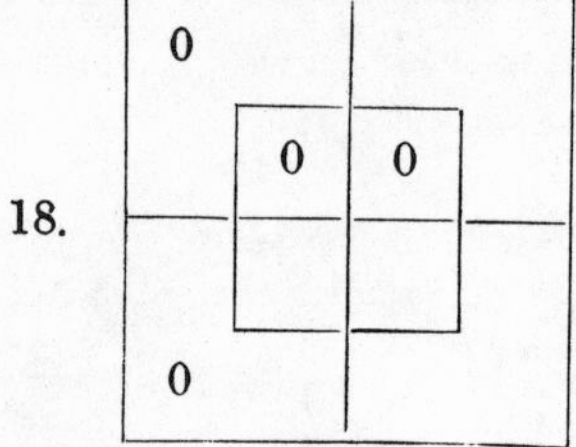

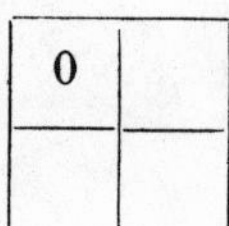

Let "persons" be Universe; m = "just";
x = "my cousins"; y = "judges".

$$\left.\begin{array}{l}\text{No } x \text{ are } m;\\ \text{No } y \text{ are } m'.\end{array}\right\} \therefore \text{ No } x \text{ are } y.$$

i. e. None of my cousins are judges.

[See p. 53]

19. 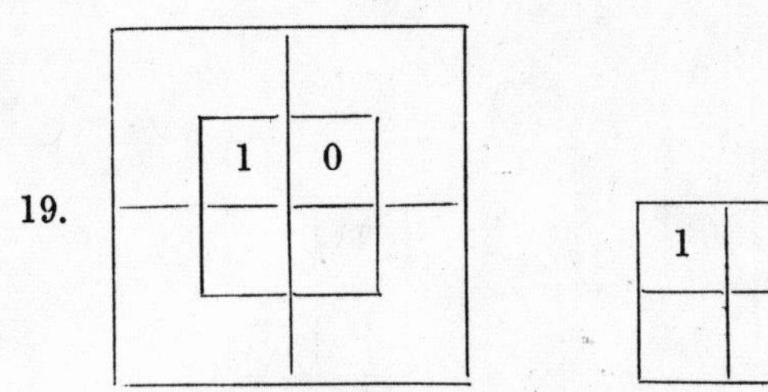

Let " periods " be Universe ; m = " days " ;
x = " rainy " ; y = " tiresome ".

Some m are x ;
All xm are y. } ∴ Some x are y.

i. e. Some rainy periods are tiresome.

N.B. These are not legitimate Premisses, since the Conclusion is really part of the second Premiss, so that the first Premiss is superfluous. This may be shown, in letters, thus :—

" All xm are y " contains " Some xm are y ", which contains " Some x are y ". Or, in words, " All rainy days are tiresome " contains " Some rainy days are tiresome ", which contains " Some rainy periods are tiresome ".

Moreover, the first Premiss, besides being superfluous, is actually contained in the second ; since it is equivalent to " Some rainy days exist ", which, as we know, is implied in the Proposition " All rainy days are tiresome ".

Altogether, a *most* unsatisfactory Pair of Premisses !
[See p. 53]

20. 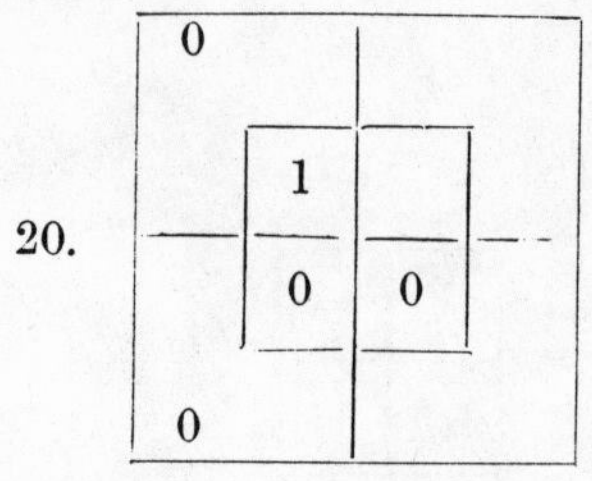

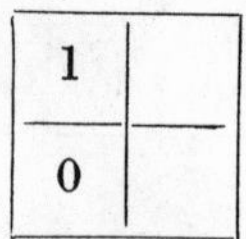

Let "things" be Universe; m = "medicine";
x = "nasty"; y = "senna".

All m are x;
All y are m. } ∴ All y are x.

i. e. Senna is nasty.

[See remarks on No. 7, p. 60.]

21. 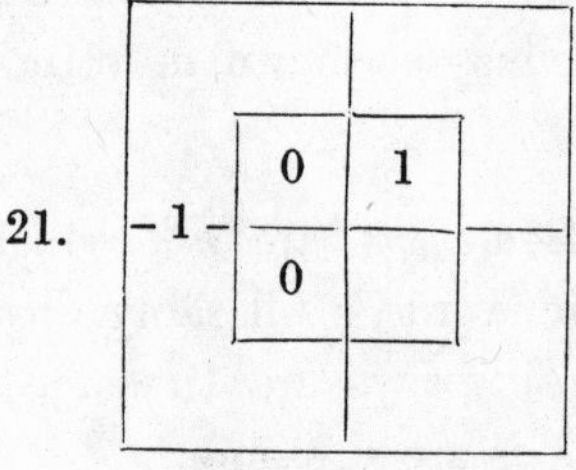

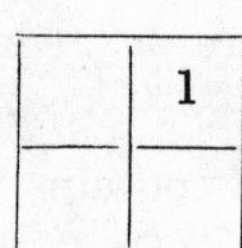

Let "persons" be Universe; m = "Jews";
x = "rich"; y = "Patagonians".

Some m are x;
All y are m'. } ∴ Some x are y'.

i. e. Some rich persons are not Patagonians.

[See p. 53]

22. 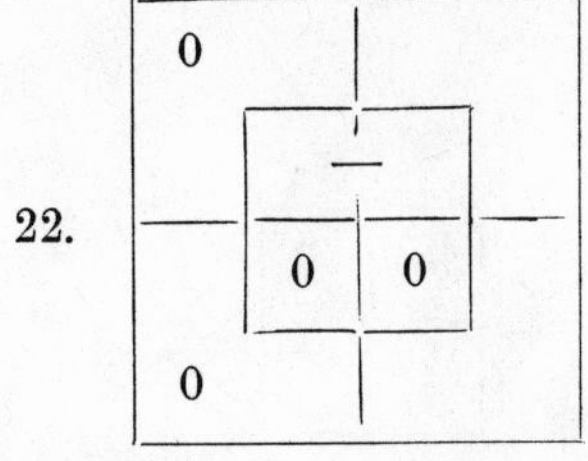

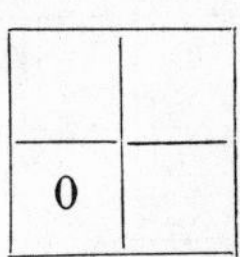

Let "creatures" be Universe; m = "teetotalers";
x = "that like sugar"; y = "nightingales".

All m are x;
No y are m'. } ∴ No y are x'.

i. e. No nightingales dislike sugar.

23. 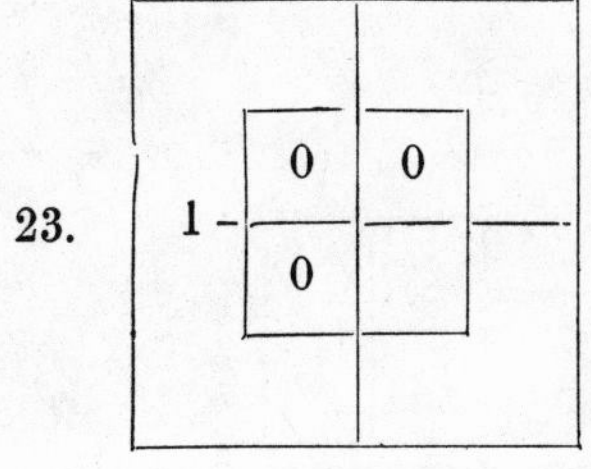

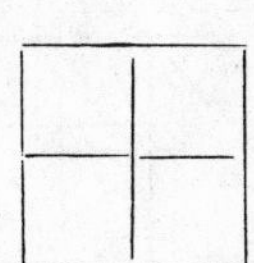

Let "food" be Universe; m = "wholesome";
x = "muffins"; y = "buns".

No x are m;
All y are m. }

There is 'no information' for the smaller Diagram; so no Conclusion can be drawn.

[See p. 53]

24. 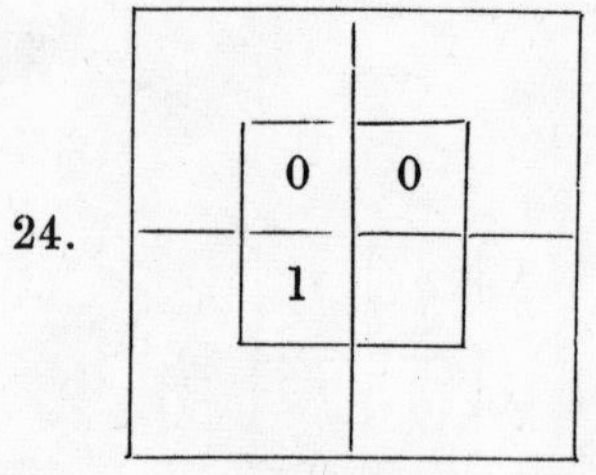

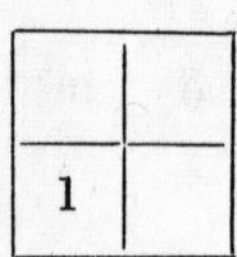

Let "creatures" be Universe; m = "that run well";
x = "fat"; y = "greyhounds".

No x are m;
Some y are m. } ∴ Some y are x'.

i. e. Some greyhounds are not fat.

25. 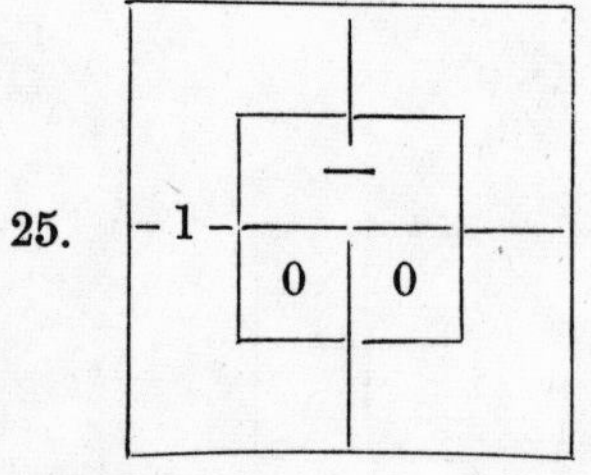

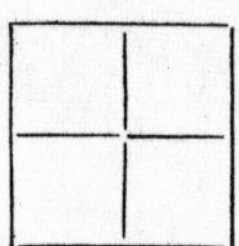

Let "persons" be Universe; m = "soldiers";
x = "that march"; y = "youths".

All m are x;
Some y are m'. }

There is 'no information' for the smaller Diagram; so no Conclusion can be drawn.

[See p. 53]

26. 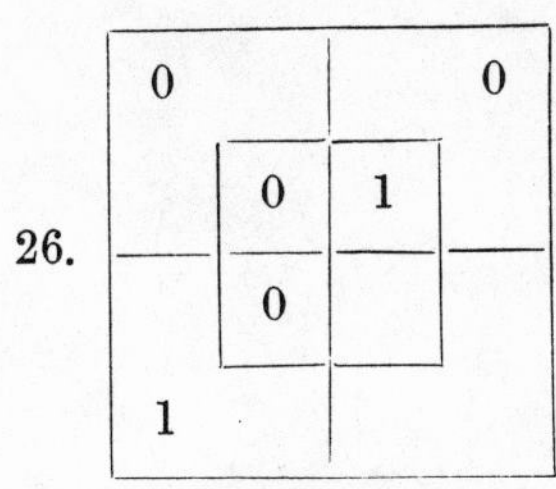

Let "food" be Universe; m = "sweet";
x = "sugar"; y = "salt".

All x are m;
All y are m'.
∴ All x are y'.
All y are x'.

i. e. Sugar is not salt.
Salt is not sugar.

27. 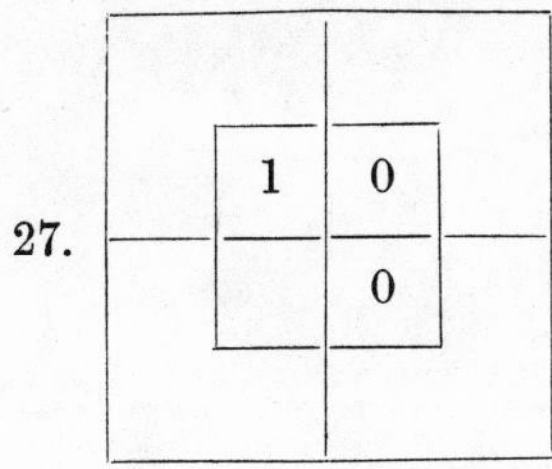

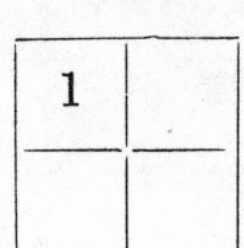

Let "Things" be Universe; m = "eggs";
x = "hard-boiled"; y = "crackable".

Some m are x;
No m are y'.
∴ Some x are y.

i. e. Some hard-boiled things can be cracked.

[See p. 53]

28. 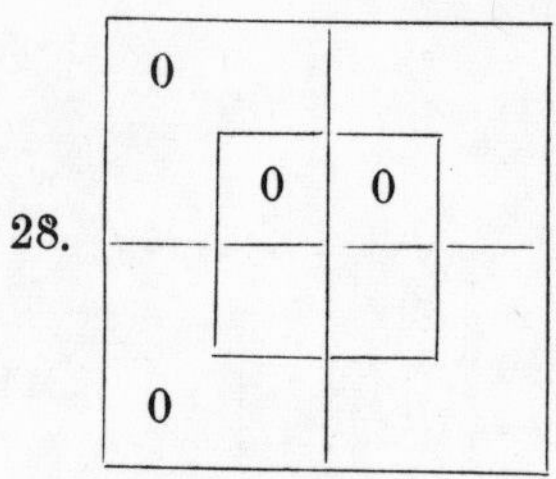

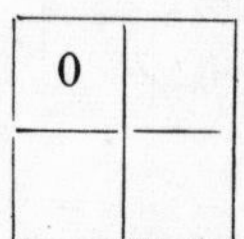

Let "persons" be Universe; m = "Jews"; x = "that are in the house"; y = "that are in the garden".

$$\left.\begin{array}{l}\text{No } m \text{ are } x;\\ \text{No } m' \text{ are } y.\end{array}\right\} \therefore \text{No } x \text{ are } y.$$

i.e. No persons, that are in the house, are also in the garden.

29. 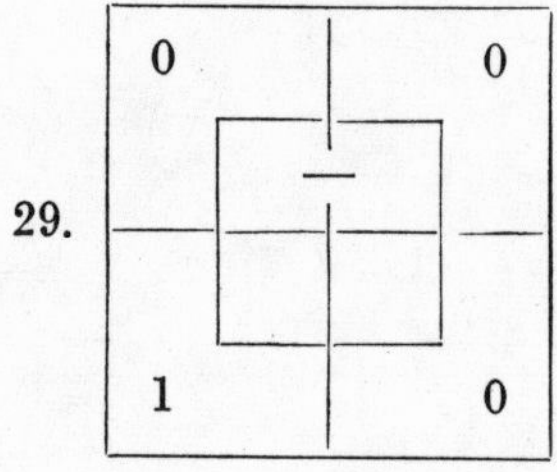

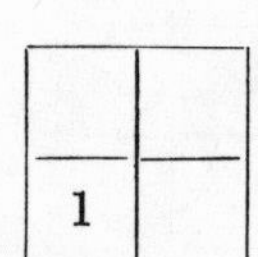

Let "Things" be Universe; m = "noisy"; x = "battles"; y = "that may escape notice".

$$\left.\begin{array}{l}\text{All } x \text{ are } m;\\ \text{All } m' \text{ are } y.\end{array}\right\} \therefore \text{Some } x' \text{ are } y.$$

i.e. Some things, that are not battles, may escape notice.

[See pp. 53, 54]

30. 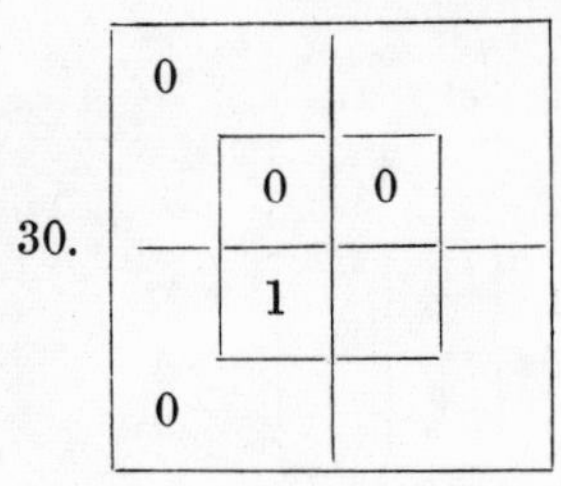

Let "persons" be Universe; m = "Jews";
x = "mad"; y = "Rabbis".

$\left.\begin{array}{l}\text{No } m \text{ are } x;\\ \text{All } y \text{ are } m.\end{array}\right\} \therefore \text{All } y \text{ are } x'.$

i. e. All Rabbis are sane.

31. 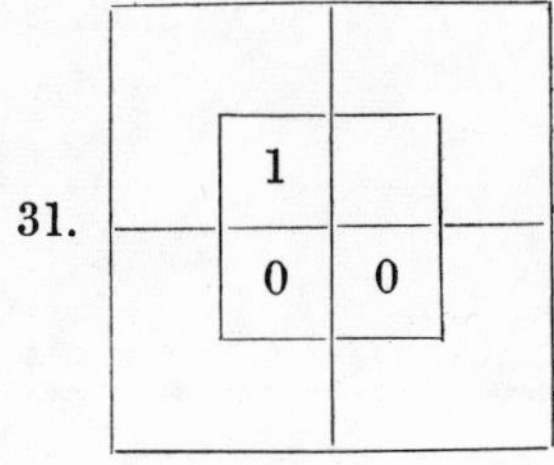

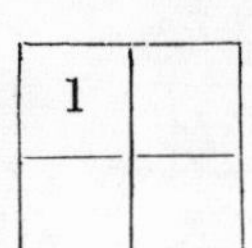

Let "Things" be Universe; m = "fish";
x = "that can swim"; y = "skates".

$\left.\begin{array}{l}\text{No } m \text{ are } x';\\ \text{Some } y \text{ are } m.\end{array}\right\} \therefore \text{Some } y \text{ are } x.$

i. e. Some skates can swim.

[See p. 54]

32. 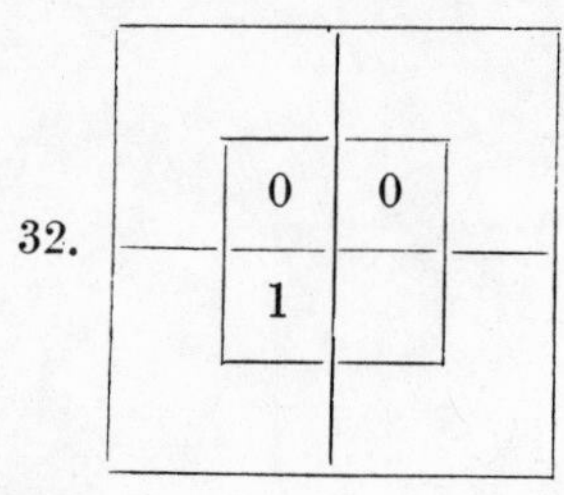

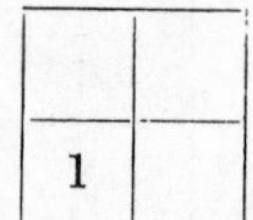

Let "people" be Universe; m = "passionate"; x = "reasonable"; y = "orators".

$$\left.\begin{array}{l}\text{All } m \text{ are } x'; \\ \text{Some } y \text{ are } m.\end{array}\right\} \therefore \text{ Some } y \text{ are } x'.$$

i. e. Some orators are unreasonable.

[See remarks on No. 7, p. 60.]

[See p. 54]

CHAPTER IV.

HIT OR MISS.

"Thou canst not hit it, hit it, hit it,
Thou canst not hit it, my good man."

---

1. Pain is wearisome;
   No pain is eagerly wished for.
2. No bald person needs a hair-brush;
   No lizards have hair.
3. All thoughtless people do mischief;
   No thoughtful person forgets a promise.
4. I do not like John;
   Some of my friends like John.
5. No potatoes are pine-apples;
   All pine-apples are nice.
6. No pins are ambitious;
   No needles are pins.
7. All my friends have colds;
   No one can sing who has a cold.
8. All these dishes are well-cooked;
   Some dishes are unwholesome if not well-cooked.

9. No medicine is nice;
   Senna is a medicine.
10. Some oysters are silent;
    No silent creatures are amusing.
11. All wise men walk on their feet;
    All unwise men walk on their hands.
12. "Mind your own business;
    This quarrel is no business of yours."
13. No bridges are made of sugar;
    Some bridges are picturesque.
14. No riddles interest me that can be solved;
    All these riddles are insoluble.
15. John is industrious;
    All industrious people are happy.
16. No frogs write books;
    Some people use ink in writing books.
17. No pokers are soft;
    All pillows are soft.
18. No antelope is ungraceful;
    Graceful animals delight the eye.
19. Some uncles are ungenerous;
    All merchants are generous.
20. No unhappy people chuckle;
    No happy people groan.
21. Audible music causes vibration in the air;
    Inaudible music is not worth paying for.

22. He gave me five pounds;
I was delighted.

23. No old Jews are fat millers;
All my friends are old millers.

24. Flour is good for food;
Oatmeal is a kind of flour.

25. Some dreams are terrible;
No lambs are terrible.

26. No rich man begs in the street;
All who are not rich should keep accounts.

27. No thieves are honest;
Some dishonest people are found out.

28. All wasps are unfriendly;
All puppies are friendly.

29. All improbable stories are doubted;
None of these stories are probable.

30. "He told me you had gone away."
"He never says one word of truth."

31. His songs never last an hour;
A song, that lasts an hour, is tedious.

32. No bride-cakes are wholesome;
Unwholesome food should be avoided.

33. No old misers are cheerful;
Some old misers are thin.

34. All ducks waddle;
Nothing that waddles is graceful.

35. No Professors are ignorant;
Some ignorant people are conceited.

36. Toothache is never pleasant;
Warmth is never unpleasant.

37. Bores are terrible;
You are a bore.

38. Some mountains are insurmountable;
All stiles can be surmounted.

39. No Frenchmen like plumpudding;
All Englishmen like plumpudding.

40. No idlers win fame;
Some painters are not idle.

41. No lobsters are unreasonable;
No reasonable creatures expect impossibilities.

42. No kind deed is unlawful;
What is lawful may be done without fear.

43. No fossils can be crossed in love;
An oyster may be crossed in love.

44. "This is beyond endurance!"
"Well, nothing beyond endurance
has ever happened to *me*."

45. All uneducated men are shallow;
All these students are educated.

46. All my cousins are unjust;
No judges are unjust.

47. No country, that has been explored,
is infested by dragons;
Unexplored countries are fascinating.

48. No misers are generous;
Some old men are not generous.

49. A prudent man shuns hyænas;
No banker is imprudent.

50. Some poetry is original;
No original work is producible at will.

51. No misers are unselfish;
None but misers save egg-shells.

52. All pale people are phlegmatic;
No one, who is not pale, looks poetical.

53. All spiders spin webs;
Some creatures, that do not spin webs, are savage.

54. None of my cousins are just;
All judges are just.

55. John is industrious;
No industrious people are unhappy.

56. Umbrellas are useful on a journey;
What is useless on a journey should be left behind.

57. Some pillows are soft;
No pokers are soft.

58. I am old and lame;
No old merchant is a lame gambler.

59. No eventful journey is ever forgotten;
Uneventful journeys are not worth writing a book about.

60. Sugar is sweet;
Some sweet things are liked by children.

61. Richard is out of temper;
No one but Richard can ride that horse.

62. All jokes are meant to amuse;
No Act of Parliament is a joke.

63. "I saw it in a newspaper."
"All newspapers tell lies."

64. No nightmare is pleasant;
Unpleasant experiences are not anxiously desired.

65. Prudent travellers carry plenty of small change;
Imprudent travellers lose their luggage.

66. All wasps are unfriendly;
No puppies are unfriendly.

67. He called here yesterday;
He is no friend of mine.

68. No quadrupeds can whistle;
Some cats are quadrupeds.

69. No cooked meat is sold by butchers;
No uncooked meat is served at dinner.

70. Gold is heavy;
Nothing but gold will silence him.

71. Some pigs are wild;
There are no pigs that are not fat.

72. No emperors are dentists;
All dentists are dreaded by children.

73. All, who are not old, like walking;
Neither you nor I are old.

74. All blades are sharp;
Some grasses are blades.

75. No dictatorial person is popular;
She is dictatorial.

76. Some sweet things are unwholesome;
No muffins are sweet.

77. No military men write poetry;
No generals are civilians.

78. Bores are dreaded;
A bore is never begged to prolong his visit.

79. All owls are satisfactory;
Some excuses are unsatisfactory.

80. All my cousins are unjust;
All judges are just.

81. Some buns are rich;
All buns are nice.

82. No medicine is nice;
No pills are unmedicinal.

83. Some lessons are difficult;
What is difficult needs attention.

84. No unexpected pleasure annoys me;
Your visit is an unexpected pleasure.

85. Caterpillars are not eloquent;
Jones is eloquent.

86. Some bald people wear wigs;
All your children have hair.

87. All wasps are unfriendly;
Unfriendly creatures are always unwelcome.

88. No bankrupts are rich;
Some merchants are not bankrupts.

89. Weasels sometimes sleep;
All animals sometimes sleep.

90. Ill-managed concerns are unprofitable;
Railways are never ill-managed.

91. Everybody has seen a pig;
Nobody admires a pig.

Extract a Pair of Premisses out of each of the following: and deduce the Conclusion, if there is one:—

92. "The Lion, as any one can tell you who has been chased by them as often as *I* have, is a very savage animal: and there are certain individuals among them, though I will not guarantee it as a general law, who do not drink coffee."

93. "It was most absurd of you to offer it! You might have known, if you had had any sense, that no old sailors ever like gruel!"

"But I thought, as he was an uncle of yours——"

"An uncle of mine, indeed! Stuff!"

"You may call it stuff, if you like. All I know is, *my* uncles are all old men: and they like gruel like anything!"

"Well, then *your* uncles are ——"

94. "Do come away! I can't stand this squeezing any more. No crowded shops are comfortable, you know very well."

"Well, who expects to be comfortable, out shopping?"

"Why, *I* do, of course! And I'm sure there are some shops, further down the street, that are not crowded. So ——"

95. "They say no doctors are metaphysical organists: and that lets me into a little fact about *you*, you know."

"Why, how do you make *that* out? You never heard me play the organ."

"No, doctor, but I've heard you talk about Browning's poetry: and that showed me that you're *metaphysical*, at any rate. So ——"

Extract a Syllogism out of each of the following: and test its correctness:—

96. "Don't talk to me! I've known more rich merchants than you have: and I can tell you not *one* of them was ever an old miser since the world began!"

"And what has that got to do with old Mr. Brown?"

"Why, isn't he very rich?"

"Yes, of course he is. And what then?"

"Why, don't you see that it's absurd to call him a miserly merchant? Either he's not a merchant, or he's not a miser!"

97. "It *is* so kind of you to enquire! I'm really feeling a great deal better to-day."

"And is it Nature, or Art, that is to have the credit of this happy change?"

"Art, I think. The Doctor has given me some of that patent medicine of his."

"Well, I'll never call him a humbug again. There's *somebody*, at any rate, that feels better after taking his medicine!"

98. "No, I don't like you one bit. And I'll go and play with my doll. *Dolls* are never unkind."

"So you like a doll better than a cousin? Oh you little silly!"

"Of course I do! *Cousins* are never kind——at least no cousins *I've* ever seen."

"Well, and what does *that* prove, I'd like to know! If you mean that cousins aren't dolls, who ever said they were?"

99. "What are you talking about geraniums for? You can't tell one flower from another, at this distance! I grant you they're all *red* flowers: it doesn't need a telescope to know *that*."

"Well, some geraniums are red, aren't they?"

"I don't deny it. And what then? I suppose you'll be telling me some of those flowers are geraniums!"

"Of course that's what I should tell you, if you'd the sense to follow an argument! But what's the good of proving anything to *you*, I should like to know?"

100. "Boys, you've passed a fairly good examination, all things considered. Now let me give you a word of advice before I go. Remember that all, who are really anxious to learn, work *hard*."

"I thank you, Sir, in the name of my scholars! And proud am I to think there are *some* of them, at least, that are really *anxious* to learn."

"Very glad to hear it: and how do you make it out to be so?"

"Why, Sir, *I* know how hard they work——some of them, that is. Who should know better?"

Extract from the following speech a series of Syllogisms, or arguments having the form of Syllogisms: and test their correctness.

It is supposed to be spoken by a fond mother, in answer to a friend's cautious suggestion that she is perhaps a *little* overdoing it, in the way of lessons, with her children.

101. "Well, they've got their own way to make in the world. *We* can't leave them a fortune apiece!

And money's not to be had, as *you* know, without money's worth: they must *work* if they want to live. And how are they to work, if they don't know anything? Take my word for it, there's no place for ignorance in *these* times! And all authorities agree that the time to learn is when you're young. One's got no memory afterwards, worth speaking of. A child will learn more in an hour than a grown man in five. So those, that have to learn, must learn when they're young, if ever they're to learn at all. Of course that doesn't do unless children are *healthy*: I quite allow *that.* Well, the doctor tells me no children are healthy unless they've got a good colour in their cheeks. And only just look at my darlings! Why, their cheeks bloom like peonies! Well, now, they tell me that, to keep children in health, you should never give them more than six hours altogether at lessons in the day, and at least two half-holidays in the week. And that's *exactly* our plan, I can assure you! We never go beyond six hours, and every Wednesday and Saturday, as ever is, not one syllable of lessons do they do after their one o'clock dinner! So how you can imagine I'm running any risk in the education of my precious pets is more than *I* can understand, I promise you!"

THE END.

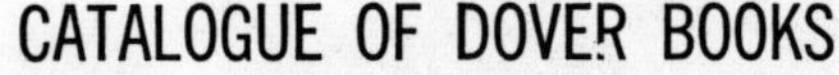
CATALOGUE OF DOVER BOOKS

The more difficult books are indicated by an asterisk (*)

Books Explaining Science and Mathematics

WHAT IS SCIENCE?, N. Campbell. The role of experiment and measurement, the function of mathematics, the nature of scientific laws, the difference between laws and theories, the limitations of science, and many similarly provocative topics are treated clearly and without technicalities by an eminent scientist. "Still an excellent introduction to scientific philosophy," H. Margenau in PHYSICS TODAY. "A first-rate primer . . . deserves a wide audience," SCIENTIFIC AMERICAN. 192pp. 5⅜ x 8. S43 Paperbound **$1.25**

THE NATURE OF PHYSICAL THEORY, P. W. Bridgman. A Nobel Laureate's clear, non-technical lectures on difficulties and paradoxes connected with frontier research on the physical sciences. Concerned with such central concepts as thought, logic, mathematics, relativity, probability, wave mechanics, etc. he analyzes the contributions of such men as Newton, Einstein, Bohr, Heisenberg, and many others. "Lucid and entertaining . . . recommended to anyone who wants to get some insight into current philosophies of science," THE NEW PHILOSOPHY. Index. xi + 138pp. 5⅜ x 8. S33 Paperbound **$1.25**

EXPERIMENT AND THEORY IN PHYSICS, Max Born. A Nobel Laureate examines the nature of experiment and theory in theoretical physics and analyzes the advances made by the great physicists of our day: Heisenberg, Einstein, Bohr, Planck, Dirac, and others. The actual process of creation is detailed step-by-step by one who participated. A fine examination of the scientific method at work. 44pp. 5⅜ x 8. S308 Paperbound **75¢**

THE PSYCHOLOGY OF INVENTION IN THE MATHEMATICAL FIELD, J. Hadamard. The reports of such men as Descartes, Pascal, Einstein, Poincaré, and others are considered in this investigation of the method of idea-creation in mathematics and other sciences and the thinking process in general. How do ideas originate? What is the role of the unconscious? What is Poincaré's forgetting hypothesis? are some of the fascinating questions treated. A penetrating analysis of Einstein's thought processes concludes the book. xiii + 145pp. 5⅜ x 8. T107 Paperbound **$1.25**

THE NATURE OF LIGHT AND COLOUR IN THE OPEN AIR, M. Minnaert. Why are shadows sometimes blue, sometimes green, or other colors depending on the light and surroundings? What causes mirages? Why do multiple suns and moons appear in the sky? Professor Minnaert explains these unusual phenomena and hundreds of others in simple, easy-to-understand terms based on optical laws and the properties of light and color. No mathematics is required but artists, scientists, students, and everyone fascinated by these "tricks" of nature will find thousands of useful and amazing pieces of information. Hundreds of observational experiments are suggested which require no special equipment. 200 illustrations; 42 photos. xvi + 362pp. 5⅜ x 8. T196 Paperbound **$1.95**

THE UNIVERSE OF LIGHT, W. Bragg. Sir William Bragg, Nobel Laureate and great modern physicist, is also well known for his powers of clear exposition. Here he analyzes all aspects of light for the layman: lenses, reflection, refraction, the optics of vision, x-rays, the photoelectric effect, etc. He tells you what causes the color of spectra, rainbows, and soap bubbles, how magic mirrors work, and much more. Dozens of simple experiments are described. Preface. Index. 199 line drawings and photographs, including 2 full-page color plates. x + 283pp. 5⅜ x 8. T538 Paperbound **$1.85**

SOAP-BUBBLES: THEIR COLOURS AND THE FORCES THAT MOULD THEM, C. V. Boys. For continuing popularity and validity as scientific primer, few books can match this volume of easily-followed experiments, explanations. Lucid exposition of complexities of liquid films, surface tension and related phenomena, bubbles' reaction to heat, motion, music, magnetic fields. Experiments with capillary attraction, soap bubbles on frames, composite bubbles, liquid cylinders and jets, bubbles other than soap, etc. Wonderful introduction to scientific method, natural laws that have many ramifications in areas of modern physics. Only complete edition in print. New Introduction by S. Z. Lewin, New York University. 83 illustrations; 1 full-page color plate. xii + 190pp. 5⅜ x 8½. T542 Paperbound **95¢**

THE STORY OF X-RAYS FROM RONTGEN TO ISOTOPES, A. R. Bleich, M.D. This book, by a member of the American College of Radiology, gives the scientific explanation of x-rays, their applications in medicine, industry and art, and their danger (and that of atmospheric radiation) to the individual and the species. You learn how radiation therapy is applied against cancer, how x-rays diagnose heart disease and other ailments, how they are used to examine mummies for information on diseases of early societies, and industrial materials for hidden weaknesses. 54 illustrations show x-rays of flowers, bones, stomach, gears with flaws, etc. 1st publication. Index. xix + 186pp. 5⅜ x 8. T622 Paperbound **$1.35**

SPINNING TOPS AND GYROSCOPIC MOTION, John Perry. A classic elementary text of the dynamics of rotation — the behavior and use of rotating bodies such as gyroscopes and tops. In simple, everyday English you are shown how quasi-rigidity is induced in discs of paper, smoke rings, chains, etc., by rapid motions; why a gyrostat falls and why a top rises; precession; how the earth's motion affects climate; and many other phenomena. Appendix on practical use of gyroscopes. 62 figures. 128pp. 5⅜ x 8. T416 Paperbound **$1.00**

SNOW CRYSTALS, W. A. Bentley, M. J. Humphreys. For almost 50 years W. A. Bentley photographed snow flakes in his laboratory in Jericho, Vermont; in 1931 the American Meteorological Society gathered together the best of his work, some 2400 photographs of snow flakes, plus a few ice flowers, windowpane frosts, dew, frozen rain, and other ice formations. Pictures were selected for beauty and scientific value. A very valuable work to anyone in meteorology, cryology; most interesting to layman; extremely useful for artist who wants beautiful, crystalline designs. All copyright free. Unabridged reprint of 1931 edition. 2453 illustrations. 227pp. 8 x 10½. T287 Paperbound **$3.00**

A DOVER SCIENCE SAMPLER, edited by George Barkin. A collection of brief, non-technical passages from 44 Dover Books Explaining Science for the enjoyment of the science-minded browser. Includes work of Bertrand Russell, Poincaré, Laplace, Max Born, Galileo, Newton; material on physics, mathematics, metallurgy, anatomy, astronomy, chemistry, etc. You will be fascinated by Martin Gardner's analysis of the sincere pseudo-scientist, Moritz's account of Newton's absentmindedness, Bernard's examples of human vivisection, etc. Illustrations from the Diderot Pictorial Encyclopedia and De Re Metallica. 64 pages. **FREE**

THE STORY OF ATOMIC THEORY AND ATOMIC ENERGY, J. G. Feinberg. A broader approach to subject of nuclear energy and its cultural implications than any other similar source. Very readable, informal, completely non-technical text. Begins with first atomic theory, 600 B.C. and carries you through the work of Mendelejeff, Röntgen, Madame Curie, to Einstein's equation and the A-bomb. New chapter goes through thermonuclear fission, binding energy, other events up to 1959. Radioactive decay and radiation hazards, future benefits, work of Bohr, moderns, hundreds more topics. "Deserves special mention . . . not only authoritative but thoroughly popular in the best sense of the word," Saturday Review. Formerly, "The Atom Story." Expanded with new chapter. Three appendixes. Index. 34 illustrations. vii + 243pp. 5⅜ x 8. T625 Paperbound **$1.45**

THE STRANGE STORY OF THE QUANTUM, AN ACCOUNT FOR THE GENERAL READER OF THE GROWTH OF IDEAS UNDERLYING OUR PRESENT ATOMIC KNOWLEDGE, B. Hoffmann. Presents lucidly and expertly, with barest amount of mathematics, the problems and theories which led to modern quantum physics. Dr. Hoffmann begins with the closing years of the 19th century, when certain trifling discrepancies were noticed, and with illuminating analogies and examples takes you through the brilliant concepts of Planck, Einstein, Pauli, Broglie, Bohr, Schroedinger, Heisenberg, Dirac, Sommerfeld, Feynman, etc. This edition includes a new, long postscript carrying the story through 1958. "Of the books attempting an account of the history and contents of our modern atomic physics which have come to my attention, this is the best," H. Margenau, Yale University, in "American Journal of Physics." 32 tables and line illustrations. Index. 275pp. 5⅜ x 8. T518 Paperbound **$1.50**

SPACE AND TIME, E. Borel. Written by a versatile mathematician of world renown with his customary lucidity and precision, this introduction to relativity for the layman presents scores of examples, analogies, and illustrations that open up new ways of thinking about space and time. It covers abstract geometry and geographical maps, continuity and topology, the propagation of light, the special theory of relativity, the general theory of relativity, theoretical researches, and much more. Mathematical notes. 2 Indexes. 4 Appendices. 15 figures. xvi + 243pp. 5⅜ x 8. T592 Paperbound **$1.45**

FROM EUCLID TO EDDINGTON: A STUDY OF THE CONCEPTIONS OF THE EXTERNAL WORLD, Sir Edmund Whittaker. A foremost British scientist traces the development of theories of natural philosophy from the western rediscovery of Euclid to Eddington, Einstein, Dirac, etc. The inadequacy of classical physics is contrasted with present day attempts to understand the physical world through relativity, non-Euclidean geometry, space curvature, wave mechanics, etc. 5 major divisions of examination: Space; Time and Movement; the Concepts of Classical Physics; the Concepts of Quantum Mechanics; the Eddington Universe. 212pp. 5⅜ x 8. T491 Paperbound **$1.35**

***THE EVOLUTION OF SCIENTIFIC THOUGHT FROM NEWTON TO EINSTEIN, A. d'Abro.** A detailed account of the evolution of classical physics into modern relativistic theory and the concommitant changes in scientific methodology. The breakdown of classical physics in the face of non-Euclidean geometry and the electromagnetic equations is carefully discussed and then an exhaustive analysis of Einstein's special and general theories of relativity and their implications is given. Newton, Riemann, Weyl, Lorentz, Planck, Maxwell, and many others are considered. A non-technical explanation of space, time, electromagnetic waves, etc. as understood today. "Model of semi-popular exposition," NEW REPUBLIC. 21 diagrams. 482pp. 5⅜ x 8.
T2 Paperbound **$2.00**

EINSTEIN'S THEORY OF RELATIVITY, Max Born. Nobel Laureate explains Einstein's special and general theories of relativity, beginning with a thorough review of classical physics in simple, non-technical language. Exposition of Einstein's work discusses concept of simultaneity, kinematics, relativity of arbitrary motions, the space-time continuum, geometry of curved surfaces, etc., steering middle course between vague popularizations and complex scientific presentations. 1962 edition revised by author takes into account latest findings, predictions of theory and implications for cosmology, indicates what is being sought in unified field theory. Mathematics very elementary, illustrative diagrams and experiments informative but simple. Revised 1962 edition. Revised by Max Born, assisted by Gunther Leibfried and Walter Biem. Index. 143 illustrations. vii + 376pp. 5⅜ x 8.
S769 Paperbound **$2.00**

PHILOSOPHY AND THE PHYSICISTS, L. Susan Stebbing. A philosopher examines the philosophical aspects of modern science, in terms of a lively critical attack on the ideas of Jeans and Eddington. Such basic questions are treated as the task of science, causality, determinism, probability, consciousness, the relation of the world of physics to the world of everyday experience. The author probes the concepts of man's smallness before an inscrutable universe, the tendency to idealize mathematical construction, unpredictability theorems and human freedom, the supposed opposition between 19th century determinism and modern science, and many others. Introduces many thought-stimulating ideas about the implications of modern physical concepts. xvi + 295pp. 5⅜ x 8. T480 Paperbound **$1.65**

THE RESTLESS UNIVERSE, Max Born. A remarkably lucid account by a Nobel Laureate of recent theories of wave mechanics, behavior of gases, electrons and ions, waves and particles, electronic structure of the atom, nuclear physics, and similar topics. "Much more thorough and deeper than most attempts . . . easy and delightful," CHEMICAL AND ENGINEERING NEWS. Special feature: 7 animated sequences of 60 figures each showing such phenomena as gas molecules in motion, the scattering of alpha particles, etc. 11 full-page plates of photographs. Total of nearly 600 illustrations. 351pp. 6⅛ x 9¼. T412 Paperbound **$2.00**

THE COMMON SENSE OF THE EXACT SCIENCES, W. K. Clifford. For 70 years a guide to the basic concepts of scientific and mathematical thought. Acclaimed by scientists and laymen alike, it offers a wonderful insight into concepts such as the extension of meaning of symbols, characteristics of surface boundaries, properties of plane figures, measurement of quantities, vectors, the nature of position, bending of space, motion, mass and force, and many others. Prefaces by Bertrand Russell and Karl Pearson. Critical introduction by James Newman. 130 figures. 249pp. 5⅜ x 8. T61 Paperbound **$1.60**

MATTER AND LIGHT, THE NEW PHYSICS, Louis de Broglie. Non-technical explanations by a Nobel Laureate of electro-magnetic theory, relativity, matter, light and radiation, wave mechanics, quantum physics, philosophy of science, and similar topics. This is one of the simplest yet most accurate introductions to the work of men like Planck, Einstein, Bohr, and others. Only 2 of the 21 chapters require a knowledge of mathematics. 300pp. 5⅜ x 8.
T35 Paperbound **$1.75**

SCIENCE, THEORY AND MAN, Erwin Schrödinger. This is a complete and unabridged reissue of SCIENCE AND THE HUMAN TEMPERAMENT plus an additional essay: "What Is an Elementary Particle?" Nobel Laureate Schrödinger discusses such topics as nature of scientific method, the nature of science, chance and determinism, science and society, conceptual models for physical entities, elementary particles and wave mechanics. Presentation is popular and may be followed by most people with little or no scientific training. "Fine practical preparation for a time when laws of nature, human institutions . . . are undergoing a critical examination without parallel," Waldemar Kaempffert, N. Y. TIMES. 192pp. 5⅜ x 8.
T428 Paperbound **$1.35**

CONCERNING THE NATURE OF THINGS, Sir William Bragg. The Nobel Laureate physicist in his Royal Institute Christmas Lectures explains such diverse phenomena as the formation of crystals, how uranium is transmuted to lead, the way X-rays work, why a spinning ball travels in a curved path, the reason why bubbles bounce from each other, and many other scientific topics that are seldom explained in simple terms. No scientific background needed—book is easy enough that any intelligent adult or youngster can understand it. Unabridged. 32pp. of photos; 57 figures. xii + 232pp. 5⅜ x 8. T31 Paperbound **$1.35**

***THE RISE OF THE NEW PHYSICS (formerly THE DECLINE OF MECHANISM), A. d'Abro.** This authoritative and comprehensive 2 volume exposition is unique in scientific publishing. Written for intelligent readers not familiar with higher mathematics, it is the only thorough explanation in non-technical language of modern mathematical-physical theory. Combining both history and exposition, it ranges from classical Newtonian concepts up through the electronic theories of Dirac and Heisenberg, the statistical mechanics of Fermi, and Einstein's relativity theories. "A must for anyone doing serious study in the physical sciences," J. OF FRANKLIN INST. 97 illustrations. 991pp. 2 volumes. T3 Vol. 1, Paperbound **$2.00**
T4 Vol. 2, Paperbound **$2.00**

CATALOGUE OF DOVER BOOKS

SCIENCE AND HYPOTHESIS, Henri Poincaré. Creative psychology in science. How such concepts as number, magnitude, space, force, classical mechanics were developed and how the modern scientist uses them in his thought. Hypothesis in physics, theories of modern physics. Introduction by Sir James Larmor. "Few mathematicians have had the breadth of vision of Poincaré, and none is his superior in the gift of clear exposition," E. T. Bell. Index. 272pp. 5⅜ x 8.
S221 Paperbound **$1.35**

THE VALUE OF SCIENCE, Henri Poincaré. Many of the most mature ideas of the "last scientific universalist" conveyed with charm and vigor for both the beginning student and the advanced worker. Discusses the nature of scientific truth, whether order is innate in the universe or imposed upon it by man, logical thought versus intuition (relating to mathematics through the works of Weierstrass, Lie, Klein, Riemann), time and space (relativity, psychological time, simultaneity), Hertz's concept of force, interrelationship of mathematical physics to pure math, values within disciplines of Maxwell, Carnot, Mayer, Newton, Lorentz, etc. Index. iii + 147pp. 5⅜ x 8. S469 Paperbound **$1.35**

THE SKY AND ITS MYSTERIES, E. A. Beet. One of the most lucid books on the mysteries of the universe; covers history of astronomy from earliest observations to modern theories of expanding universe, source of stellar energy, birth of planets, origin of moon craters, possibilities of life on other planets. Discusses effects of sunspots on weather; distance, age of stars; methods and tools of astronomers; much more. Expert and fascinating. "Eminently readable book," London Times. Bibliography. Over 50 diagrams, 12 full-page plates. Fold-out star map. Introduction. Index. 238pp. 5¼ x 7½. T627 Clothbound **$3.50**

OUT OF THE SKY: AN INTRODUCTION TO METEORITICS, H. H. Nininger. A non-technical yet comprehensive introduction to the young science of meteoritics: all aspects of the arrival of cosmic matter on our planet from outer space and the reaction and alteration of this matter in the terrestrial environment. Essential facts and major theories presented by one of the world's leading experts. Covers ancient reports of meteors; modern systematic investigations; fireball clusters; meteorite showers; tektites; planetoidal encounters; etc. 52 full-page plates with over 175 photographs. 22 figures. Bibliography and references. Index. viii + 336pp. 5⅜ x 8.
T519 Paperbound **$1.85**

THE REALM OF THE NEBULAE, E. Hubble. One of great astronomers of our day records his formulation of concept of "island universes." Covers velocity-distance relationship; classification, nature, distances, general types of nebulae; cosmological theories. A fine introduction to modern theories for layman. No math needed. New introduction by A. Sandage. 55 illustrations, photos. Index. iv + 201pp. 5⅜ x 8. S455 Paperbound **$1.50**

AN ELEMENTARY SURVEY OF CELESTIAL MECHANICS, Y. Ryabov. Elementary exposition of gravitational theory and celestial mechanics. Historical introduction and coverage of basic principles, including: the ecliptic, the orbital plane, the 2- and 3-body problems, the discovery of Neptune, planetary rotation, the length of the day, the shapes of galaxies, satellites (detailed treatment of Sputnik I), etc. First American reprinting of successful Russian popular exposition. Follow actual methods of astrophysicists with only high school math! Appendix. 58 figures. 165pp. 5⅜ x 8. T756 Paperbound **$1.25**

GREAT IDEAS AND THEORIES OF MODERN COSMOLOGY, Jagjit Singh. Companion volume to author's popular "Great Ideas of Modern Mathematics" (Dover, $1.55). The best non-technical survey of post-Einstein attempts to answer perhaps unanswerable questions of origin, age of Universe, possibility of life on other worlds, etc. Fundamental theories of cosmology and cosmogony recounted, explained, evaluated in light of most recent data: Einstein's concepts of relativity, space-time; Milne's a priori world-system; astrophysical theories of Jeans, Eddington; Hoyle's "continuous creation;" contributions of dozens more scientists. A faithful, comprehensive critical summary of complex material presented in an extremely well-written text intended for laymen. Original publication. Index. xii + 276pp. 5⅜ x 8½. T925 Paperbound **$1.85**

BASIC ELECTRICITY, Bureau of Naval Personnel. Very thorough, easily followed course in basic electricity for beginner, layman, or intermediate student. Begins with simplest definitions, presents coordinated, systematic coverage of basic theory and application: conductors, insulators, static electricity, magnetism, production of voltage, Ohm's law, direct current series and parallel circuits, wiring techniques, electromagnetism, alternating current, capacitance and inductance, measuring instruments, etc.; application to electrical machines such as alternating and direct current generators, motors, transformers, magnetic magnifiers, etc. Each chapter contains problems to test progress; answers at rear. No math needed beyond algebra. Appendices on signs, formulas, etc. 345 illustrations. 448pp. 7½ x 10.
S973 Paperbound **$2.95**

ELEMENTARY METALLURGY AND METALLOGRAPHY, A. M. Shrager. An introduction to common metals and alloys; stress is upon steel and iron, but other metals and alloys also covered. All aspects of production, processing, working of metals. Designed for student who wishes to enter metallurgy, for bright high school or college beginner, layman who wants background on extremely important industry. Questions, at ends of chapters, many microphotographs, glossary. Greatly revised 1961 edition. 195 illustrations, tables. ix + 389pp. 5⅜ x 8.
S138 Paperbound **$2.25**

BRIDGES AND THEIR BUILDERS, D. B. Steinman & S. R. Watson. Engineers, historians, and every person who has ever been fascinated by great spans will find this book an endless source of information and interest. Greek and Roman structures, Medieval bridges, modern classics such as the Brooklyn Bridge, and the latest developments in the science are retold by one of the world's leading authorities on bridge design and construction. BRIDGES AND THEIR BUILDERS is the only comprehensive and accurate semi-popular history of these important measures of progress in print. New, greatly revised, enlarged edition. 23 photos; 26 line-drawings. Index. xvii + 401pp. 5⅜ x 8. T431 Paperbound **$2.00**

FAMOUS BRIDGES OF THE WORLD, D. B. Steinman. An up-to-the-minute new edition of a book that explains the fascinating drama of how the world's great bridges came to be built. The author, designer of the famed Mackinac bridge, discusses bridges from all periods and all parts of the world, explaining their various types of construction, and describing the problems their builders faced. Although primarily for youngsters, this cannot fail to interest readers of all ages. 48 illustrations in the text. 23 photographs. 99pp. 6⅛ x 9¼. T161 Paperbound **$1.00**

HOW DO YOU USE A SLIDE RULE? by A. A. Merrill. A step-by-step explanation of the slide rule that presents the fundamental rules clearly enough for the non-mathematician to understand. Unlike most instruction manuals, this work concentrates on the two most important operations: multiplication and division. 10 easy lessons, each with a clear drawing, for the reader who has difficulty following other expositions. 1st publication. Index. 2 Appendices. 10 illustrations. 78 problems, all with answers. vi + 36 pp. 6⅛ x 9¼. T62 Paperbound **60¢**

HOW TO CALCULATE QUICKLY, H. Sticker. A tried and true method for increasing your "number sense" — the ability to see relationships between numbers and groups of numbers. Addition, subtraction, multiplication, division, fractions, and other topics are treated through techniques not generally taught in schools: left to right multiplication, division by inspection, etc. This is not a collection of tricks which work only on special numbers, but a detailed well-planned course, consisting of over 9,000 problems that you can work in spare moments. It is excellent for anyone who is inconvenienced by slow computational skills. 5 or 10 minutes of this book daily will double or triple your calculation speed. 9,000 problems, answers. 256pp. 5⅜ x 8. T295 Paperbound **$1.00**

MATHEMATICAL FUN, GAMES AND PUZZLES, Jack Frohlichstein. A valuable service for parents of children who have trouble with math, for teachers in need of a supplement to regular upper elementary and junior high math texts (each section is graded—easy, average, difficult—for ready adaptation to different levels of ability), and for just anyone who would like to develop basic skills in an informal and entertaining manner. The author combines ten years of experience as a junior high school math teacher with a method that uses puzzles and games to introduce the basic ideas and operations of arithmetic. Stress on everyday uses of math: banking, stock market, personal budgets, insurance, taxes. Intellectually stimulating and practical, too. 418 problems and diversions with answers. Bibliography. 120 illustrations. xix + 306pp. 5⅝ x 8½. T789 Paperbound **$1.75**

GREAT IDEAS OF MODERN MATHEMATICS: THEIR NATURE AND USE, Jagjit Singh. Reader with only high school math will understand main mathematical ideas of modern physics, astronomy, genetics, psychology, evolution, etc. better than many who use them as tools, but comprehend little of their basic structure. Author uses his wide knowledge of non-mathematical fields in brilliant exposition of differential equations, matrices, group theory, logic, statistics, problems of mathematical foundations, imaginary numbers, vectors, etc. Original publication. 2 appendixes. 2 indexes. 65 illustr. 322pp. 5⅜ x 8. S587 Paperbound **$1.75**

***MATHEMATICS IN ACTION, O. G. Sutton.** Everyone with a command of high school algebra will find this book one of the finest possible introductions to the application of mathematics to physical theory. Ballistics, numerical analysis, waves and wavelike phenomena, Fourier series, group concepts, fluid flow and aerodynamics, statistical measures, and meteorology are discussed with unusual clarity. Some calculus and differential equations theory is developed by the author for the reader's help in the more difficult sections. 88 figures. Index. viii + 236pp. 5⅜ x 8. T440 Clothbound **$3.50**

***INTRODUCTION TO SYMBOLIC LOGIC AND ITS APPLICATIONS, Rudolph Carnap.** One of the clearest, most comprehensive, and rigorous introductions to modern symbolic logic, by perhaps its greatest living master. Not merely elementary theory, but demonstrated applications in mathematics, physics, and biology. Symbolic languages of various degrees of complexity are analyzed, and one constructed. "A creation of the rank of a masterpiece," Zentralblatt für Mathematik und Ihre Grenzgebiete. Over 300 exercises. 5 figures. Bibliography. Index. xvi + 241pp. 5⅜ x 8. S453 Paperbound **$1.85**

***HIGHER MATHEMATICS FOR STUDENTS OF CHEMISTRY AND PHYSICS, J. W. Mellor.** Not abstract, but practical, drawing its problems from familiar laboratory material, this book covers theory and application of differential calculus, analytic geometry, functions with singularities, integral calculus, infinite series, solution of numerical equations, differential equations, Fourier's theorem and extensions, probability and the theory of errors, calculus of variations, determinants, etc. "If the reader is not familiar with this book, it will repay him to examine it," CHEM. & ENGINEERING NEWS. 800 problems. 189 figures. 2 appendices; 30 tables of integrals, probability functions, etc. Bibliography. xxi + 641pp. 5⅜ x 8. S193 Paperbound **$2.25**

THE FOURTH DIMENSION SIMPLY EXPLAINED, edited by Henry P. Manning. Originally written as entries in contest sponsored by "Scientific American," then published in book form, these 22 essays present easily understood explanations of how the fourth dimension may be studied, the relationship of non-Euclidean geometry to the fourth dimension, analogies to three-dimensional space, some fourth-dimensional absurdities and curiosities, possible measurements and forms in the fourth dimension. In general, a thorough coverage of many of the simpler properties of fourth-dimensional space. Multi-points of view on many of the most important aspects are valuable aid to comprehension. Introduction by Dr. Henry P. Manning gives proper emphasis to points in essays, more advanced account of fourth-dimensional geometry. 82 figures. 251pp. 5⅜ x 8.
T711 Paperbound **$1.35**

TRIGONOMETRY REFRESHER FOR TECHNICAL MEN, A. A. Klaf. A modern question and answer text on plane and spherical trigonometry. Part I covers plane trigonometry: angles, quadrants, trigonometrical functions, graphical representation, interpolation, equations, logarithms, solution of triangles, slide rules, etc. Part II discusses applications to navigation, surveying, elasticity, architecture, and engineering. Small angles, periodic functions, vectors, polar coordinates, De Moivre's theorem, fully covered. Part III is devoted to spherical trigonometry and the solution of spherical triangles, with applications to terrestrial and astronomical problems. Special time-savers for numerical calculation. 913 questions answered for you! 1738 problems; answers to odd numbers. 494 figures. 14 pages of functions, formulae. Index. x + 629pp. 5⅜ x 8.
T371 Paperbound **$2.00**

CALCULUS REFRESHER FOR TECHNICAL MEN. A. A. Klaf. Not an ordinary textbook but a unique refresher for engineers, technicians, and students. An examination of the most important aspects of differential and integral calculus by means of 756 key questions. Part I covers simple differential calculus: constants, variables, functions, increments, derivatives, logarithms, curvature, etc. Part II treats fundamental concepts of integration: inspection, substitution, transformation, reduction, areas and volumes, mean value, successive and partial integration, double and triple integration. Stresses practical aspects! A 50 page section gives applications to civil and nautical engineering, electricity, stress and strain, elasticity, industrial engineering, and similar fields. 756 questions answered. 556 problems; solutions to odd numbers. 36 pages of constants, formulae. Index. v + 431pp. 5⅜ x 8.
T370 Paperbound **$2.00**

PROBABILITIES AND LIFE, Emile Borel. One of the leading French mathematicians of the last 100 years makes use of certain results of mathematics of probabilities and explains a number of problems that for the most part, are related to everyday living or to illness and death: computation of life expectancy tables, chances of recovery from various diseases, probabilities of job accidents, weather predictions, games of chance, and so on. Emphasis on results not processes, though some indication is made of mathematical proofs. Simple in style, free of technical terminology, limited in scope to everyday situations, it is comprehensible to laymen, fine reading for beginning students of probability. New English translation. Index. Appendix. vi + 87pp. 5⅜ x 8½.
T121 Paperbound **$1.00**

POPULAR SCIENTIFIC LECTURES, Hermann von Helmholtz. 7 lucid expositions by a pre-eminent scientific mind: "The Physiological Causes of Harmony in Music," "On the Relation of Optics to Painting," "On the Conservation of Force," "On the Interaction of Natural Forces," "On Goethe's Scientific Researches" into theory of color, "On the Origin and Significance of Geometric Axioms," "On Recent Progress in the Theory of Vision." Written with simplicity of expression, stripped of technicalities, these are easy to understand and delightful reading for anyone interested in science or looking for an introduction to serious study of acoustics or optics. Introduction by Professor Morris Kline, Director, Division of Electromagnetic Research, New York University, contains astute, impartial evaluations. Selected from "Popular Lectures on Scientific Subjects," 1st and 2nd series. xii + 286pp. 5⅜ x 8½.
T799 Paperbound **$1.45**

SCIENCE AND METHOD, Henri Poincaré. Procedure of scientific discovery, methodology, experiment, idea-germination—the intellectual processes by which discoveries come into being. Most significant and most interesting aspects of development, application of ideas. Chapters cover selection of facts, chance, mathematical reasoning, mathematics, and logic; Whitehead, Russell, Cantor; the new mechanics, etc. 288pp. 5⅜ x 8.
S222 Paperbound **$1.35**

HEAT AND ITS WORKINGS, Morton Mott-Smith, Ph.D. An unusual book; to our knowledge the only middle-level survey of this important area of science. Explains clearly such important concepts as physiological sensation of heat and Weber's law, measurement of heat, evolution of thermometer, nature of heat, expansion and contraction of solids, Boyle's law, specific heat. BTU's and calories, evaporation, Andrews's isothermals, radiation, the relation of heat to light, many more topics inseparable from other aspects of physics. A wide, non-mathematical yet thorough explanation of basic ideas, theories, phenomena for laymen and beginning scientists illustrated by experiences of daily life. Bibliography. 50 illustrations. x + 165pp. 5⅜ x 8½.
T978 Paperbound **$1.00**

History of Science and Mathematics

THE STUDY OF THE HISTORY OF MATHEMATICS, THE STUDY OF THE HISTORY OF SCIENCE, G. Sarton. Two books bound as one. Each volume contains a long introduction to the methods and philosophy of each of these historical fields, covering the skills and sympathies of the historian, concepts of history of science, psychology of idea-creation, and the purpose of history of science. Prof. Sarton also provides more than 80 pages of classified bibliography. Complete and unabridged. Indexed. 10 illustrations. 188pp. 5⅜ x 8. T240 Paperbound **$1.25**

A HISTORY OF PHYSICS, Florian Cajori, Ph.D. First written in 1899, thoroughly revised in 1929, this is still best entry into antecedents of modern theories. Precise non-mathematical discussion of ideas, theories, techniques, apparatus of each period from Greeks to 1920's, analyzing within each period basic topics of matter, mechanics, light, electricity and magnetism, sound, atomic theory, etc. Stress on modern developments, from early 19th century to present. Written with critical eye on historical development, significance. Provides most of needed historical background for student of physics. Reprint of second (1929) edition. Index. Bibliography in footnotes. 16 figures. xv + 424pp. 5⅜ x 8. T970 Paperbound **$2.00**

A HISTORY OF ASTRONOMY FROM THALES TO KEPLER, J. L. E. Dreyer. Formerly titled A HISTORY OF PLANETARY SYSTEMS FROM THALES TO KEPLER. This is the only work in English which provides a detailed history of man's cosmological views from prehistoric times up through the Renaissance. It covers Egypt, Babylonia, early Greece, Alexandria, the Middle Ages, Copernicus, Tycho Brahe, Kepler, and many others. Epicycles and other complex theories of positional astronomy are explained in terms nearly everyone will find clear and easy to understand. "Standard reference on Greek astronomy and the Copernican revolution," SKY AND TELESCOPE. Bibliography. 21 diagrams. Index. xvii + 430pp. 5⅜ x 8. S79 Paperbound **$1.98**

A SHORT HISTORY OF ASTRONOMY, A. Berry. A popular standard work for over 50 years, this thorough and accurate volume covers the science from primitive times to the end of the 19th century. After the Greeks and Middle Ages, individual chapters analyze Copernicus, Brahe, Galileo, Kepler, and Newton, and the mixed reception of their startling discoveries. Post-Newtonian achievements are then discussed in unusual detail: Halley, Bradley, Lagrange, Laplace, Herschel, Bessel, etc. 2 indexes. 104 illustrations, 9 portraits. xxxi + 440pp. 5⅜ x 8. T210 Paperbound **$2.00**

PIONEERS OF SCIENCE, Sir Oliver Lodge. An authoritative, yet elementary history of science by a leading scientist and expositor. Concentrating on individuals—Copernicus, Brahe, Kepler, Galileo, Descartes, Newton, Laplace, Herschel, Lord Kelvin, and other scientists—the author presents their discoveries in historical order, adding biographical material on each man and full, specific explanations of their achievements. The full, clear discussions of the accomplishments of post-Newtonian astronomers are features seldom found in other books on the subject. Index. 120 illustrations. xv + 404pp. 5⅜ x 8. T716 Paperbound **$1.65**

THE BIRTH AND DEVELOPMENT OF THE GEOLOGICAL SCIENCES, F. D. Adams. The most complete and thorough history of the earth sciences in print. Geological thought from earliest recorded times to the end of the 19th century—covers over 300 early thinkers and systems: fossils and hypothetical explanations of them, vulcanists vs. neptunists, figured stones and paleontology, generation of stones, and similar topics. 91 illustrations, including medieval, renaissance woodcuts, etc. 632 footnotes and bibliographic notes. Index. 511pp. 5⅜ x 8. T5 Paperbound **$2.25**

THE STORY OF ALCHEMY AND EARLY CHEMISTRY, J. M. Stillman. "Add the blood of a red-haired man"—a recipe typical of the many quoted in this authoritative and readable history of the strange beliefs and practices of the alchemists. Concise studies of every leading figure in alchemy and early chemistry through Lavoisier, in this curious epic of superstition and true science, constructed from scores of rare and difficult Greek, Latin, German, and French texts. Foreword by S. W. Young. 246-item bibliography. Index. xiii + 566pp. 5⅜ x 8. S628 Paperbound **$2.45**

HISTORY OF MATHEMATICS, D. E. Smith. Most comprehensive non-technical history of math in English. Discusses the lives and works of over a thousand major and minor figures, from Euclid to Descartes, Gauss, and Riemann. Vol. I: A chronological examination, from primitive concepts through Egypt, Babylonia, Greece, the Orient, Rome, the Middle Ages, the Renaissance, and up to 1900. Vol. 2: The development of ideas in specific fields and problems, up through elementary calculus. Two volumes, total of 510 illustrations, 1355pp. 5⅜ x 8. Set boxed in attractive container. T429,430 Paperbound the set **$5.00**

Nature

AN INTRODUCTION TO BIRD LIFE FOR BIRD WATCHERS, Aretas A. Saunders. Fine, readable introduction to birdwatching. Includes a great deal of basic information on about 160 different varieties of wild birds—elementary facts not easily found elsewhere. Complete guide to identification procedures, methods of observation, important habits of birds, finding nests, food, etc. "Could make bird watchers of readers who never suspected they were vulnerable to that particular virus," CHICAGO SUNDAY TRIBUNE. Unabridged, corrected edition. Bibliography. Index. 22 line drawings by D. D'Ostilio. Formerly "The Lives of Wild Birds." 256pp. 5⅜ x 8½. T1139 Paperbound **$1.00**

LIFE HISTORIES OF NORTH AMERICAN BIRDS, Arthur Cleveland Bent. Bent's historic, all-encompassing series on North American birds, originally produced under the auspices of the Smithsonian Institution, now being republished in its entirety by Dover Publications. The twenty-volume collection forms the most comprehensive, most complete, most-used source of information in existence. Each study describes in detail the characteristics, range, distribution, habits, migratory patterns, courtship procedures, plumage, eggs, voice, enemies, etc. of the different species and subspecies of the birds that inhabit our continent, utilizing reports of hundreds of contemporary observers as well as the writings of the great naturalists of the past. Invaluable to the ornithologist, conservationist, amateur naturalist, and birdwatcher. All books in the series contain numerous photographs to provide handy guides for identification and study.

LIFE HISTORIES OF NORTH AMERICAN BIRDS OF PREY. Including hawks, eagles, falcons, buzzards, condors, owls, etc. Index. Bibliographies of 923 items. 197 full-page plates containing close to 400 photographs. Total of 907pp. 5⅜ x 8½.
Vol. I: T931 Paperbound **$2.50**
Vol. II: T932 Paperbound **$2.50**
The set Paperbound **$5.00**

LIFE HISTORIES OF NORTH AMERICAN SHORE BIRDS. Including 81 varieties of such birds as sandpipers, woodcocks, snipes, phalaropes, oyster catchers, and many others. Index for each volume. Bibliographies of 449 entries. 121 full-page plates including over 200 photographs. Total of 860 pp. 5⅜ x 8½.
Vol. I: T933 Paperbound **$2.35**
Vol. II: T934 Paperbound **$2.35**
The set Paperbound **$4.70**

LIFE HISTORIES OF NORTH AMERICAN WILD FOWL. Including 73 varieties of ducks, geese, mergansers, swans, etc. Index for each volume. Bibliographies of 268 items. 106 full-page plates containing close to 200 photographs. Total of 685pp. 5⅜ x 8½.
Vol. I: T285 Paperbound **$2.50**
Vol. II: T286 Paperbound **$2.50**
The set Paperbound **$5.00**

LIFE HISTORIES OF NORTH AMERICAN GULLS AND TERNS. 50 different varieties of gulls and terns. Index. Bibliography. 93 plates including 149 photographs. xii + 337pp. 5⅜ x 8½. T1029 Paperbound **$2.75**

LIFE HISTORIES OF NORTH AMERICAN GALLINACEOUS BIRDS. Including partridge, quail, grouse, pheasant, pigeons, doves, and others. Index. Bibliography. 93 full-page plates including 170 photographs. xiii + 490pp. 5⅜ x 8½. T1028 Paperbound **$2.75**

THE MALAY ARCHIPELAGO, Alfred Russel Wallace. The record of the explorations (8 years, 14,000 miles) of the Malay Archipelago by a great scientific observer. A contemporary of Darwin, Wallace independently arrived at the concept of evolution by natural selection, applied the new theories of evolution to later genetic discoveries, and made significant contributions to biology, zoology, and botany. This work is still one of the classics of natural history and travel. It contains the author's reports of the different native peoples of the islands, descriptions of the island groupings, his accounts of the animals, birds, and insects that flourished in this area. The reader is carried through strange lands, alien cultures, and new theories, and will share in an exciting, unrivalled travel experience. Unabridged reprint of the 1922 edition, with 62 drawings and maps. 3 appendices, one on cranial measurements. xvii + 515pp. 5⅜ x 8. T187 Paperbound **$2.00**

THE TRAVELS OF WILLIAM BARTRAM, edited by **Mark Van Doren.** This famous source-book of American anthropology, natural history, geography is the record kept by Bartram in the 1770's, on travels through the wilderness of Florida, Georgia, the Carolinas. Containing accurate and beautiful descriptions of Indians, settlers, fauna, flora, it is one of the finest pieces of Americana ever written. Introduction by Mark Van Doren. 13 original illustrations. Index. 448pp. 5⅜ x 8. T13 Paperbound **$2.00**

COMMON SPIDERS OF THE UNITED STATES, J. H. Emerton. Only non-technical, but thorough, reliable guide to spiders for the layman. Over 200 spiders from all parts of the country, arranged by scientific classification, are identified by shape and color, number of eyes, habitat and range, habits, etc. Full text, 501 line drawings and photographs, and valuable introduction explain webs, poisons, threads, capturing and preserving spiders, etc. Index. New synoptic key by S. W. Frost. xxiv + 225pp. 5⅜ x 8. T223 Paperbound **$1.45**

LIFE HISTORIES OF NORTH AMERICAN MARSH BIRDS. A wealth of data on 54 different kinds of marsh bird (flamingo, ibis, bittern, heron, egret, crane, crake, rail, coot, etc.). Index. Bibliography. 98 full-page plates containing 179 black-and-white photographs. xiv + 392pp. 5⅜ x 8½. T1082 Paperbound **$2.75**

LIFE HISTORIES OF NORTH AMERICAN DIVING BIRDS. Thirty-six different diving birds including grebe, loon, auk, murre, puffin, and the like. Index. Bibliography. 55 full-page plates (92 photographs). xiv + 239pp. 5⅜ x 8½. T1091 Paperbound **$2.75**

LIFE HISTORIES OF NORTH AMERICAN WOOD WARBLERS. Covers about 58 types. Index. Bibliography. 83 full-page plates containing 125 black-and-white photographs. xi + 734pp. of text. 5⅜ x 8½.
Vol. I: T1153 Paperbound **$2.50**
Vol. II: T1154 Paperbound **$2.50**
The set Paperbound **$5.00**

LIFE HISTORIES OF NORTH AMERICAN FLYCATCHERS, LARKS, SWALLOWS, AND THEIR ALLIES. Complete information on about 78 different varieties. Index. Bibliography. 70 full-page plates (117 photographs). xi + 555pp. of text. 5⅜ x 8½. T1090 Paperbound **$2.75**

AMERICAN WILDLIFE, AND PLANTS: A GUIDE TO WILDLIFE FOOD HABITS, A. C. Martin, H. S. Zim, A. L. Nelson. Result of 75 years of research by U. S. Fish and Wildlife Service into food and feeding habits of more than 1,000 species of birds and mammals, their distribution in America, migratory habits, and the most important plant-animal relationships. Treats over 300 common species of birds, fur and game animals, small mammals, hoofed browsers, fish, amphibians, reptiles by group, giving data on their food, ranges, habits and economies. Also focuses on the different genera of plants that furnish food for our wildlife, animals that use them, and their value. Only thorough study of its kind in existence. "Of immense value to sportsmen, naturalists, bird students, foresters, landscape architects, botanists," NATURE. "Undoubtedly an essential handbook," SCIENTIFIC MONTHLY. Unabridged republication of 1951 edition. Over 600 illustrations, maps, etc. Classified bibliography. Index. x + 500pp. 5⅜ x 8. T793 Paperbound **$2.25**

HOW TO KNOW THE WILD FLOWERS, Mrs. Wm. Starr Dana. A Guide to the names, haunts, and habits of wild flowers. Well-known classic of nature lore. Informative and delightful. Plants classified by color and season of their typical flowers for easy identification. Thorough coverage of more than 1,000 important flowering, berry-bearing and foliage plants of Eastern and Central United States and Canada. Complete botanical information about each important plant. Also history, uses, folklore, habitat, etc. Nomenclature modernized by C. J. Hylander. 174 full-page illustrations by Marion Satterlee. xii + 481pp. 5⅜ x 8½.
T332 Paperbound **$1.85**

HOW PLANTS GET THEIR NAMES, L. H. Bailey. Introduction to botanical nomenclature for the horticulturist and garden-lover. Discussions of Carl Linnaeus, "father of botany," and analysis of his definitions of genus and species, a brief history of the science before Linnaean systematization, a chapter on plant identification, a mine of information on the rules of nomenclature and Latin stems and word-endings used in botanical nomenclature, with pronunciation guides. An important section contains a full list of generic terms of horticultural literature and common Latin words and their English botanical applications and meanings. "Written with knowledge and authority, charm and eloquence and poetic imagination on the varied aspects of the author's specialty," New York Times. 11 illustrations. vi + 181pp. 5⅜ x 8½. T796 Paperbound **$1.25**

THE CACTACEAE: DESCRIPTIONS AND ILLUSTRATIONS OF PLANTS OF THE CACTUS FAMILY, N. L. Britton and J. N. Rose. Definitive study of plants of the Cactus Family. The authors devoted more than 15 years of research to this monumental task and produced an exhaustive, rigorously scientific account never likely to be superseded. 3 major classifications, or tribes, are recognized, under which they arrange and describe in full detail 124 genera and 1,235 species of cactus from all over the world. Complete data on each species: leaves, flowers, seeds, fruit, distribution, growth, spines, stem structure, economic uses, etc. In addition, 125 keys facilitate identification of genera and species. For teachers and students of botany and forestry, naturalists, conservationists, and nature lovers, this is an indispensable work. Unabridged republication of second (1937) edition. First edition originally published under the auspices of the Carnegie Institution, Washington, D.C. 4 vols. bound as 2. 1279 illustrations, photographs, sketches, etc. 137 plates. Total of xxvii + 1039pp. 8 x 10¼. T771 Clothbound, 2-volume set **$20.00**

GUIDE TO SOUTHERN TREES, Elwood S. and J. George Harrar. A handy, comprehensive 700-page manual with numerous illustrations and information on more than 350 different kinds of trees, covering the entire area south of the Mason-Dixon line from the Atlantic Ocean to the Florida Keys and western Texas. Descriptions range from the common pine, cypress, walnut, beech, and elm to such rare species as Franklinia, etc. A mine of information on leaves, flowers, twigs, bark, fruit, distribution etc. of each kind of tree. Eminently readable, written in non-technical language, it is an indispensable handbook for all lovers of the outdoors. Revised edition. Index. 81-item bibliography. Glossary. 200 full-page illustrations. ix + 709pp. 4⅝ x 6⅜. T945 Paperbound **$2.25**

WESTERN FOREST TREES, James B. Berry. For years a standard guide to the trees of the Western United States. Covers over 70 different subspecies, ranging from the Pacific shores to western South Dakota, New Mexico, etc. Much information on range and distribution, growth habits, appearance, leaves, bark, fruit, twigs, etc. for each tree discussed, plus material on wood of the trees and its uses. Basic division (Trees with needle-like leaves, scale-like leaves, and compound, lobed or divided, and simple broadleaf trees), along with almost 100 illustrations (mostly full-size) of buds, leaves, etc., aids in easy identification of just about any tree of the area. Many subsidiary keys. Revised edition. Introduction. 12 photos. 85 illustrations by Mary E. Eaton. Index. xii + 212pp. 5⅜ x 8.
T1138 Paperbound **$1.35**

MANUAL OF THE TREES OF NORTH AMERICA (EXCLUSIVE OF MEXICO), Charles Sprague Sargent. The magnum opus of the greatest American dendrologist. Based on 44 years of original research, this monumental work is still the most comprehensive and reliable sourcebook on the subject. Includes 185 genera and 717 species of trees (and many shrubs) found in the U.S., Canada, and Alaska. 783 illustrative drawings by C. E. Faxon and Mary W. Gill. An all-encompassing lifetime reference book for students, teachers of botany and forestry, naturalists, conservationists, and all nature lovers. Includes an 11-page analytical key to genera to help the beginner locate any tree by its leaf characteristics. Within the text over 100 further keys aid in easy identification. Synopsis of families. Glossary. Index. 783 illustrations, 1 map. Total of 1 + 891pp. 5⅜ x 8.
T277 Vol. I Paperbound **$2.25**
T278 Vol. II Paperbound **$2.25**
The set **$4.50**

TREES OF THE EASTERN AND CENTRAL UNITED STATES AND CANADA, W. M. Harlow, Professor of Wood Technology, College of Forestry, State University of N. Y., Syracuse, N. Y. This middle-level text is a serious work covering more than 140 native trees and important escapes, with information on general appearance, growth habit, leaf forms, flowers, fruit, bark, and other features. Commercial use, distribution, habitat, and woodlore are also given. Keys within the text enable you to locate various species with ease. With this book you can identify at sight almost any tree you are likely to encounter; you will know which trees have edible fruit, which are suitable for house planting, and much other useful and interesting information. More than 600 photographs and figures. xiii + 288pp. 4⅝ x 6½.
T395 Paperbound **$1.35**

FRUIT KEY AND TWIG KEY TO TREES AND SHRUBS (FRUIT KEY TO NORTHEASTERN TREES, TWIG TREE TO DECIDUOUS WOODY PLANTS OF EASTERN NORTH AMERICA), W. M. Harlow. The only guides with photographs of every twig and fruit described—especially valuable to the novice. The fruit key (both deciduous trees and evergreens) has an introduction explaining seeding, organs involved, fruit types and habits. The twig key introduction treats growth and morphology. In the keys proper, identification is easy and almost automatic. This exceptional work, widely used in university courses, is especially useful for identification in winter, or from the fruit or seed only. Over 350 photos, up to 3 times natural size. Bibliography, glossary, index of common and scientific names, in each key. xvii + 125pp. 5⅝ x 8⅜.
T511 Paperbound **$1.25**

HOW TO KNOW THE FERNS, F. T. Parsons. Ferns, among our most lovely native plants, are all too little known. This modern classic of nature lore will enable the layman to identify any American fern he is likely to come across. After an introduction on the structure and life of ferns, the 57 most important ferns are fully pictured and described (arranged upon a simple identification key). Index of Latin and English names. 61 illustrations and 42 full-page plates. xiv + 215pp. 5⅜ x 8.
T740 Paperbound **$1.35**

OUR SMALL NATIVE ANIMALS: THEIR HABITS AND CARE, R. Snedigar, Curator of Reptiles, Chicago Zoological Park. An unusual nature handbook containing all the vital facts of habitat, distribution, foods, and special habits in brief life histories of 114 different species of squirrels, chipmunks, rodents, larger mammals, birds, amphibians, lizards and snakes. Liberally sprinkled with first-hand anecdotes. A wealth of information on capturing and caring for these animals: proper pens and cages, correct diet, curing diseases, special equipment required, etc. Addressed to the teacher interested in classroom demonstrations, the camp director, and to anyone who ever wanted a small animal for a pet. Revised edition, New preface. Index. 62 halftones. 14 line drawings. xviii + 296pp. 5⅜ x 8⅛.
T1022 Paperbound **$1.75**

INSECT LIFE AND INSECT NATURAL HISTORY, S. W. Frost. Unusual for emphasizing habits, social life, and ecological relations of insects, rather than more academic aspects of classification and morphology. Prof. Frost's enthusiasm and knowledge are everywhere evident as he discusses insect associations, and specialized habits like leaf-mining, leaf-rolling, and case-making, the gall insects, the boring insects, aquatic insects, etc. He examines all sorts of matters not usually covered in general works, such as: insects as human food; insect music and musicians; insect response to electric and radio waves; use of insects in art and literature. The admirably executed purpose of this book, which covers the middle ground between elementary treatment and scholarly monographs, is to excite the reader to observe for himself. Over 700 illustrations. Extensive bibliography. x + 524pp. 5⅜ x 8.
T517 Paperbound **$2.25**

Puzzles, Mathematical Recreations

SYMBOLIC LOGIC and THE GAME OF LOGIC, Lewis Carroll. "Symbolic Logic" is not concerned with modern symbolic logic, but is instead a collection of over 380 problems posed with charm and imagination, using the syllogism, and a fascinating diagrammatic method of drawing conclusions. In "The Game of Logic" Carroll's whimsical imagination devises a logical game played with 2 diagrams and counters (included) to manipulate hundreds of tricky syllogisms. The final section, "Hit or Miss" is a lagniappe of 101 additional puzzles in the delightful Carroll manner. Until this reprint edition, both of these books were rarities costing up to $15 each. Symbolic Logic: Index. xxxi + 199pp. The Game of Logic: 96pp. 2 vols. bound as one. 5⅜ x 8. T492 Paperbound **$1.50**

PILLOW PROBLEMS and A TANGLED TALE, Lewis Carroll. One of the rarest of all Carroll's works, "Pillow Problems" contains 72 original math puzzles, all typically ingenious. Particularly fascinating are Carroll's answers which remain exactly as he thought them out, reflecting his actual mental process. The problems in "A Tangled Tale" are in story form, originally appearing as a monthly magazine serial. Carroll not only gives the solutions, but uses answers sent in by readers to discuss wrong approaches and misleading paths, and grades them for insight. Both of these books were rarities until this edition, "Pillow Problems" costing up to $25, and "A Tangled Tale" $15. Pillow Problems: Preface and Introduction by Lewis Carroll. xx + 109pp. A Tangled Tale: 6 illustrations. 152pp. Two vols. bound as one. 5⅜ x 8. T493 Paperbound **$1.50**

AMUSEMENTS IN MATHEMATICS, Henry Ernest Dudeney. The foremost British originator of mathematical puzzles is always intriguing, witty, and paradoxical in this classic, one of the largest collections of mathematical amusements. More than 430 puzzles, problems, and paradoxes. Mazes and games, problems on number manipulation, unicursal and other route problems, puzzles on measuring, weighing, packing, age, kinship, chessboards, joiners', crossing river, plane figure dissection, and many others. Solutions. More than 450 illustrations. vii + 258pp. 5⅜ x 8. T473 Paperbound **$1.25**

THE CANTERBURY PUZZLES, Henry Dudeney. Chaucer's pilgrims set one another problems in story form. Also Adventures of the Puzzle Club, the Strange Escape of the King's Jester, the Monks of Riddlewell, the Squire's Christmas Puzzle Party, and others. All puzzles are original, based on dissecting plane figures, arithmetic, algebra, elementary calculus and other branches of mathematics, and purely logical ingenuity. "The limit of ingenuity and intricacy," The Observer. Over 110 puzzles. Full Solutions. 150 illustrations. vii + 225pp. 5⅜ x 8. T474 Paperbound **$1.25**

MATHEMATICAL EXCURSIONS, H. A. Merrill. Even if you hardly remember your high school math, you'll enjoy the 90 stimulating problems contained in this book and you will come to understand a great many mathematical principles with surprisingly little effort. Many useful shortcuts and diversions not generally known are included: division by inspection, Russian peasant multiplication, memory systems for pi, building odd and even magic squares, square roots by geometry, dyadic systems, and many more. Solutions to difficult problems. 50 illustrations. 145pp. 5⅜ x 8. T350 Paperbound **$1.00**

MAGIC SQUARES AND CUBES, W. S. Andrews. Only book-length treatment in English, a thorough non-technical description and analysis. Here are nasik, overlapping, pandiagonal, serrated squares; magic circles, cubes, spheres, rhombuses. Try your hand at 4-dimensional magical figures! Much unusual folklore and tradition included. High school algebra is sufficient. 754 diagrams and illustrations. viii + 419pp. 5⅜ x 8. T658 Paperbound **$1.85**

CALIBAN'S PROBLEM BOOK: MATHEMATICAL, INFERENTIAL AND CRYPTOGRAPHIC PUZZLES, H. Phillips (Caliban), S. T. Shovelton, G. S. Marshall. 105 ingenious problems by the greatest living creator of puzzles based on logic and inference. Rigorous, modern, piquant; reflecting their author's unusual personality, these intermediate and advanced puzzles all involve the ability to reason clearly through complex situations; some call for mathematical knowledge, ranging from algebra to number theory. Solutions. xi + 180pp. 5⅜ x 8. T736 Paperbound **$1.25**

MATHEMATICAL PUZZLES FOR BEGINNERS AND ENTHUSIASTS, G. Mott-Smith. 188 mathematical puzzles based on algebra, dissection of plane figures, permutations, and probability, that will test and improve your powers of inference and interpretation. The Odic Force, The Spider's Cousin, Ellipse Drawing, theory and strategy of card and board games like tit-tat-toe, go moku, salvo, and many others. 100 pages of detailed mathematical explanations. Appendix of primes, square roots, etc. 135 illustrations. 2nd revised edition. 248pp. 5⅜ x 8. T198 Paperbound **$1.00**

MATHEMAGIC, MAGIC PUZZLES, AND GAMES WITH NUMBERS, R. V. Heath. More than 60 new puzzles and stunts based on the properties of numbers. Easy techniques for multiplying large numbers mentally, revealing hidden numbers magically, finding the date of any day in any year, and dozens more. Over 30 pages devoted to magic squares, triangles, cubes, circles, etc. Edited by J. S. Meyer. 76 illustrations. 128pp. 5⅜ x 8. T110 Paperbound **$1.00**

MATHEMATICAL RECREATIONS, M. Kraitchik. One of the most thorough compilations of unusual mathematical problems for beginners and advanced mathematicians. Historical problems from Greek, Medieval, Arabic, Hindu sources. 50 pages devoted to pastimes derived from figurate numbers, Mersenne numbers, Fermat numbers, primes and probability. 40 pages of magic, Euler, Latin, panmagic squares. 25 new positional and permutational games of permanent value: fairy chess, latruncles, reversi, jinx, ruma, lasca, tricolor, tetrachrome, etc. Complete rigorous solutions. Revised second edition. 181 illustrations. 333pp. 5⅜ x 8.
T163 Paperbound **$1.75**

MATHEMATICAL PUZZLES OF SAM LOYD, selected and edited by M. Gardner. Choice puzzles by the greatest American puzzle creator and innovator. Selected from his famous collection, "Cyclopedia of Puzzles," they retain the unique style and historical flavor of the originals. There are posers based on arithmetic, algebra, probability, game theory, route tracing, topology, counter, sliding block, operations research, geometrical dissection. Includes the famous "14-15" puzzle which was a national craze, and his "Horse of a Different Color" which sold millions of copies. 117 of his most ingenious puzzles in all, 120 line drawings and diagrams. Solutions. Selected references. xx + 167pp. 5⅜ x 8. T498 Paperbound **$1.00**

MATHEMATICAL PUZZLES OF SAM LOYD, Vol. II, selected and edited by Martin Gardner. The outstanding 2nd selection from the great American innovator's "Cyclopedia of Puzzles": speed and distance problems, clock problems, plane and solid geometry, calculus problems, etc. Analytical table of contents that groups the puzzles according to the type of mathematics necessary to solve them. 166 puzzles, 150 original line drawings and diagrams. Selected references. xiv + 177pp. 5⅜ x 8. T709 Paperbound **$1.00**

ARITHMETICAL EXCURSIONS: AN ENRICHMENT OF ELEMENTARY MATHEMATICS, H. Bowers and J. Bowers. A lively and lighthearted collection of facts and entertainments for anyone who enjoys manipulating numbers or solving arithmetical puzzles: methods of arithmetic never taught in school, little-known facts about the most simple numbers, and clear explanations of more sophisticated topics; mysteries and folklore of numbers, the "Hin-dog-abic" number system, etc. First publication. Index. 529 numbered problems and diversions, all with answers. Bibliography. 60 figures. xiv + 320pp. 5⅜ x 8. T770 Paperbound **$1.65**

CRYPTANALYSIS, H. F. Gaines. Formerly entitled ELEMENTARY CRYPTANALYSIS, this introductory-intermediate level text is the best book in print on cryptograms and their solution. It covers all major techniques of the past, and contains much that is not generally known except to experts. Full details about concealment, substitution, and transposition ciphers; periodic mixed alphabets, multafid, Kasiski and Vigenere methods, Ohaver patterns, Playfair, and scores of other topics. 6 language letter and word frequency appendix. 167 problems, now furnished with solutions. Index. 173 figures. vi + 230pp. 5⅜ x 8.
T97 Paperbound **$2.00**

CRYPTOGRAPHY, L. D. Smith. An excellent introductory work on ciphers and their solution, the history of secret writing, and actual methods and problems in such techniques as transposition and substitution. Appendices describe the enciphering of Japanese, the Baconian biliteral cipher, and contain frequency tables and a bibliography for further study. Over 150 problems with solutions. 160pp. 5⅜ x 8. T247 Paperbound **$1.00**

PUZZLE QUIZ AND STUNT FUN, J. Meyer. The solution to party doldrums. 238 challenging puzzles, stunts and tricks. Mathematical puzzles like The Clever Carpenter, Atom Bomb; mysteries and deductions like The Bridge of Sighs, The Nine Pearls, Dog Logic; observation puzzles like Cigarette Smokers, Telephone Dial; over 200 others including magic squares, tongue twisters, puns, anagrams, and many others. All problems solved fully. 250pp. 5⅜ x 8.
T337 Paperbound **$1.00**

101 PUZZLES IN THOUGHT AND LOGIC, C. R. Wylie, Jr. Brand new problems you need no special knowledge to solve! Take the kinks out of your mental "muscles" and enjoy solving murder problems, the detection of lying fishermen, the logical identification of color by a blindman, and dozens more. Introduction with simplified explanation of general scientific method and puzzle solving. 128pp. 5⅜ x 8. T367 Paperbound **$1.00**

MY BEST PROBLEMS IN MATHEMATICS, Hubert Phillips ("Caliban"). Only elementary mathematics needed to solve these 100 witty, catchy problems by a master problem creator. Problems on the odds in cards and dice, problems in geometry, algebra, permutations, even problems that require no math at all—just a logical mind, clear thinking. Solutions completely worked out. If you enjoy mysteries, alerting your perceptive powers and exercising your detective's eye, you'll find these cryptic puzzles a challenging delight. Original 1961 publication. 100 puzzles, solutions. x + 107pp. 5⅝ x 8. T91 Paperbound **$1.00**

MY BEST PUZZLES IN LOGIC AND REASONING, Hubert Phillips ("Caliban"). A new collection of 100 inferential and logical puzzles chosen from the best that have appeared in England, available for first time in U.S. By the most endlessly resourceful puzzle creator now living. All data presented are both necessary and sufficient to allow a single unambiguous answer. No special knowledge is required for problems ranging from relatively simple to completely original one-of-a-kinds. Guaranteed to please beginners and experts of all ages. Original publication. 100 puzzles, full solutions. x + 107pp. 5⅜ x 8. T119 Paperbound **$1.00**

THE BOOK OF MODERN PUZZLES, G. L. Kaufman. A completely new series of puzzles as fascinating as crossword and deduction puzzles but based upon different principles and techniques. Simple 2-minute teasers, word labyrinths, design and pattern puzzles, logic and observation puzzles — over 150 braincrackers. Answers to all problems. 116 illustrations. 192pp. 5⅜ x 8.
T143 Paperbound **$1.00**

NEW WORD PUZZLES, G. L. Kaufman. 100 ENTIRELY NEW puzzles based on words and their combinations that will delight crossword puzzle, Scrabble and Jotto fans. Chess words, based on the moves of the chess king; design-onyms, symmetrical designs made of synonyms; rhymed double-crostics; syllable sentences; addle letter anagrams; alphagrams; linkograms; and many others all brand new. Full solutions. Space to work problems. 196 figures. vi + 122pp. 5⅜ x 8.
T344 Paperbound **$1.00**

MAZES AND LABYRINTHS: A BOOK OF PUZZLES, W. Shepherd. Mazes, formerly associated with mystery and ritual, are still among the most intriguing of intellectual puzzles. This is a novel and different collection of 50 amusements that embody the principle of the maze: mazes in the classical tradition; 3-dimensional, ribbon, and Möbius-strip mazes; hidden messages; spatial arrangements; etc.—almost all built on amusing story situations. 84 illustrations. Essay on maze psychology. Solutions. xv + 122pp. 5⅜ x 8.
T731 Paperbound **$1.00**

MAGIC TRICKS & CARD TRICKS, W. Jonson. Two books bound as one. 52 tricks with cards, 37 tricks with coins, bills, eggs, smoke, ribbons, slates, etc. Details on presentation, misdirection, and routining will help you master such famous tricks as the Changing Card, Card in the Pocket, Four Aces, Coin Through the Hand, Bill in the Egg, Afghan Bands, and over 75 others. If you follow the lucid exposition and key diagrams carefully, you will finish these two books with an astonishing mastery of magic. 106 figures. 224pp. 5⅜ x 8.
T909 Paperbound **$1.00**

PANORAMA OF MAGIC, Milbourne Christopher. A profusely illustrated history of stage magic, a unique selection of prints and engravings from the author's private collection of magic memorabilia, the largest of its kind. Apparatus, stage settings and costumes; ingenious ads distributed by the performers and satiric broadsides passed around in the streets ridiculing pompous showmen; programs; decorative souvenirs. The lively text, by one of America's foremost professional magicians, is full of anecdotes about almost legendary wizards: Dede, the Egyptian; Philadelphia, the wonder-worker; Robert-Houdin, "the father of modern magic;" Harry Houdini; scores more. Altogether a pleasure package for anyone interested in magic, stage setting and design, ethnology, psychology, or simply in unusual people. A Dover original. 295 illustrations; 8 in full color. Index. viii + 216pp. 8⅜ x 11¼.
T774 Paperbound **$2.25**

HOUDINI ON MAGIC, Harry Houdini. One of the greatest magicians of modern times explains his most prized secrets. How locks are picked, with illustrated picks and skeleton keys; how a girl is sawed into twins; how to walk through a brick wall — Houdini's explanations of 44 stage tricks with many diagrams. Also included is a fascinating discussion of great magicians of the past and the story of his fight against fraudulent mediums and spiritualists. Edited by W.B. Gibson and M.N. Young. Bibliography. 155 figures, photos. xv + 280pp. 5⅜ x 8.
T384 Paperbound **$1.25**

MATHEMATICS, MAGIC AND MYSTERY, Martin Gardner. Why do card tricks work? How do magicians perform astonishing mathematical feats? How is stage mind-reading possible? This is the first book length study explaining the application of probability, set theory, theory of numbers, topology, etc., to achieve many startling tricks. Non-technical, accurate, detailed! 115 sections discuss tricks with cards, dice, coins, knots, geometrical vanishing illusions, how a Curry square "demonstrates" that the sum of the parts may be greater than the whole, and dozens of others. No sleight of hand necessary! 135 illustrations. xii + 174pp. 5⅜ x 8.
T335 Paperbound **$1.00**

EASY-TO-DO ENTERTAINMENTS AND DIVERSIONS WITH COINS, CARDS, STRING, PAPER AND MATCHES, R. M. Abraham. Over 300 tricks, games and puzzles will provide young readers with absorbing fun. Sections on card games; paper-folding; tricks with coins, matches and pieces of string; games for the agile; toy-making from common household objects; mathematical recreations; and 50 miscellaneous pastimes. Anyone in charge of groups of youngsters, including hard-pressed parents, and in need of suggestions on how to keep children sensibly amused and quietly content will find this book indispensable. Clear, simple text, copious number of delightful line drawings and illustrative diagrams. Originally titled "Winter Nights Entertainments." Introduction by Lord Baden Powell. 329 illustrations. v + 186pp. 5⅜ x 8½.
T921 Paperbound **$1.00**

STRING FIGURES AND HOW TO MAKE THEM, Caroline Furness Jayne. 107 string figures plus variations selected from the best primitive and modern examples developed by Navajo, Apache, pygmies of Africa, Eskimo, in Europe, Australia, China, etc. The most readily understandable, easy-to-follow book in English on perennially popular recreation. Crystal-clear exposition; step-by-step diagrams. Everyone from kindergarten children to adults looking for unusual diversion will be endlessly amused. Index. Bibliography. Introduction by A. C. Haddon. 17 full-page plates. 960 illustrations. xxiii + 401pp. 5⅜ x 8½.
T152 Paperbound **$2.00**

Entertainments, Humor

ODDITIES AND CURIOSITIES OF WORDS AND LITERATURE, C. Bombaugh, edited by M. Gardner. The largest collection of idiosyncratic prose and poetry techniques in English, a legendary work in the curious and amusing bypaths of literary recreations and the play technique in literature—so important in modern works. Contains alphabetic poetry, acrostics, palindromes, scissors verse, centos, emblematic poetry, famous literary puns, hoaxes, notorious slips of the press, hilarious mistranslations, and much more. Revised and enlarged with modern material by Martin Gardner. 368pp. 5⅜ x 8. T759 Paperbound **$1.50**

A NONSENSE ANTHOLOGY, collected by **Carolyn Wells.** 245 of the best nonsense verses ever written, including nonsense puns, absurd arguments, mock epics and sagas, nonsense ballads, odes, "sick" verses, dog-Latin verses, French nonsense verses, songs. By Edward Lear, Lewis Carroll, Gelett Burgess, W. S. Gilbert, Hilaire Belloc, Peter Newell, Oliver Herford, etc., 83 writers in all plus over four score anonymous nonsense verses. A special section of limericks, plus famous nonsense such as Carroll's "Jabberwocky" and Lear's "The Jumblies" and much excellent verse virtually impossible to locate elsewhere. For 50 years considered the best anthology available. Index of first lines specially prepared for this edition. Introduction by Carolyn Wells. 3 indexes: Title, Author, First lines. xxxiii + 279pp. T499 Paperbound **$1.35**

THE BAD CHILD'S BOOK OF BEASTS, MORE BEASTS FOR WORSE CHILDREN, and A MORAL ALPHABET, H. Belloc. Hardly an anthology of humorous verse has appeared in the last 50 years without at least a couple of these famous nonsense verses. But one must see the entire volumes—with all the delightful original illustrations by Sir Basil Blackwood—to appreciate fully Belloc's charming and witty verses that play so subacidly on the platitudes of life and morals that beset his day—and ours. A great humor classic. Three books in one. Total of 157pp. 5⅜ x 8. T749 Paperbound **$1.00**

THE DEVIL'S DICTIONARY, Ambrose Bierce. Sardonic and irreverent barbs puncturing the pomposities and absurdities of American politics, business, religion, literature, and arts, by the country's greatest satirist in the classic tradition. Epigrammatic as Shaw, piercing as Swift, American as Mark Twain, Will Rogers, and Fred Allen, Bierce will always remain the favorite of a small coterie of enthusiasts, and of writers and speakers whom he supplies with "some of the most gorgeous witticisms of the English language" (H. L. Mencken). Over 1000 entries in alphabetical order. 144pp. 5⅜ x 8. T487 Paperbound **$1.00**

THE PURPLE COW AND OTHER NONSENSE, Gelett Burgess. The best of Burgess's early nonsense, selected from the first edition of the "Burgess Nonsense Book." Contains many of his most unusual and truly awe-inspiring pieces: 36 nonsense quatrains, the Poems of Patagonia, Alphabet of Famous Goops, and the other hilarious (and rare) adult nonsense that place him in the forefront of American humorists. All pieces are accompanied by the original Burgess illustrations. 123 illustrations. xiii + 113pp. 5⅜ x 8. T772 Paperbound **$1.00**

MY PIOUS FRIENDS AND DRUNKEN COMPANIONS and MORE PIOUS FRIENDS AND DRUNKEN COMPANIONS, Frank Shay. Folksingers, amateur and professional, and everyone who loves singing: here, available for the first time in 30 years, is this valued collection of 132 ballads, blues, vaudeville numbers, drinking songs, sea chanties, comedy songs. Songs of pre-Beatnik Bohemia; songs from all over America, England, France, Australia; the great songs of the Naughty Nineties and early twentieth-century America. Over a third with music. Woodcuts by John Held, Jr. convey perfectly the brash insouciance of an era of rollicking unabashed song. 12 illustrations by John Held, Jr. Two indexes (Titles and First lines and Choruses). Introductions by the author. Two volumes bound as one. Total of xvi + 235pp. 5⅜ x 8½. T946 Paperbound **$1.25**

HOW TO TELL THE BIRDS FROM THE FLOWERS, R. W. Wood. How not to confuse a carrot with a parrot, a grape with an ape, a puffin with nuffin. Delightful drawings, clever puns, absurd little poems point out far-fetched resemblances in nature. The author was a leading physicist. Introduction by Margaret Wood White. 106 illus. 60pp. 5⅜ x 8. T523 Paperbound **75¢**

PECK'S BAD BOY AND HIS PA, George W. Peck. The complete edition, containing both volumes, of one of the most widely read American humor books. The endless ingenious pranks played by bad boy "Hennery" on his pa and the grocery man, the outraged pomposity of Pa, the perpetual ridiculing of middle class institutions, are as entertaining today as they were in 1883. No pale sophistications or subtleties, but rather humor vigorous, raw, earthy, imaginative, and, as folk humor often is, sadistic. This peculiarly fascinating book is also valuable to historians and students of American culture as a portrait of an age. 100 original illustrations by True Williams. Introduction by E. F. Bleiler. 347pp. 5⅜ x 8. T497 Paperbound **$1.35**

CATALOGUE OF DOVER BOOKS

THE HUMOROUS VERSE OF LEWIS CARROLL. Almost every poem Carroll ever wrote, the largest collection ever published, including much never published elsewhere: 150 parodies, burlesques, riddles, ballads, acrostics, etc., with 130 original illustrations by Tenniel, Carroll, and others. "Addicts will be grateful . . . there is nothing for the faithful to do but sit down and fall to the banquet," N. Y. Times. Index to first lines. xiv + 446pp. 5⅜ x 8.
T654 Paperbound **$1.85**

DIVERSIONS AND DIGRESSIONS OF LEWIS CARROLL. A major new treasure for Carroll fans! Rare privately published humor, fantasy, puzzles, and games by Carroll at his whimsical best, with a new vein of frank satire. Includes many new mathematical amusements and recreations, among them the fragmentary Part III of "Curiosa Mathematica." Contains "The Rectory Umbrella," "The New Belfry," "The Vision of the Three T's," and much more. New 32-page supplement of rare photographs taken by Carroll. x + 375pp. 5⅜ x 8.
T732 Paperbound **$1.65**

THE COMPLETE NONSENSE OF EDWARD LEAR. This is the only complete edition of this master of gentle madness available at a popular price. A BOOK OF NONSENSE, NONSENSE SONGS, MORE NONSENSE SONGS AND STORIES in their entirety with all the old favorites that have delighted children and adults for years. The Dong With A Luminous Nose, The Jumblies, The Owl and the Pussycat, and hundreds of other bits of wonderful nonsense. 214 limericks, 3 sets of Nonsense Botany, 5 Nonsense Alphabets, 546 drawings by Lear himself, and much more. 320pp. 5⅜ x 8. T167 Paperbound **$1.00**

THE MELANCHOLY LUTE, The Humorous Verse of Franklin P. Adams ("FPA"). The author's own selection of light verse, drawn from thirty years of FPA's column, "The Conning Tower," syndicated all over the English-speaking world. Witty, perceptive, literate, these ninety-six poems range from parodies of other poets, Millay, Longfellow, Edgar Guest, Kipling, Masefield, etc., and free and hilarious translations of Horace and other Latin poets, to satiric comments on fabled American institutions—the New York Subways, preposterous ads, suburbanites, sensational journalism, etc. They reveal with vigor and clarity the humor, integrity and restraint of a wise and gentle American satirist. Introduction by Robert Hutchinson. vi + 122pp. 5⅜ x 8½. T108 Paperbound **$1.00**

SINGULAR TRAVELS, CAMPAIGNS, AND ADVENTURES OF BARON MUNCHAUSEN, R. E. Raspe, with 90 illustrations by Gustave Doré. The first edition in over 150 years to reestablish the deeds of the Prince of Liars exactly as Raspe first recorded them in 1785—the genuine Baron Munchausen, one of the most popular personalities in English literature. Included also are the best of the many sequels, written by other hands. Introduction on Raspe by J. Carswell. Bibliography of early editions. xliv + 192pp. 5⅜ x 8. T698 Paperbound **$1.00**

THE WIT AND HUMOR OF OSCAR WILDE, ed. by Alvin Redman. Wilde at his most brilliant, in 1000 epigrams exposing weaknesses and hypocrisies of "civilized" society. Divided into 49 categories—sin, wealth, women, America, etc.—to aid writers, speakers. Includes excerpts from his trials, books, plays, criticism. Formerly "The Epigrams of Oscar Wilde." Introduction by Vyvyan Holland, Wilde's only living son. Introductory essay by editor. 260pp. 5⅜ x 8. T602 Paperbound **$1.00**

MAX AND MORITZ, Wilhelm Busch. Busch is one of the great humorists of all time, as well as the father of the modern comic strip. This volume, translated by H. A. Klein and other hands, contains the perennial favorite "Max and Moritz" (translated by C. T. Brooks), Plisch and Plum, Das Rabennest, Eispeter, and seven other whimsical, sardonic, jovial, diabolical cartoon and verse stories. Lively English translations parallel the original German. This work has delighted millions, since it first appeared in the 19th century, and is guaranteed to please almost anyone. Edited by H. A. Klein, with an afterword. x + 205pp. 5⅝ x 8½.
T181 Paperbound **$1.00**

HYPOCRITICAL HELENA, Wilhelm Busch. A companion volume to "Max and Moritz," with the title piece (Die Fromme Helena) and 10 other highly amusing cartoon and verse stories, all newly translated by H. A. Klein and M. C. Klein: Adventure on New Year's Eve (Abenteuer in der Neujahrsnacht), Hangover on the Morning after New Year's Eve (Der Katzenjammer am Neujahrsmorgen), etc. English and German in parallel columns. Hours of pleasure, also a fine language aid. x + 205pp. 5⅝ x 8½. T184 Paperbound **$1.00**

THE BEAR THAT WASN'T, Frank Tashlin. What does it mean? Is it simply delightful wry humor, or a charming story of a bear who wakes up in the midst of a factory, or a satire on Big Business, or an existential cartoon-story of the human condition, or a symbolization of the struggle between conformity and the individual? New York Herald Tribune said of the first edition: ". . . a fable for grownups that will be fun for children. Sit down with the book and get your own bearings." Long an underground favorite with readers of all ages and opinions. v + 51pp. Illustrated. 5⅜ x 8½. T939 Paperbound **75¢**

RUTHLESS RHYMES FOR HEARTLESS HOMES and MORE RUTHLESS RHYMES FOR HEARTLESS HOMES, Harry Graham ("Col. D. Streamer"). Two volumes of Little Willy and 48 other poetic disasters. A bright, new reprint of oft-quoted, never forgotten, devastating humor by a precursor of today's "sick" joke school. For connoisseurs of wicked, wacky humor and all who delight in the comedy of manners. Original drawings are a perfect complement. 61 illustrations. Index. vi + 69pp. Two vols. bound as one. 5⅜ x 8½.
T930 Paperbound **75¢**

Chess, Checkers, Games, Go

THE ADVENTURE OF CHESS, Edward Lasker. A lively history of chess, from its ancient beginnings in the Indian 4-handed game of Chaturanga, through to the great players of our day, as told by one of America's finest masters. He introduces such unusual sidelights and amusing oddities as Maelzel's chess-playing automaton that beat Napoleon 3 times. Major discussion of chess-playing machines and personal memories of Nimzovich, Capablanca, etc. 5-page chess primer. 11 illustrations, 53 diagrams. 296pp. 5⅜ x 8. S510 Paperbound **$1.45**

A TREASURY OF CHESS LORE, edited by Fred Reinfeld. A delightful collection of anecdotes, short stories, aphorisms by and about the masters, poems, accounts of games and tournaments, photography. Hundreds of humorous, pithy, satirical, wise, and historical episodes, comments, and word portraits. A fascinating "must" for chess players; revealing and perhaps seductive to those who wonder what their friends see in the game. 48 photographs (14 full page plates) 12 diagrams. xi + 306pp. 5⅜ x 8. T458 Paperbound **$1.75**

HOW DO YOU PLAY CHESS? by Fred Reinfeld. A prominent expert covers every basic rule of chess for the beginner in 86 questions and answers: moves, powers of pieces, rationale behind moves, how to play forcefully, history of chess, and much more. Bibliography of chess publications. 11 board diagrams. 48 pages. **FREE**

THE PLEASURES OF CHESS, Assiac. Internationally known British writer, influential chess columnist, writes wittily about wide variety of chess subjects: Anderssen's "Immortal Game;" only game in which both opponents resigned at once; psychological tactics of Reshevsky, Lasker; varieties played by masters for relaxation, such as "losing chess;" sacrificial orgies; etc. These anecdotes, witty observations will give you fresh appreciation of game. 43 problems. 150 diagrams. 139pp. 5⅜ x 8. T597 Paperbound **$1.25**

WIN AT CHESS, F. Reinfeld. 300 practical chess situations from actual tournament play to sharpen your chess eye and test your skill. Traps, sacrifices, mates, winning combinations, subtle exchanges, show you how to WIN AT CHESS. Short notes and tables of solutions and alternative moves help you evaluate your progress. Learn to think ahead playing the "crucial moments" of historic games. 300 diagrams. Notes and solutions. Formerly titled CHESS QUIZ. vi + 120pp. 5⅜ x 8. T438 Paperbound **$1.00**

THE ART OF CHESS, James Mason. An unabridged reprinting of the latest revised edition of the most famous general study of chess ever written. Also included, a complete supplement by Fred Reinfeld, "How Do You Play Chess?", invaluable to beginners for its lively question and answer method. Mason, an early 20th century master, teaches the beginning and intermediate player more than 90 openings, middle game, end game, how to see more moves ahead, to plan purposefully, attack, sacrifice, defend, exchange, and govern general strategy. Supplement. 448 diagrams. 1947 Reinfeld-Bernstein text. Bibliography. xvi + 340pp. 5⅜ x 8. T463 Paperbound **$1.85**

THE PRINCIPLES OF CHESS, James Mason. This "great chess classic" (N. Y. Times) is a general study covering all aspects of the game: basic forces, resistance, obstruction, opposition, relative values, mating, typical end game situations, combinations, much more. The last section discusses openings, with 50 games illustrating modern master play of Rubinstein, Spielmann, Lasker, Capablanca, etc., selected and annotated by Fred Reinfeld. Will improve the game of any intermediate-skilled player, but is so forceful and lucid that an absolute beginner might use it to become an accomplished player. 1946 Reinfeld edition. 166 diagrams. 378pp. 5⅜ x 8. T646 Paperbound **$1.85**

LASKER'S MANUAL OF CHESS, Dr. Emanuel Lasker. Probably the greatest chess player of modern times, Dr. Emanuel Lasker held the world championship 28 years, independent of passing schools or fashions. This unmatched study of the game, chiefly for intermediate to skilled players, analyzes basic methods, combinations, position play, the aesthetics of chess, dozens of different openings, etc., with constant reference to great modern games. Contains a brilliant exposition of Steinitz's important theories. Introduction by Fred Reinfeld. Tables of Lasker's tournament record. 3 indices. 308 diagrams. 1 photograph. xxx + 349pp. 5⅜ x 8. T640 Paperbound **$2.00**

THE ART OF CHESS COMBINATION, E. Znosko-Borovsky. Proves that combinations, perhaps the most aesthetically satisfying, successful technique in chess, can be an integral part of your game, instead of a haphazard occurrence. Games of Capablanca, Rubinstein, Nimzovich, Bird, etc. grouped according to common features, perceptively analyzed to show that every combination begins in certain simple ideas. Will help you to plan many moves ahead. Technical terms almost completely avoided. "In the teaching of chess he may claim to have no superior," P. W. Sergeant. Introduction. Exercises. Solutions. Index. 223pp. 5⅜ x 8. T583 Paperbound **$1.45**

CATALOGUE OF DOVER BOOKS

MODERN IDEAS IN CHESS, Richard Reti. An enduring classic, because of its unrivalled explanation of the way master chess had developed in the past hundred years. Reti, who was an outstanding theoretician and player, explains each advance in chess by concentrating on the games of the single master most closely associated with it: Morphy, Anderssen, Steinitz, Lasker, Alekhine, other world champions. Play the games in this volume, study Reti's perceptive observations, and have a living picture of the road chess has travelled. Introduction. 34 diagrams. 192pp. 5⅜ x 8. T638 Paperbound **$1.25**

THE BOOK OF THE NEW YORK INTERNATIONAL CHESS TOURNAMENT, 1924, annotated by A. Alekhine and edited by H. Helms. Long a rare collector's item, this is the book of one of the most brilliant tournaments of all time, during which Capablanca, Lasker, Alekhine, Reti, and others immeasurably enriched chess theory in a thrilling contest. All 110 games played, with Alekhine's unusually penetrating notes. 15 photographs. xi + 271pp. 5⅜ x 8. T752 Paperbound **$1.85**

KERES' BEST GAMES OF CHESS, selected, annotated by F. Reinfeld. 90 best games, 1931-1948, by one of boldest, most exciting players of modern chess. Games against Alekhine, Bogolyubov, Capablanca, Euwe, Fine, Reshevsky, other masters, show his treatments of openings such as Giuoco Piano, Alekhine Defense, Queen's Gambit Declined; attacks, sacrifices, alternative methods. Preface by Keres gives personal glimpses, evaluations of rivals. 110 diagrams. 272pp. 5⅜ x 8. T593 Paperbound **$1.35**

HYPERMODERN CHESS as developed in the games of its greatest exponent, ARON NIMZOVICH, edited by Fred Reinfeld. An intensely original player and analyst, Nimzovich's extraordinary approaches startled and often angered the chess world. This volume, designed for the average player, shows in his victories over Alekhine, Lasker, Marshall, Rubinstein, Spielmann, and others, how his iconoclastic methods infused new life into the game. Use Nimzovich to invigorate your play and startle opponents. Introduction. Indices of players and openings. 180 diagrams. viii + 220pp. 5⅜ x 8. T448 Paperbound **$1.35**

THE DEVELOPMENT OF A CHESS GENIUS: 100 INSTRUCTIVE GAMES OF ALEKHINE, F. Reinfeld. 100 games of the chess giant's formative years, 1905-1914, from age 13 to maturity, each annotated and commented upon by Fred Reinfeld. Included are matches against Bogolyubov, Capablanca, Tarrasch, and many others. You see the growth of an inexperienced genius into one of the greatest players of all time. Many of these games have never appeared before in book form. "One of America's most significant contributions to the chess world," Chess Life. New introduction. Index of players, openings. 204 illustrations. xv +227pp. 5¾ x 8. T551 Paperbound **$1.35**

RESHEVSKY'S BEST GAMES OF CHESS, Samuel Reshevsky. One time 4-year-old chess genius, 5-time winner U. S. Chess Championship, selects, annotates 110 of his best games, illustrating theories, favorite methods of play against Capablanca, Alekhine, Bogolyubov, Kashdan, Vidmar, Botvinnik, others. Clear, non-technical style. Personal impressions of opponents, autobiographical material, tournament match record. Formerly "Reshevsky on Chess." 309 diagrams, 2 photos. 288pp. 5⅜ x 8. T606 Paperbound **$1.25**

ONE HUNDRED SELECTED GAMES, Mikhail Botvinnik. Author's own choice of his best games before becoming World Champion in 1948, beginning with first big tournament, the USSR Championship, 1927. Shows his great power of analysis as he annotates these games, giving strategy, technique against Alekhine, Capablanca, Euwe, Keres, Reshevsky, Smyslov, Vidmar, many others. Discusses his career, methods of play, system of training. 6 studies of endgame positions. 221 diagrams. 272pp. 5⅜ x 8. T620 Paperbound **$1.50**

RUBINSTEIN'S CHESS MASTERPIECES, selected, annotated by Hans Kmoch. Thoroughgoing mastery of opening, middle game; faultless technique in endgame, particularly rook and pawn endings; ability to switch from careful positional play to daring combinations; all distinguish the play of Rubinstein. 100 best games, against Janowski, Nimzowitch, Tarrasch, Vidmar, Capablanca, other greats, carefully annotated, will improve your game rapidly. Biographical introduction, B. F. Winkelman. 103 diagrams. 192pp. 5⅜ x 8. T617 Paperbound **$1.25**

TARRASCH'S BEST GAMES OF CHESS, selected & annotated by Fred Reinfeld. First definitive collection of games by Siegbert Tarrasch, winner of 7 international tournaments, and the leading theorist of classical chess. 183 games cover fifty years of play against Mason, Mieses, Paulsen, Teichmann, Pillsbury, Janwoski, others. Reinfeld includes Tarrasch's own analyses of many of these games. A careful study and replaying of the games will give you a sound understanding of classical methods, and many hours of enjoyment. Introduction. Indexes. 183 diagrams. xxiv + 386pp. 5⅜ x 8. T644 Paperbound **$2.00**

MARSHALL'S BEST GAMES OF CHESS, F. J. Marshall. Grandmaster, U. S. Champion for 27 years, tells story of career; presents magnificent collection of 140 of best games, annotated by himself. Games against Alekhine, Capablanca, Emanuel Lasker, Janowski, Rubinstein, Pillsbury, etc. Special section analyzes openings such as King's Gambit, Ruy Lopez, Alekhine's Defense, Giuoco Piano, others. A study of Marshall's brilliant offensives, slashing attacks, extraordinary sacrifices, will rapidly improve your game. Formerly "My Fifty Years of Chess." Introduction. 19 diagrams. 13 photos. 250pp. 5⅜ x 8. T604 Paperbound **$1.45**

THE HASTINGS CHESS TOURNAMENT, 1895, edited by Horace F. Cheshire. This is the complete tournament book of the famous Hastings 1895 tournament. One of the most exciting tournaments ever to take place, it evoked the finest play from such players as Dr. Lasker, Steinitz, Tarrasch, Harry Pillsbury, Mason, Tchigorin, Schlecter, and others. It was not only extremely exciting as an event, it also created first-rate chess. This book contains fully annotated all 230 games, full information about the playing events, biographies of the players, and much other material that makes it a chess classic. 22 photos, 174 diagrams. x + 370pp. 5⅝ x 8½. T288 Paperbound **$2.00**

THE BOOK OF THE NOTTINGHAM INTERNATIONAL CHESS TOURNAMENT, 1936, Annotated by Dr. Alexander Alekhine. The Nottingham 1936 tournament is regarded by many chess enthusiasts as the greatest tournament of recent years. It brought together all the living former world champions, the current chess champion, and the future world champion: Dr. Lasker, Capablanca, Alekhine, Euwe, Botvinnik, and Reshevsky, Fine, Flohr, Tartakover, Vidmar, and Bogoljubov. The play was brilliant throughout. This volume contains all 105 of the games played, provided with the remarkable annotations of Alekhine. 1 illustration, 121 diagrams. xx + 291pp. 5⅜ x 8½. T189 Paperbound **$1.85**

CHESS FOR FUN AND CHESS FOR BLOOD, Edward Lasker. A genial, informative book by one of century's leading masters. Incisive comments on chess as a form of art and recreation, on how a master prepares for and plays a tournament. Best of all is author's move-by-move analysis of his game with Dr. Emanuel Lasker in 1924 World Tournament, a charming and thorough recreation of one of the great games in history: the author's mental processes; how his calculations were upset; how both players blundered; the surprising outcome. Who could not profit from this study-in-depth? For the enthusiast who likes to read about chess as well as play it. Corrected (1942) edition. Preface contains 8 letters to author about the fun of chess. 95 illustrations by Maximilian Mopp. 224pp. 5⅜ x 8½. T146 Paperbound **$1.25**

HOW NOT TO PLAY CHESS, Eugene A. Znosko-Borovsky. Sticking to a few well-chosen examples and explaining every step along the way, an outstanding chess expositor shows how to avoid playing a hit-or-miss game and instead develop general plans of action based on positional analysis: weak and strong squares, the notion of the controlled square, how to seize control of open lines, weak points in the pawn structure, and so on. Definition and illustration of typical chess mistakes plus 20 problems (from master games) added by Fred Reinfeld for the 1949 edition and a number of good-to-memorize tips make this a lucid book that can teach in a few hours what might otherwise take years to learn. 119pp. 5⅜ x 8. T920 Paperbound **$1.00**

THE SOVIET SCHOOL OF CHESS, A. Kotov and M. Yudovich. 128 master games, most unavailable elsewhere, by 51 outstanding players, including Botvinnik, Keres, Smyslov, Tal, against players like Capablanca, Euwe, Reshevsky. All carefully annotated, analyzed. Valuable biographical information about each player, early history of Russian chess, careers and contributions of Chigorin and Alekhine, development of Soviet school from 1920 to present with full over-all study of main features of its games, history of Russian chess literature. The most comprehensive work on Russian chess ever printed, the richest single sourcebook for up-to-date Russian theory and strategy. New introduction. Appendix of Russian Grandmasters, Masters, Master Composers. Two indexes (Players, Games). 30 photographs. 182 diagrams. vi + 390pp. 5⅜ x 8. T26 Paperbound **$2.00**

THE ART OF THE CHECKMATE, Georges Renaud and Victor Kahn. Two former national chess champions of France examine 127 games, identify 23 kinds of mate, and show the rationale for each. These include Legal's pseudo sacrifice, the double check, the smothered mate, Greco's mate, Morphy's mate, the mate of two bishops, two knights, many, many more. Analysis of ideas, not memorization problems. Review quizzes with answers help readers gauge progress. 80 quiz examples and solutions. 299 diagrams. vi + 208pp. T106 Paperbound **$1.35**

HOW TO SOLVE CHESS PROBLEMS, K. S. Howard. Full of practical suggestions for the fan or the beginner—who knows only the moves of the chessmen. Contains preliminary section and 58 two-move, 46 three-move, and 8 four-move problems composed by 27 outstanding American problem creators in the last 30 years. Explanation of all terms and exhaustive index. "Just what is wanted for the student," Brian Harley. 112 problems, solutions. vi +171pp. 5⅜ x 8. T748 Paperbound **$1.00**

CHESS STRATEGY, Edward Lasker. Keres, Fine, and other great players have acknowledged their debt to this book, which has taught just about the whole modern school how to play forcefully and intelligently. Covers fundamentals, general strategic principles, middle and end game, objects of attack, etc. Includes 48 dramatic games from master tournaments, all fully analyzed. "Best textbook I know in English," J. R. Capablanca. New introduction by author. Table of openings. Index. 167 illustrations. vii + 282pp. 5⅜ x 8. T528 Paperbound **$1.50**

REINFELD ON THE END GAME IN CHESS, F. Reinfeld. Formerly titled PRACTICAL END-GAME PLAY, this book contains clear, simple analyses of 62 end games by such masters as Alekhine, Tarrasch, Marshall, Morphy, Capablanca, and many others. Primary emphasis is on the general principles of transition from middle play to end play. This book is unusual in analyzing weak or incorrect moves to show how error occurs and how to avoid it. Covers king and pawn, minor piece, queen endings, weak squares, centralization, tempo moves, and many other vital factors. 62 diagrams. vi + 177pp. 5⅜ x 8. T417 Paperbound **$1.25**

THE AMERICAN TWO-MOVE CHESS PROBLEM, Kenneth S. Howard. One of this country's foremost contemporary problem composers selects an interesting, diversified collection of the best two-movers by 58 top American composers. Involving complete blocks, mutates, line openings and closings, other unusual moves, these problems will help almost any player improve his strategic approach. Probably has no equal for all around artistic excellence, surprising keymoves, interesting strategy. Includes 30-page history of development of American two-mover from Loyd, its founder, to the present. Index of composers. vii + 99pp. 5⅜ x 8½.
T997 Paperbound **$1.00**

WIN AT CHECKERS, M. Hopper. (Formerly CHECKERS). The former World's Unrestricted Checker Champion discusses the principles cf the game, expert's shots and traps, problems for the beginner, standard openings, locating your best move, the end game, opening "blitzkrieg" moves, ways to draw when you are behind your opponent, etc. More than 100 detailed questions and answers anticipate your problems. Appendix. 75 problems with solutions and diagrams. Index. 79 figures. xi + 107pp. 5⅜ x 8. T363 Paperbound **$1.00**

GAMES ANCIENT AND ORIENTAL, AND HOW TO PLAY THEM, E. Falkener. A connoisseur's selection of exciting and different games: Oriental varieties of chess, with unusual pieces and moves (including Japanese shogi); the original pachisi; go; reconstructions of lost Roman and Egyptian games; and many more. Full rules and sample games. Now play at home the games that have entertained millions, not on a fad basis, but for millennia. 345 illustrations and figures. iv + 366pp. 5⅜ x 8. T739 Paperbound **$2.00**

GO AND GO-MOKU, Edward Lasker. A fascinating Oriental game, Go, is winning new devotees in America daily. Rules that you can learn in a few minutes—a wealth of combinations that makes it more profound than chess! This is an easily followed step-by-step explanation of this 2000-year-old game, beginning with fundamentals. New chapter on advanced strategy in this edition! Also contains rules for Go-Moku, a very easy sister game. 72 diagrams. xix + 215pp. 5⅜ x 8. T613 Paperbound **$1.50**

HOW TO FORCE CHECKMATE, F. Reinfeld. Formerly titled CHALLENGE TO CHESSPLAYERS, this is an invaluable collection of 300 lightning strokes selected from actual masters' play, which will demonstrate how to smash your opponent's game with strong decisive moves. No board needed — clear, practical diagrams and easy-to-understand solutions. Learn to plan up to three moves ahead and play a superior end game. 300 diagrams. 111pp. 5⅜ x 8.
T439 Paperbound **$1.25**

CHESSBOARD MAGIC! A COLLECTION OF 160 BRILLIANT ENDINGS, I. Chernev. Contains 160 endgame compositions, all illustrating not only ingenuity of composition, but inherent beauty of solution. In one, five Knights are needed to force mate; in another White forces stalemate though Black finishes eight passed pawns ahead; 150 more, all remarkable, all will sharpen your imagination and increase your skill. "Inexhaustible source of entertainment, an endless feast of delight," Reuben Fine, Grandmaster. Introduction. 160 diagrams. Index of composers. vii + 172pp. 5⅜ x 8. T607 Paperbound **$1.00**

LEARN CHESS FROM THE MASTERS, F. Reinfeld. Formerly titled CHESS BY YOURSELF, this book contains 10 games which you play against such masters as Marshall, Bronstein, Najdorf, and others, and an easy system for grading each move you make against a variety of other possible moves. Detailed annotations reveal the principles of the game through actual play. 91 diagrams. viii + 144pp. 5⅜ x 8. T362 Paperbound **$1.00**

MORPHY'S GAMES OF CHESS, edited by Philip W. Sergeant. You can put boldness into your game by following the brilliant, forceful moves of the man who has been called the greatest chess player of all time. Here are 300 of Morphy's best games carefully annotated to reveal Morphy's principles. 54 classics against masters like Anderssen, Harrwitz, Bird, Paulsen, and others. 52 games at odds; 54 blindfold games; plus over 100 others. Unabridged reissue of the latest revised edition. Bibliography. New introduction by Fred Reinfeld. Annotations and introduction by Sergeant. Index. 235 diagrams. x + 352pp. 5⅜ x 8. T386 Paperbound **$1.85**

CHESS PRAXIS, Aron Nimzovich. Nimzovich was the stormy petrel of chess in the first decades of this century, and his system, known as hypermodern chess, revolutionized all play since his time. Casting aside the classical chess theory of Steinitz and Tarrasch, he created his own analysis of chess, considering dynamic patterns as they emerge during play. This is the fullest exposition of his ideas, and it is easily one of the dozen greatest books ever written on chess. Nimzovich illustrates each of his principles with at least two games, and shows how he applied his concepts successfully in games against such masters as Alekhine, Tarrasch, Reti, Rubinstein, Capablanca, Spielmann and others. Indispensable to every serious chess player. Translated by J. DuMont. 135 diagrams, 1 photo. xi + 364pp. 5½ x 8⅝.
T296 Paperbound **$2.00**

CHESS AND CHECKERS: THE WAY TO MASTERSHIP, Edward Lasker. Complete, lucid instructions for the beginner—and valuable suggestions for the advanced player! For both games the great master and teacher presents fundamentals, elementary tactics, and steps toward becoming a superior player. He concentrates on general principles rather than a mass of rules, comprehension rather than brute memory. Historical introduction. 118 diagrams. xiv + 167pp. 5⅜ x 8. T657 Paperbound **$1.15**

Fiction

THE LAND THAT TIME FORGOT and THE MOON MAID, Edgar Rice Burroughs. In the opinion of many, Burroughs' best work. The first concerns a strange island where evolution is individual rather than phylogenetic. Speechless anthropoids develop into intelligent human beings within a single generation. The second projects the reader far into the future and describes the first voyage to the Moon (in the year 2025), the conquest of the Earth by the Moon, and years of violence and adventure as the enslaved Earthmen try to regain possession of their planet. "An imaginative tour de force that keeps the reader keyed up and expectant," NEW YORK TIMES. Complete, unabridged text of the original two novels (three parts in each). 5 illustrations by J. Allen St. John. vi + 552pp. 5⅜ x 8½.
T1020 Clothbound **$3.75**
T358 Paperbound **$2.00**

AT THE EARTH'S CORE, PELLUCIDAR, TANAR OF PELLUCIDAR: THREE SCIENCE FICTION NOVELS BY EDGAR RICE BURROUGHS. Complete, unabridged texts of the first three Pellucidar novels. Tales of derring-do by the famous master of science fiction. The locale for these three related stories is the inner surface of the hollow Earth where we discover the world of Pellucidar, complete with all types of bizarre, menacing creatures, strange peoples, and alluring maidens—guaranteed to delight all Burroughs fans and a wide circle of adventure lovers. Illustrated by J. Allen St. John and P. F. Berdanier. vi + 433pp. 5⅜ x 8½.
T1051 Paperbound **$2.00**

THREE MARTIAN NOVELS, Edgar Rice Burroughs. Contains: Thuvia, Maid of Mars; The Chessmen of Mars; and The Master Mind of Mars. High adventure set in an imaginative and intricate conception of the Red Planet. Mars is peopled with an intelligent, heroic human race which lives in densely populated cities and with fierce barbarians who inhabit dead sea bottoms. Other exciting creatures abound amidst an inventive framework of Martian history and geography. Complete unabridged reprintings of the first edition. 16 illustrations by J. Allen St. John. vi + 499pp. 5⅜ x 8½.
T39 Paperbound **$1.85**

TO THE SUN? and OFF ON A COMET!, Jules Verne. Complete texts of two of the most imaginative flights into fancy in world literature display the high adventure that have kept Verne's novels read for nearly a century. Only unabridged edition of the best translation, by Edward Roth. Large, easily readable type. 50 illustrations selected from first editions. 462pp. 5⅜ x 8.
T634 Paperbound **$1.75**

FROM THE EARTH TO THE MOON and ALL AROUND THE MOON, Jules Verne. Complete editions of two of Verne's most successful novels, in finest Edward Roth translations, now available after many years out of print. Verne's visions of submarines, airplanes, television, rockets, interplanetary travel; of scientific and not-so-scientific beliefs; of peculiarities of Americans; all delight and engross us today as much as when they first appeared. Large, easily readable type. 42 illus. from first French edition. 476pp. 5⅜ x 8.
T633 Paperbound **$1.75**

THREE PROPHETIC NOVELS BY H. G. WELLS, edited by E. F. Bleiler. Complete texts of "When the Sleeper Wakes" (1st book printing in 50 years), "A Story of the Days to Come," "The Time Machine" (1st complete printing in book form). Exciting adventures in the future are as enjoyable today as 50 years ago when first printed. Predict TV, movies, intercontinental airplanes, prefabricated houses, air-conditioned cities, etc. First important author to foresee problems of mind control, technological dictatorships. "Absolute best of imaginative fiction," N. Y. Times. Introduction. 335pp. 5⅜ x 8.
T605 Paperbound **$1.50**

SEVEN SCIENCE FICTION NOVELS, H. G. Wells. Full unabridged texts of 7 science-fiction novels of the master. Ranging from biology, physics, chemistry, astronomy to sociology and other studies, Mr. Wells extrapolates whole worlds of strange and intriguing character. "One will have to go far to match this for entertainment, excitement, and sheer pleasure . . . ," NEW YORK TIMES. Contents: The Time Machine, The Island of Dr. Moreau, First Men in the Moon, The Invisible Man, The War of the Worlds, The Food of the Gods, In the Days of the Comet. 1015pp. 5⅜ x 8.
T264 Clothbound **$4.50**

28 SCIENCE FICTION STORIES OF H. G. WELLS. Two full unabridged novels, MEN LIKE GODS and STAR BEGOTTEN, plus 26 short stories by the master science-fiction writer of all time. Stories of space, time, invention, exploration, future adventure—an indispensable part of the library of everyone interested in science and adventure. PARTIAL CONTENTS: Men Like Gods, The Country of the Blind, In the Abyss, The Crystal Egg, The Man Who Could Work Miracles, A Story of the Days to Come, The Valley of Spiders, and 21 more! 928pp. 5⅜ x 8.
T265 Clothbound **$4.50**

THE WAR IN THE AIR, IN THE DAYS OF THE COMET, THE FOOD OF THE GODS: THREE SCIENCE FICTION NOVELS BY H. G. WELLS. Three exciting Wells offerings bearing on vital social and philosophical issues of his and our own day. Here are tales of air power, strategic bombing, East vs. West, the potential miracles of science, the potential disasters from outer space, the relationship between scientific advancement and moral progress, etc. First reprinting of "War in the Air" in almost 50 years. An excellent sampling of Wells at his storytelling best. Complete, unabridged reprintings. 16 illustrations. 645pp. 5⅜ x 8½.
T1135 Paperbound **$2.00**

CATALOGUE OF DOVER BOOKS

3 ADVENTURE NOVELS by H. Rider Haggard. Complete texts of "She," "King Solomon's Mines," "Allan Quatermain." Qualities of discovery, desire for immortality, search for the primitive, for what is unadorned by civilization, have kept these novels of African adventure excitingly alive to readers from R. L. Stevenson to George Orwell. 636pp. 5⅜ x 8.
T584 Paperbound **$2.00**

THE CASTING AWAY OF MRS. LECKS AND MRS. ALESHINE, F. R. Stockton. A charming light novel by Frank Stockton, one of America's finest humorists (and author of "The Lady, or the Tiger?"). This book has made millions of Americans laugh at the reflection of themselves in two middle-aged American women involved in some of the strangest adventures on record. You will laugh, too, as they endure shipwreck, desert island, and blizzard with maddening tranquillity. Also contains complete text of "The Dusantes," sequel to "The Casting Away." 49 original illustrations by F. D. Steele. vii + 142pp. 5⅜ x 8. T743 Paperbound **$1.00**

THREE PROPHETIC NOVELS OF H. G. WELLS. Complete texts of 3 timeless science fiction novels by the greatest master of the art, with remarkable prophecies of technological and social changes that are really taking place!—"When the Sleeper Wakes" (first printing in 50 years), "A Story of the Days to Come," and "The Time Machine" (only truly complete text available). Introduction by E. F. Bleiler. "The absolute best of imaginative fiction," N. Y. Times. 335pp. 5⅜ x 8.
T605 Paperbound **$1.45**

SEVEN SCIENCE FICTION NOVELS, H. G. Wells. Full unabridged texts of 7 science-fiction novels of the master. Ranging from biology, physics, chemistry, astronomy, to sociology and other studies, Mr. Wells extrapolates whole worlds of strange and intriguing character. "One will have to go far to match this for entertainment, excitement, and sheer pleasure . . ." NEW YORK TIMES. Contents: The Time Machine, The Island of Dr. Moreau, The First Men in the Moon, The Invisible Man, The War of the Worlds, The Food of the Gods, In The Days of the Comet. 1015pp. 5⅜ x 8.
T264 Clothbound **$4.50**

THE PRISONER OF ZENDA and RUPERT OF HENTZAU, Anthony Hope. The first edition to contain the complete story of the English diplomat who becomes King for a Day in the ancient aristocratic Kingdom of Ruritania. Long a favorite of devotees of high adventure, romance, grand intigue. Intelligent thrills presented with verve and elegant excitement. Unabridged reprints. Two volumes bound as one. 14 illustrations by Charles Dana Gibson. 420pp. 5⅜ x 8.
T69 Paperbound **$1.35**

TWO LITTLE SAVAGES, Ernest Thompson Seton. A lively narrative of the adventures of two real boys who decide to go Indian, combined with a storehouse of survival information: how to make a fire without matches, use an axe expertly, smudge mosquitoes, distinguish animal tracks, make mocassins, bows and arrows, learn the stars, etc. A classic of nature and boyhood, certain to awaken nature-interest in any youngster—or oldster. Highly recommended to Scouts, hunters, campers, bird-watchers or even city-dwellers who like to learn about the ways of nature. 293 illustrations by the author. x + 286pp. 5⅜ x 8½.
T985 Paperbound **$1.50**

THREE MARTIAN NOVELS, Edgar Rice Burroughs. Complete unabridged reprinting, in one volume, of Thuvia, Maid of Mars; Chessmen of Mars; The Master Mind of Mars. Hours of science-fiction adventure by a modern master storyteller. Reset in large clear type for easy reading. 16 illustrations by J. Allen St. John, vi + 490 pp. 5⅜ x 8½. T39 Paperbound **$1.75**

THE LAND THAT TIME FORGOT, and THE MOON MAID, Edgar Rice Burroughs. Two of Burroughs's rarest novels, considered by most authorities to be his best work. The first is adventure on a lost island where evolution is an individual matter and rapid, rather than slow and in terms of species; the second is the story of the first exploration of the Moon, the weird cultures that inhabit its interior, the conquest of the Earth by the Moon, and the millennia of struggle between the invaders and the earthmen. Packed full of thrills, thought-provoking. 5 illustrations by J. Allan St. John. 5⅜ x 8½.
T358 Paperbound **$2.00**
T1020 Clothbound **$3.75**

PIRATES OF VENUS, LOST ON VENUS, Edgar Rice Burroughs. These are the first two novels describing the adventures of Carson Napier on mysterious Venus. Thrilling adventures and exciting science-fiction situations among the towering jungles, monster-filled seas, and fantastic cities of the Second Planet. Complete and unabridged. Illustrations from original periodical publications. Illustrations by Matania. vi + 340pp. 5⅜ x 8½.
T1053 Paperbound **$1.75**

A PRINCESS OF MARS, A FIGHTING MAN OF MARS, Edgar Rice Burroughs. Two fantastic novels of Mars. "A Princess of Mars" explains how John Carter first came to Mars, and his adventures among the dying civilizations. "A Fighting Man of Mars", an independent novel set in the same adventurous environment, provides hours of thrills among lost cities and monsters. Illustrated by J. Allan St. John. 5⅜ x 8½. T1055 Paperbound **$1.75**

Social Sciences

SOCIAL THOUGHT FROM LORE TO SCIENCE, H. E. Barnes and H. Becker. An immense survey of sociological thought and ways of viewing, studying, planning, and reforming society from earliest times to the present. Includes thought on society of preliterate peoples, ancient non-Western cultures, and every great movement in Europe, America, and modern Japan. Analyzes hundreds of great thinkers: Plato, Augustine, Bodin, Vico, Montesquieu, Herder, Comte, Marx, etc. Weighs the contributions of utopians, sophists, fascists and communists; economists, jurists, philosophers, ecclesiastics, and every 19th and 20th century school of scientific sociology, anthropology, and social psychology throughout the world. Combines topical, chronological, and regional approaches, treating the evolution of social thought as a process rather than as a series of mere topics. "Impressive accuracy, competence, and discrimination . . . easily the best single survey," Nation. Thoroughly revised, with new material up to 1960. 2 indexes. Over 2200 bibliographical notes. Three volume set. Total of 1586pp. 5⅜ x 8.
T901 Vol I Paperbound **$2.35**
T902 Vol II Paperbound **$2.35**
T903 Vol III Paperbound **$2.35**
The set **$7.05**

FOLKWAYS, William Graham Sumner. A classic of sociology, a searching and thorough examination of patterns of behaviour from primitive, ancient Greek and Judaic, Medieval Christian, African, Oriental, Melanesian, Australian, Islamic, to modern Western societies. Thousands of illustrations of social, sexual, and religious customs, mores, laws, and institutions. Hundreds of categories: Labor, Wealth, Abortion, Primitive Justice, Life Policy, Slavery, Cannibalism, Uncleanness and the Evil Eye, etc. Will extend the horizon of every reader by showing the relativism of his own culture. Prefatory note by A. G. Keller. Introduction by William Lyon Phelps. Bibliography. Index. xiii + 692pp. 5⅜ x 8. T508 Paperbound **$2.49**

PRIMITIVE RELIGION, P. Radin. A thorough treatment by a noted anthropologist of the nature and origin of man's belief in the supernatural and the influences that have shaped religious expression in primitive societies. Ranging from the Arunta, Ashanti, Aztec, Bushman, Crow, Fijian, etc., of Africa, Australia, Pacific Islands, the Arctic, North and South America, Prof. Radin integrates modern psychology, comparative religion, and economic thought with first-hand accounts gathered by himself and other scholars of primitive initiations, training of the shaman, and other fascinating topics. "Excellent," NATURE (London). Unabridged reissue of 1st edition. New author's preface. Bibliographic notes. Index. x + 322pp. 5⅜ x 8.
T393 Paperbound **$1.85**

PRIMITIVE MAN AS PHILOSOPHER, P. Radin. A standard anthropological work covering primitive thought on such topics as the purpose of life, marital relations, freedom of thought, symbolism, death, resignation, the nature of reality, personality, gods, and many others. Drawn from factual material gathered from the Winnebago, Oglala Sioux, Maori, Baganda, Batak, Zuni, among others, it does not distort ideas by removing them from context but interprets strictly within the original framework. Extensive selections of original primitive documents. Bibliography. Index. xviii + 402pp. 5⅜ x 8. T392 Paperbound **$2.25**

A TREATISE ON SOCIOLOGY, THE MIND AND SOCIETY, Vilfredo Pareto. This treatise on human society is one of the great classics of modern sociology. First published in 1916, its careful catalogue of the innumerable manifestations of non-logical human conduct (Book One); the theory of "residues," leading to the premise that sentiment not logic determines human behavior (Book Two), and of "derivations," beliefs derived from desires (Book Three); and the general description of society made up of non-elite and elite, consisting of "foxes" who live by cunning and "lions" who live by force, stirred great controversy. But Pareto's passion for isolation and classification of elements and factors, and his allegiance to scientific method as the key tool for scrutinizing the human situation made his a truly twentieth-century mind and his work a catalytic influence on certain later social commentators. These four volumes (bound as two) require no special training to be appreciated and any reader who wishes to gain a complete understanding of modern sociological theory, regardless of special field of interest, will find them a must. Reprint of revised (corrected) printing of original edition. Translated by Andrew Bongiorno and Arthur Livingston. Index. Bibliography. Appendix containing index-summary of theorems. 48 diagrams. Four volumes bound as two. Total of 2063pp. 5⅜ x 8½. The set Clothbound **$15.00**

THE POLISH PEASANT IN EUROPE AND AMERICA, William I. Thomas, Florian Znaniecki. A seminal sociological study of peasant primary groups (family and community) and the disruptions produced by a new industrial system and immigration to America. The peasant's family, class system, religious and aesthetic attitudes, and economic life are minutely examined and analyzed in hundreds of pages of primary documentation, particularly letters between family members. The disorientation caused by new environments is scrutinized in detail (a 312-page autobiography of an immigrant is especially valuable and revealing) in an attempt to find common experiences and reactions. The famous "Methodological Note" sets forth the principles which guided the authors. When out of print this set has sold for as much as $50. 2nd revised edition. 2 vols. Vol. 1: xv + 1115pp. Vol. 2: 1135pp. Index. 6 x 9.
T478 Clothbound 2 vol. set **$12.50**

Music

A GENERAL HISTORY OF MUSIC, Charles Burney. A detailed coverage of music from the Greeks up to 1789, with full information on all types of music: sacred and secular, vocal and instrumental, operatic and symphonic. Theory, notation, forms, instruments, innovators, composers, performers, typical and important works, and much more in an easy, entertaining style. Burney covered much of Europe and spoke with hundreds of authorities and composers so that this work is more than a compilation of records . . . it is a living work of careful and first-hand scholarship. Its account of thoroughbass (18th century) Italian music is probably still the best introduction on the subject. A recent NEW YORK TIMES review said, "Surprisingly few of Burney's statements have been invalidated by modern research . . . still of great value." Edited and corrected by Frank Mercer. 35 figures. Indices. 1915pp. 5⅜ x 8. 2 volumes. T36 The Set, Clothbound **$12.50**

A DICTIONARY OF HYMNOLOGY, John Julian. This exhaustive and scholarly work has become known as an invaluable source of hundreds of thousands of important and often difficult to obtain facts on the history and use of hymns in the western world. Everyone interested in hymns will be fascinated by the accounts of famous hymns and hymn writers and amazed by the amount of practical information he will find. More than 30,000 entries on individual hymns, giving authorship, date and circumstances of composition, publication, textual variations, translations, denominational and ritual usage, etc. Biographies of more than 9,000 hymn writers, and essays on important topics such as Christmas carols and children's hymns, and much other unusual and valuable information. A 200 page double-columned index of first lines — the largest in print. Total of 1786 pages in two reinforced clothbound volumes. 6¼ x 9¼. The set, T333 Clothbound **$17.50**

MUSIC IN MEDIEVAL BRITAIN, F. Ll. Harrison. The most thorough, up-to-date, and accurate treatment of the subject ever published, beautifully illustrated. Complete account of institutions and choirs; carols, masses, and motets; liturgy and plainsong; and polyphonic music from the Norman Conquest to the Reformation. Discusses the various schools of music and their reciprocal influences; the origin and development of new ritual forms; development and use of instruments; and new evidence on many problems of the period. Reproductions of scores, over 200 excerpts from medieval melodies. Rules of harmony and dissonance; influence of Continental styles; great composers (Dunstable, Cornysh, Fairfax, etc.); and much more. Register and index of more than 400 musicians. Index of titles. General Index. 225-item bibliography. 6 Appendices. xix + 491pp. 5⅝ x 8¾. T705 Clothbound **$10.00**

THE MUSIC OF SPAIN, Gilbert Chase. Only book in English to give concise, comprehensive account of Iberian music; new Chapter covers music since 1941. Victoria, Albéniz, Cabezón, Pedrell, Turina, hundreds of other composers; popular and folk music; the Gypsies; the guitar; dance, theatre, opera, with only extensive discussion in English of the Zarzuela; virtuosi such as Casals; much more. "Distinguished . . . readable," Saturday Review. 400-item bibliography. Index. 27 photos. 383pp. 5⅜ x 8. T549 Paperbound **$2.00**

ON STUDYING SINGING, Sergius Kagen. An intelligent method of voice-training, which leads you around pitfalls that waste your time, money, and effort. Exposes rigid, mechanical systems, baseless theories, deleterious exercises. "Logical, clear, convincing . . . dead right," Virgil Thomson, N.Y. Herald Tribune. "I recommend this volume highly," Maggie Teyte, Saturday Review. 119pp. 5⅜ x 8. T622 Paperbound **$1.25**

WILLIAM LAWES, M. Lefkowitz. This is the definitive work on Lawes, the versatile, prolific, and highly original "King's musician" of 17th century England. His life is reconstructed from original documents, and nearly every piece he ever wrote is examined and evaluated: his fantasias, pavans, violin "sonatas," lyra viol and bass viol suites, and music for harp and theorbo; and his songs, masques, and theater music to words by Herrick ("Gather Ye Rosebuds"), Jonson, Suckling, Shirley, and others. The author shows the innovations of dissonance, augmented triad, and other Italian influences Lawes helped introduce to England. List of Lawes' complete works and several complete scores by this major precursor of Purcell and the 18th century developments. Index. 5 Appendices. 52 musical excerpts, many never before in print. Bibliography. x + 320pp. 5⅜ x 8. T706 Clothbound **$10.00**

THE FUGUE IN BEETHOVEN'S PIANO MUSIC, J. V. Cockshoot. The first study of a neglected aspect of Beethoven's genius: his ability as a writer of fugues. Analyses of early studies and published works demonstrate his original and powerful contributions to composition. 34 works are examined, with 143 musical excerpts. For all pianists, teachers, students, and music-minded readers with a serious interest in Beethoven. Index. 93-item bibliography. Illustration of original score for "Fugue in C." xv + 212pp. 5⅝ x 8⅜. T704 Clothbound **$6.00**

CATALOGUE OF DOVER BOOKS

JOHANN SEBASTIAN BACH, Philipp Spitta. The complete and unabridged text of the definitive study of Bach. Written some 70 years ago, it is still unsurpassed for its coverage of nearly all aspects of Bach's life and work. There could hardly be a finer non-technical introduction to Bach's music than the detailed, lucid analyses which Spitta provides for hundreds of individual pieces. 26 solid pages are devoted to the B minor mass, for example, and 30 pages to the glorious St. Matthew Passion. This monumental set also includes a major analysis of the music of the 18th century: Buxtehude, Pachelbel, etc. "Unchallenged as the last word on one of the supreme geniuses of music," John Barkham, SATURDAY REVIEW SYNDICATE. Total of 1819pp. 2 volumes. Heavy cloth binding. 5⅜ x 8. T252 The set, Clothbound **$12.50**

THE LIFE OF MOZART, O. Jahn. Probably the largest amount of material on Mozart's life and works ever gathered together in one book! Its 1350 authoritative and readable pages cover every event in his life, and contain a full critique of almost every piece he ever wrote, including sketches and intimate works. There is a full historical-cultural background, and vast research into musical and literary history, sources of librettos, prior treatments of Don Juan legend, etc. This is the complete and unaltered text of the definitive Townsend translation, with foreword by Grove. 5 engraved portraits from Salzburg archives. 4 facsimiles in Mozart's hand. 226 musical examples. 4 Appendixes, including complete list of Mozart's compositions, with Köchel numbers (fragmentary works included). Total of xxviii + 1352pp. Three volume set. 5⅜ x 8.
T85 Vol. I Clothbound **$5.00**
T86 Vol. II Clothbound **$5.00**
The set **$10.00**

BEETHOVEN'S QUARTETS, J. de Marliave. The most complete and authoritative study ever written, enjoyable for scholar and layman alike. The 16 quartets and Grand Fugue are all analyzed bar by bar and theme by theme, not over-technically, but concentrating on mood and effects. Complete background material for each composition: influences, first reviews, etc. Preface by Gabriel Fauré. Introduction and notes by J. Escarra. Translated by Hilda Andrews. 321 musical examples. xxiii + 379pp. 5⅜ x 8. T694 Paperbound **$1.85**

STRUCTURAL HEARING: TONAL COHERENCE IN MUSIC, Felix Salzer. Written by a pupil of the late Heinrich Schenker, this is not only the most thorough exposition in English of the Schenker method but also extends the Schenker approach to include modern music, the middle ages, and renaissance music. It explores the phenomenon of tonal organization by means of a detailed analysis and discussion of more than 500 musical pieces. It casts new light for the reader acquainted with harmony upon the understanding of musical compositions, problems of musical coherence, and connection between theory and composition. "Has been the foundation on which all teaching in music theory has been based at this college," Leopold Mannes, President of The Mannes College of Music. 2 volumes. Total of 658pp. 6½ x 9¼.
The set, T418 Clothbound **$8.00**

ANTONIO STRADIVARI: HIS LIFE AND WORK (1644-1737), W. Henry Hill, Arthur F. Hill, and Alfred E. Hill. Still the only book that really delves into life and art of the incomparable Italian craftsman, maker of the finest musical instruments in the world today. The authors, expert violin-makers themselves, discuss Stradivari's ancestry, his construction and finishing techniques, distinguished characteristics of many of his instruments and their locations. Included, too, is story of introduction of his instruments into France, England, first revelation of their supreme merit, and information on his labels, number of instruments made, prices, mystery of ingredients of his varnish, tone of pre-1684 Stradivari violin and changes between 1684 and 1690. An extremely interesting, informative account for all music lovers, from craftsman to concert-goer. Republication of original (1902) edition. New introduction by Sydney Beck, Head of Rare Book and Manuscript Collections, Music Division, New York Public Library. Analytical index by Rembert Wurlitzer. Appendixes. 68 illustrations. 30 full-page plates. 4 in color. xxvi + 315pp. 5⅜ x 8½. T425 Paperbound **$2.25**

THREE CLASSICS IN THE AESTHETIC OF MUSIC, Claude Debussy, Ferrucio Busoni, and Charles Ives. Three very different points of view by three top-ranking modern composers. "M. Croche, the Dilettante-Hater" consists of twenty-five brief articles written by Debussy between the years 1901 and 1905, a sparkling collection of personal commentary on a wide range of topics. Busoni's "Toward a New Aesthetic of Music" considers the nature of absolute music in an attempt to suggest answers to the question, What are the aims of music?, and discusses modern systems of tonality and harmony, the concept of unity of keys, etc. Ives's "Essays Before a Sonata," a literary complement to the movements of the author's "Concord, 1845" piano sonata, contains his most mature analysis of his art. Stimulating reading for musicians, music lovers, and philosophers of the arts. iv + 188pp. 5⅜ x 8½.
T320 Paperbound **$1.45**

Dover Classical Records

Now available directly to the public exclusively from Dover: top-quality recordings of fine classical music for only $2 per record! Almost all were released by major record companies to sell for $5 and $6. These recordings were issued under our imprint only after they had passed a severe critical test. We insisted upon:

First-rate music that is enjoyable, musically important and culturally significant.

First-rate performances, where the artists have carried out the composer's intentions, in which the music is alive, vigorous, played with understanding and sensitivity.

First-rate sound—clear, sonorous, fully balanced, crackle-free, whir-free.

Have in your home music by major composers, performed by such gifted musicians as Elsner, Gitlis, Wührer, Beveridge Webster, the Barchet Quartet, Gimpel, etc. Enthusiastically received when first released, many of these performances are definitive. The records are not seconds or remainders, but brand new pressings made on pure vinyl from carefully chosen master tapes. "All purpose" 12" monaural 33⅓ rpm records, they play equally well on hi-fi and stereo equipment. Fine music for discriminating music lovers, superlatively played, flawlessly recorded: there is no better way to build your library of recorded classical music at remarkable savings. There are no strings; this is not a come-on, not a club, forcing you to buy records you may not want in order to get a few at a lower price. Buy whatever records you want in any quantity, and never pay more than $2 each. Your obligation ends with your first purchase. And that's when ours begins. Dover's money-back guarantee allows you to return any record for any reason, even if you don't like the music, for a full, immediate refund—no questions asked.

MOZART: STRING QUARTETS: IN A (K. 464) AND C ("DISSONANT") (K. 465), Barchet Quartet. The final two of the famous Haydn Quartets, high-points in the history of music. The A Major was accepted with delight by Mozart's contemporaries, but the C Major, with its dissonant opening, aroused strong protest. Today, of course, the remarkable resolutions of the dissonances are recognized as major musical achievements. "Beautiful warm playing," MUSICAL AMERICA. "Two of Mozart's loveliest quartets in a distinguished performance," REV. OF RECORDED MUSIC. (Playing time 58 mins.) HCR 5200 **$2.00**

MOZART: STRING QUARTETS: IN G (K. 80), D (K. 156), and C (K. 157), Barchet Quartet. The early chamber music of Mozart receives unfortunately little attention. First-rate music of the Italian school, it contains all the lightness and charm that belongs only to the youthful Mozart. This is currently the only separate source for the composer's work of this period. "Excellent," HIGH FIDELITY. "Filled with sunshine and youthful joy; played with verve, recorded sound live and brilliant," CHRISTIAN SCI. MONITOR. (playing time 51 mins.) HCR 5201 **$2.00**

MOZART: SERENADES: #9 IN D ("POSTHORN") (K. 320), #6 IN D ("SERENATA NOTTURNA") (K. 239), Pro Musica Orch. of Stuttgart, under Edouard van Remoortel. For Mozart, the serenade was a highly effective form, since he could bring to it the immediacy and intimacy of chamber music as well as the free fantasy of larger group music. Both these serenades are distinguished by a playful, mischievous quality, a spirit perfectly captured in this fine performance. "A triumph, polished playing from the orchestra," HI FI MUSIC AT HOME. "Sound is rich and resonant, fidelity is wonderful," REV. OF RECORDED MUSIC. (Playing time 51 mins.) HCR 5202 **$2.00**

MOZART: DIVERTIMENTO FOR VIOLIN, VIOLA AND CELLO IN E FLAT (K. 563); ADAGIO AND FUGUE IN F MINOR (K. 404a), Kehr Trio. The divertimento is one of Mozart's most beloved pieces, called by Einstein "the finest and most perfect trio ever heard." It is difficult to imagine a music lover who will not be delighted by it. This is the only recording of the lesser known Adagio and Fugue, written in 1782 and influenced by Bach's Well-Tempered Clavichord. "Extremely beautiful recording, strongly recommended," THE OBSERVER. "Superior to rival editions," HIGH FIDELITY. (Playing time 51 mins.) HCR 5203 **$2.00**

SCHUMANN: KREISLERIANA (OPUS 16) AND FANTASIA IN C (OPUS 17), Vlado Perlemuter, Piano. The vigorous Romantic imagination and the remarkable emotional qualities of Schumann's piano music raise it to a special eminence in 19th-century creativity. Both these pieces are rooted to the composer's tortuous romance with his future wife, Clara, and both receive brilliant treatment at the hands of Vlado Perlemuter, Paris Conservatory, proclaimed by Alfred Cortot "not only a great virtuoso but also a great musician." "The best Kreisleriana to date," BILLBOARD. (Playing time 55 mins.) HCR 5204 **$2.00**

DONIZETTI, BETLY (LA CAPANNA SVIZZERA), Soloists of Compagnia del Teatro dell'Opera Comica di Roma, Societa del Quartetto, Rome, Chorus and Orch. Betly, a delightful one-act opera written in 1836, is similar in style and story to one of Donizetti's better-known operas, L'Elisir. Betly is lighthearted and farcical, with bright melodies and a freshness characteristic of the best of Donizetti. Libretto (English and Italian) included. "The chief honors go to Angela Tuccari who sings the title role, and the record is worth having for her alone," M. Rayment, GRAMOPHONE REC. REVIEW. "The interpretation . . . is excellent . . . This is a charming record which we recommend to lovers of little-known works," DISQUES.
HCR 5218 **$2.00**

ROSSINI: L'OCCASIONE FA IL LADRO (IL CAMBIO DELLA VALIGIA), Soloists of Compagnia del Teatro dell'Opera Comica di Roma, Societa del Quartetto, Rome, Chorus and Orch. A charming one-act opera buffa, this is one of the first works of Rossini's maturity, and it is filled with the wit, gaiety and sparkle that make his comic operas second only to Mozart's. Like other Rossini works, L'Occasione makes use of the theme of impersonation and attendant amusing confusions. This is the only recording of this important buffa. Full libretto (English and Italian) included. "A major rebirth, a stylish performance . . . the Roman recording engineers have outdone themselves," H. Weinstock, SAT. REVIEW. (Playing time 53 mins.)
HCR 5219 **$2.00**

DOWLAND: "FIRST BOOKE OF AYRES," Pro Musica Antiqua of Brussels, Safford Cape, Director. This is the first recording to include all 22 of the songs of this great collection, written by John Dowland, one of the most important writers of songs of 16th and 17th century England. The participation of the Brussels Pro Musica under Safford Cape insures scholarly accuracy and musical artistry. "Powerfully expressive and very beautiful," B. Haggin. "The musicianly singers . . . never fall below an impressive standard," Philip Miller. Text included. (Playing time 51 mins.)
HCR 5220 **$2.00**

FRENCH CHANSONS AND DANCES OF THE 16TH CENTURY, Pro Musica Antiqua of Brussels, Safford Cape, Director. A remarkable selection of 26 three- or four-part chansons and delightful dances from the French Golden Age—by such composers as Orlando Lasso, Crecquillon, Claude Gervaise, etc. Text and translation included. "Delightful, well-varied with respect to mood and to vocal and instrumental color," HIGH FIDELITY. "Performed with . . . discrimination and musical taste, full of melodic distinction and harmonic resource," Irving Kolodin. (Playing time 39 mins.)
HCR 5221 **$2.00**

GALUPPI: CONCERTI A QUATRO: #1 IN G MINOR, #2 IN G, #3 IN D, #4 IN C MINOR, #5 IN E FLAT, AND #6 IN B FLAT, Biffoli Quartet. During Baldassare Galuppi's lifetime, his instrumental music was widely renowned, and his contemporaries Mozart and Haydn thought highly of his work. These 6 concerti reflect his great ability; and they are among the most interesting compositions of the period. They are remarkable for their unusual combinations of timbres and for emotional elements that were only then beginning to be introduced into music. Performed by the well-known Biffoli Quartet, this is the only record devoted exclusively to Galuppi. (Playing time 47 mins.)
HCR 5222 **$2.00**

HAYDN: DIVERTIMENTI FOR WIND BAND, IN C; IN F; DIVERTIMENTO A NOVE STROMENTI IN C FOR STRINGS AND WIND INSTRUMENTS, reconstructed by H. C. Robbins Landon, performed by members of Vienna State Opera Orch.; MOZART DIVERTIMENTI IN C, III (K. 187) AND IV (K. 188), Salzburg Wind Ensemble. Robbins Landon discovered Haydn manuscripts in a Benedictine monastery in Lower Austria, edited them and restored their original instrumentation The result is this magnificent record. Two little-known divertimenti by Mozart—of great charm and appeal—are also included. None of this music is available elsewhere (Playing time 58 mins.)
HCR 5223 **$2.00**

PURCELL: TRIO SONATAS FROM "SONATAS OF FOUR PARTS" (1697): #9 IN F ("GOLDEN"), #7 IN C, #1 IN B MINOR, #10 IN D, #4 IN D MINOR, #2 IN E FLAT, AND #8 IN G MINOR, Giorgio Ciompi, and Werner Torkanowsky, Violins, Geo. Koutzen, Cello, and Herman Chessid, Harpsichord. These posthumously-published sonatas show Purcell at his most advanced and mature. They are certainly among the finest musical examples of pre-modern chamber music. Those not familiar with his instrumental music are well-advised to hear these outstanding pieces. "Performance sounds excellent," Harold Schonberg. "Some of the most noble and touching music known to anyone," AMERICAN RECORD GUIDE. (Playing time 58 mins.)
HCR 5224 **$2.00**

BARTOK: VIOLIN CONCERTO; SONATA FOR UNACCOMPANIED VIOLIN, Ivry Gitlis, Pro Musica of Vienna, under Hornstein. Both these works are outstanding examples of Bartok's final period, and they show his powers at their fullest. The Violin Concerto is, in the opinion of many authorities, Bartok's finest work, and the Sonata, his last work, is "a masterpiece" (F. Sackville West). "Wonderful, finest performance of both Bartok works I have ever heard," GRAMOPHONE. "Gitlis makes such potent and musical sense out of these works that I suspect many general music lovers (not otherwise in sympathy with modern music) will discover to their amazement that they like it. Exceptionally good sound," AUDITOR. (Playing time 54 mins.)
HCR 5211 **$2.00**

SCHUMANN: TRIOS #1 IN D MINOR (OPUS 63) AND #3 IN G MINOR (OPUS 110), Trio di Bolzano. The fiery, romantic, melodic Trio #1 and the dramatic, seldom heard Trio #3 are both movingly played by a fine chamber ensemble. No one personified Romanticism to the general public of the 1840's more than did Robert Schumann, and among his most romantic works are these trios for cello, violin and piano. "Ensemble and overall interpretation leave little to be desired," HIGH FIDELITY. "An especially understanding performance," REV. OF RECORDED MUSIC. (Playing time 54 mins.) HCR 5205 **$2.00**

SCHUBERT: QUINTET IN A ("TROUT") (OPUS 114), AND NOCTURNE IN E FLAT (OPUS 148), Friedrich Wührer, Piano and Barchet Quartet. If there is a single piece of chamber music that is a universal favorite, it is probably Schubert's "Trout" Quintet. Delightful melody, harmonic resources, musical exuberance are its characteristics. The Nocturne (played by Wührer, Barchet, and Reimann) is an exquisite piece with a deceptively simple theme and harmony. "The best Trout on the market—Wührer is a fine Viennese-style Schubertian, and his spirit infects the Barchets," ATLANTIC MONTHLY. "Exquisitely recorded," ETUDE. (Playing time 44 mins.) HCR 5206 **$2.00**

SCHUBERT: PIANO SONATAS IN C MINOR AND B (OPUS 147), Friedrich Wührer. Schubert's sonatas retain the structure of the classical form, but delight listeners with romantic freedom and a special melodic richness. The C Minor, one of the Three Grand Sonatas, is a product of the composer's maturity. The B Major was not published until 15 years after his death. "Remarkable interpretation, reproduction of the first rank," DISQUES. "A superb pianist for music like this, musicianship, sweep, power, and an ability to integrate Schubert's measures such as few pianists have had since Schnabel," Harold Schonberg. (Playing time 49 mins.) HCR 5207 **$2.00**

STRAVINSKY: VIOLIN CONCERTO IN D, Ivry Gitlis, Cologne Orchestra; DUO CONCERTANTE, Ivry Gitlis, Violin, Charlotte Zelka, Piano, Cologne Orchestra; JEU DE CARTES, Bamberg Symphony, under Hollreiser. Igor Stravinsky is probably the most important composer of this century, and these three works are among the most significant of his neoclassical period of the 30's. The Violin Concerto is one of the few modern classics. Jeu de Cartes, a ballet score, bubbles with gaiety, color and melodiousness. "Imaginatively played and beautifully recorded," E. T. Canby, HARPERS MAGAZINE. "Gitlis is excellent, Hollreiser beautifully worked out," HIGH FIDELITY. (Playing time 55 mins.) HCR 5208 **$2.00**

GEMINIANI: SIX CONCERTI GROSSI, OPUS 3, Helma Elsner, Harpsichord, Barchet Quartet, Pro Musica Orch. of Stuttgart, under Reinhardt. Francesco Geminiani (1687-1762) has been rediscovered in the same musical exploration that revealed Scarlatti, Vivaldi, and Corelli. In form he is more sophisticated than the earlier Italians, but his music delights modern listeners with its combination of contrapuntal techniques and the full harmonies and rich melodies charcteristic of Italian music. This is the only recording of the six 1733 concerti: D Major, B Flat Minor, E Minor, G Minor, E Minor (bis), and D Minor. "I warmly recommend it, spacious, magnificent, I enjoyed every bar," C. Cudworth, RECORD NEWS. "Works of real charm, recorded with understanding and style," ETUDE. (Playing time 52 mins.) HCR 5209 **$2.00**

MODERN PIANO SONATAS: BARTOK: SONATA FOR PIANO; BLOCH: SONATA FOR PIANO (1935); PROKOFIEV, PIANO SONATA #7 IN B FLAT ("STALINGRAD"); STRAVINSKY: PIANO SONATA (1924), István Nádas, Piano. Shows some of the major forces and directions in modern piano music: Stravinsky's crisp austerity; Bartok's fusion of Hungarian folk motives; incisive diverse rhythms, and driving power; Bloch's distinctive emotional vigor; Prokofiev's brilliance and melodic beauty couched in pre-Romantic forms. "A most interesting documentation of the contemporary piano sonata. Nadas is a very good pianist." HIGH FIDELITY. (Playing time 59 mins.) HCR 5215 **$2.00**

VIVALDI: CONCERTI FOR FLUTE, VIOLIN, BASSOON, AND HARPSICHORD: #8 IN G MINOR, #21 IN F, #27 IN D, #7 IN D; SONATA #1 IN A MINOR, Gastone Tassinari, Renato Giangrandi, Giorgio Semprini, Arlette Eggmann. More than any other Baroque composer, Vivaldi moved the concerto grosso closer to the solo concert we deem standard today. In these concerti he wrote virtuosi music for the solo instruments, allowing each to introduce new material or expand on musical ideas, creating tone colors unusual even for Vivaldi. As a result, this record displays a new area of his genius, offering some of his most brilliant music. Performed by a top-rank European group. (Playing time 45 mins.) HCR 5216 **$2.00**

LÜBECK: CANTATAS: HILF DEINEM VOLK; GOTT, WIE DEIN NAME, Stuttgart Choral Society, Swabian Symphony Orch.; PRELUDES AND FUGUES IN C MINOR AND IN E, Eva Hölderlin, Organ. Vincent Lübeck (1654-1740), contemporary of Bach and Buxtehude, was one of the great figures of the 18th-century North German school. These examples of Lübeck's few surviving works indicate his power and brilliance. Voice and instrument lines in the cantatas are strongly reminiscent of the organ: the preludes and fugues show the influence of Bach and Buxtehude. This is the only recording of the superb cantatas. Text and translation included. "Outstanding record," E. T. Canby, SAT. REVIEW. "Hölderlin's playing is exceptional," AM. RECORD REVIEW. "Will make [Lübeck] many new friends," Philip Miller. (Playing time 37 mins.) HCR 5217 **$2.00**

Language Books and Records

GERMAN: HOW TO SPEAK AND WRITE IT. AN INFORMAL CONVERSATIONAL METHOD FOR SELF STUDY, Joseph Rosenberg. Eminently useful for self study because of concentration on elementary stages of learning. Also provides teachers with remarkable variety of aids: 28 full- and double-page sketches with pertinent items numbered and identified in German and English; German proverbs, jokes; grammar, idiom studies; extensive practice exercises. The most interesting introduction to German available, full of amusing illustrations, photographs of cities and landmarks in German-speaking cities, cultural information subtly woven into conversational material. Includes summary of grammar, guide to letter writing, study guide to German literature by Dr. Richard Friedenthal. Index. 400 illustrations. 384pp. 5⅜ x 8½.
T271 Paperbound **$2.00**

FRENCH: HOW TO SPEAK AND WRITE IT. AN INFORMAL CONVERSATIONAL METHOD FOR SELF STUDY, Joseph Lemaitre. Even the absolute beginner can acquire a solid foundation for further study from this delightful elementary course. Photographs, sketches and drawings, sparkling colloquial conversations on a wide variety of topics (including French culture and custom), French sayings and quips, are some of aids used to demonstrate rather than merely describe the language. Thorough yet surprisingly entertaining approach, excellent for teaching and for self study. Comprehensive analysis of pronunciation, practice exercises and appendices of verb tables, additional vocabulary, other useful material. Index. Appendix. 400 illustrations. 416pp. 5⅜ x 8½.
T268 Paperbound **$2.00**

DICTIONARY OF SPOKEN SPANISH, Spanish-English, English-Spanish. Compiled from spoken Spanish, emphasizing idiom and colloquial usage in both Castilian and Latin-American. More than 16,000 entries containing over 25,000 idioms—the largest list of idiomatic constructions ever published. Complete sentences given, indexed under single words—language in immediately useable form, for travellers, businessmen, students, etc. 25 page introduction provides rapid survey of sounds, grammar, syntax, with full consideration of irregular verbs. Especially apt in modern treatment of phrases and structure. 17 page glossary gives translations of geographical names, money values, numbers, national holidays, important street signs, useful expressions of high frequency, plus unique 7 page glossary of Spanish and Spanish-American foods and dishes. Originally published as War Department Technical Manual TM 30-900. iv + 513pp. 5⅜ x 8.
T495 Paperbound **$1.75**

SPEAK MY LANGUAGE: SPANISH FOR YOUNG BEGINNERS, M. Ahlman, Z. Gilbert. Records provide one of the best, and most entertaining, methods of introducing a foreign language to children. Within the framework of a train trip from Portugal to Spain, an English-speaking child is introduced to Spanish by a native companion. (Adapted from a successful radio program of the N. Y. State Educational Department.) Though a continuous story, there are a dozen specific categories of expressions, including greetings, numbers, time, weather, food, clothes, family members, etc. Drill is combined with poetry and contextual use. Authentic background music is heard. An accompanying book enables a reader to follow the records, and includes a vocabulary of over 350 recorded expressions. Two 10″ 33⅓ records, total of 40 minutes. Book. 40 illustrations. 69pp. 5¼ x 10½.
T890 The set **$4.95**

AN ENGLISH-FRENCH-GERMAN-SPANISH WORD FREQUENCY DICTIONARY, H. S. Eaton. An indispensable language study aid, this is a semantic frequency list of the 6000 most frequently used words in 4 languages—24,000 words in all. The lists, based on concepts rather than words alone, and containing all modern, exact, and idiomatic vocabulary, are arranged side by side to form a unique 4-language dictionary. A simple key indicates the importance of the individual words within each language. Over 200 pages of separate indexes for each language enable you to locate individual words at a glance. Will help language teachers and students, authors of textbooks, grammars, and language tests to compare concepts in the various languages and to concentrate on basic vocabulary, avoiding uncommon and obsolete words. 2 Appendixes. xxi + 441pp. 6½ x 9¼.
T738 Paperbound **$2.45**

NEW RUSSIAN-ENGLISH AND ENGLISH-RUSSIAN DICTIONARY, M. A. O'Brien. Over 70,000 entries in the new orthography! Many idiomatic uses and colloquialisms which form the basis of actual speech. Irregular verbs, perfective and imperfective aspects, regular and irregular sound changes, and other features. One of the few dictionaries where accent changes within the conjugation of verbs and the declension of nouns are fully indicated. "One of the best," Prof. E. J. Simmons, Cornell. First names, geographical terms, bibliography, etc. 738pp. 4½ x 6¼.
T208 Paperbound **$2.00**

96 MOST USEFUL PHRASES FOR TOURISTS AND STUDENTS in English, French, Spanish, German, Italian. A handy folder you'll want to carry with you. How to say "Excuse me," "How much is it?", "Write it down, please," etc., in four foreign languages. Copies limited, no more than 1 to a customer.
FREE

Say It language phrase books

These handy phrase books (128 to 196 pages each) make grammatical drills unnecessary for an elementary knowledge of a spoken foreign language. Covering most matters of travel and everyday life each volume contains:

Over 1000 phrases and sentences in immediately useful forms — foreign language plus English.

Modern usage designed for Americans. Specific phrases like, "Give me small change," and "Please call a taxi."

Simplified phonetic transcription you will be able to read at sight.

The only completely indexed phrase books on the market.

Covers scores of important situations: — Greetings, restaurants, sightseeing, useful expressions, etc.

These books are prepared by native linguists who are professors at Columbia, N.Y.U., Fordham and other great universities. Use them independently or with any other book or record course. They provide a supplementary living element that most other courses lack. Individual volumes in:

Russian 75¢
Italian 75¢
Spanish 75¢
German 75¢
Hebrew 75¢
Danish 75¢
Japanese 75¢
Swedish 75¢
Dutch 75¢
Esperanto 75¢
Modern Greek 75¢
Portuguese 75¢
Norwegian 75¢
Polish 75¢
French 75¢
Yiddish 75¢
Turkish 75¢
English for German-speaking people 75¢
English for Italian-speaking people 75¢
English for Spanish-speaking people 75¢

Large clear type. 128-196 pages each. 3½ x 5¼. Sturdy paper binding.

Listen and Learn language records

LISTEN & LEARN is the only language record course designed especially to meet your travel and everyday needs. It is available in separate sets for FRENCH, SPANISH, GERMAN, JAPANESE, RUSSIAN, MODERN GREEK, PORTUGUESE, ITALIAN and HEBREW, and each set contains three 33⅓ rpm long-playing records—1½ hours of recorded speech by eminent native speakers who are professors at Columbia, New York University, Queens College.

Check the following special features found only in LISTEN & LEARN:

- **Dual-language recording. 812 selected phrases and sentences,** over 3200 words, spoken first in English, then in their foreign language equivalents. A suitable pause follows each foreign phrase, allowing you time to repeat the expression. You learn by unconscious assimilation.
- **128 to 206-page manual** contains everything on the records, plus a simple phonetic pronunciation guide.
- **Indexed for convenience. The only set on the market** that is completely indexed. No more puzzling over where to find the phrase you need. Just look in the rear of the manual.
- **Practical.** No time wasted on material you can find in any grammar. LISTEN & LEARN covers central core material with phrase approach. Ideal for the person with limited learning time.
- **Living, modern expressions,** not found in other courses. Hygienic products, modern equipment, shopping—expressions used every day, like "nylon" and "air-conditioned."
- **Limited objective.** Everything you learn, no matter where you stop, is immediately useful. You have to finish other courses, wade through grammar and vocabulary drill, before they help you.
- **High-fidelity recording.** LISTEN & LEARN records equal in clarity and surface-silence any record on the market costing up to $6.

"Excellent . . . the spoken records . . . impress me as being among the very best on the market," **Prof. Mario Pei,** Dept. of Romance Languages, Columbia University. "Inexpensive and well-done . . . it would make an ideal present," CHICAGO SUNDAY TRIBUNE. "More genuinely helpful than anything of its kind which I have previously encountered," **Sidney Clark,** well-known author of "ALL THE BEST" travel books.

UNCONDITIONAL GUARANTEE. Try LISTEN & LEARN, then return it within 10 days for full refund if you are not satisfied.

Each set contains three twelve-inch 33⅓ records, manual, and album.

SPANISH	the set **$5.95**	GERMAN	the set **$5.95**
FRENCH	the set **$5.95**	ITALIAN	the set **$5.95**
RUSSIAN	the set **$5.95**	JAPANESE	the set **$5.95**
PORTUGUESE	the set **$5.95**	MODERN GREEK	the set **$5.95**
MODERN HEBREW	the set **$5.95**		

Trubner Colloquial Manuals

These unusual books are members of the famous Trubner series of colloquial manuals. They have been written to provide adults with a sound colloquial knowledge of a foreign language, and are suited for either class use or self-study. Each book is a complete course in itself, with progressive, easy to follow lessons. Phonetics, grammar, and syntax are covered, while hundreds of phrases and idioms, reading texts, exercises, and vocabulary are included. These books are unusual in being neither skimpy nor overdetailed in grammatical matters, and in presenting up-to-date, colloquial, and practical phrase material. Bilingual presentation is stressed, to make thorough self-study easier for the reader.

COLLOQUIAL HINDUSTANI, A. H. Harley, formerly Nizam's Reader in Urdu, U. of London. 30 pages on phonetics and scripts (devanagari & Arabic-Persian) are followed by 29 lessons, including material on English and Arabic-Persian influences. Key to all exercises. Vocabulary. 5 x 7½. 147pp. Clothbound **$1.75**

COLLOQUIAL PERSIAN, L. P. Elwell-Sutton. Best introduction to modern Persian, with 90 page grammatical section followed by conversations, 35-page vocabulary. 139pp. Clothbound **$1.75**

COLLOQUIAL ARABIC, DeLacy O'Leary. Foremost Islamic scholar covers language of Egypt, Syria, Palestine, & Northern Arabia. Extremely clear coverage of complex Arabic verbs & noun plurals; also cultural aspects of language. Vocabulary. xviii + 192pp. 5 x 7½. Clothbound **$2.50**

COLLOQUIAL GERMAN, P. F. Doring. Intensive thorough coverage of grammar in easily-followed form. Excellent for brush-up, with hundreds of colloquial phrases. 34 pages of bilingual texts. 224pp. 5 x 7½. Clothbound **$1.75**

COLLOQUIAL SPANISH, W. R. Patterson. Castilian grammar and colloquial language, loaded with bilingual phrases and colloquialisms. Excellent for review or self-study. 164pp. 5 x 7½. Clothbound **$1.75**

COLLOQUIAL FRENCH, W. R. Patterson. 16th revision of this extremely popular manual. Grammar explained with model clarity, and hundreds of useful expressions and phrases; exercises, reading texts, etc. Appendixes of new and useful words and phrases. 223pp. 5 x 7½. Clothbound **$1.75**

COLLOQUIAL CZECH, J. Schwarz, former headmaster of Lingua Institute, Prague. Full easily followed coverage of grammar, hundreds of immediately useable phrases, texts. Perhaps the best Czech grammar in print. "An absolutely successful textbook," JOURNAL OF CZECHO-SLOVAK FORCES IN GREAT BRITAIN. 252pp. 5 x 7½. Clothbound **$3.00**

COLLOQUIAL RUMANIAN, G. Nandris, Professor of University of London. Extremely thorough coverage of phonetics, grammar, syntax; also included 70-page reader, and 70-page vocabulary. Probably the best grammar for this increasingly important language. 340pp. 5 x 7½. Clothbound **$2.50**

COLLOQUIAL ITALIAN, A. L. Hayward. Excellent self-study course in grammar, vocabulary, idioms, and reading. Easy progressive lessons will give a good working knowledge of Italian in the shortest possible time. 5 x 7½. Clothbound **$1.75**

COLLOQUIAL TURKISH, Yusuf Mardin. Very clear, thorough introduction to leading cultural and economic language of Near East. Begins with pronunciation and statement of vowel harmony, then 36 lessons present grammar, graded vocabulary, useful phrases, dialogues, reading, exercises. Key to exercises at rear. Turkish-English vocabulary. All in Roman alphabet. x + 288pp. 4¾ x 7¼. Clothbound **$4.00**

DUTCH-ENGLISH AND ENGLISH-DUTCH DICTIONARY, F. G. Renier. For travel, literary, scientific or business Dutch, you will find this the most convenient, practical and comprehensive dictionary on the market. More than 60,000 entries, shades of meaning, colloquialisms, idioms, compounds and technical terms. Dutch and English strong and irregular verbs. This is the only dictionary in its size and price range that indicates the gender of nouns. New orthography. xvii + 571pp. 5½ x 6¼. T224 Clothbound **$2.75**

LEARN DUTCH, F. G. Renier. This book is the most satisfactory and most easily used grammar of modern Dutch. The student is gradually led from simple lessons in pronunciation, through translation from and into Dutch, and finally to a mastery of spoken and written Dutch. Grammatical principles are clearly explained while a useful, practical vocabulary is introduced in easy exercises and readings. It is used and recommended by the Fulbright Committee in the Netherlands. Phonetic appendices. Over 1200 exercises; Dutch-English, English-Dutch vocabularies. 181pp. 4¼ x 7¼. T441 Clothbound **$2.25**

Literature, History of Literature

ARISTOTLE'S THEORY OF POETRY AND THE FINE ARTS, edited by S. H. Butcher. The celebrated Butcher translation of this great classic faced, page by page, with the complete Greek text. A 300 page introduction discussing Aristotle's ideas and their influence in the history of thought and literature, and covering art and nature, imitation as an aesthetic form, poetic truth, art and morality, tragedy, comedy, and similar topics. Modern Aristotelian criticism discussed by John Gassner. lxxvi + 421pp. 5⅜ x 8. T42 Paperbound **$2.00**

INTRODUCTIONS TO ENGLISH LITERATURE, edited by B. Dobrée. Goes far beyond ordinary histories, ranging from the 7th century up to 1914 (to the 1940's in some cases.) The first half of each volume is a specific detailed study of historical and economic background of the period and a general survey of poetry and prose, including trends of thought, influences, etc. The second and larger half is devoted to a detailed study of more than 5000 poets, novelists, dramatists; also economists, historians, biographers, religious writers, philosophers, travellers, and scientists of literary stature, with dates, lists of major works and their dates, keypoint critical bibliography, and evaluating comments. The most compendious bibliographic and literary aid within its price range.

Vol. I. THE BEGINNINGS OF ENGLISH LITERATURE TO SKELTON, (1509), W. L. Renwick, H. Orton. 450pp. 5⅛ x 7⅞. T75 Clothbound **$4.50**

Vol. II. THE ENGLISH RENAISSANCE, 1510-1688, V. de Sola Pinto. 381pp. 5⅛ x 7⅞. T76 Clothbound **$4.50**

Vol. III. AUGUSTANS AND ROMANTICS, 1689-1830, H. Dyson, J. Butt. 320pp. 5⅛ x 7⅞. T77 Clothbound **$4.50**

Vol. IV. THE VICTORIANS AND AFTER, 1830-1940's, E. Batho, B. Dobrée. 360pp. 5⅛ x 7⅞. T78 Clothbound **$4.50**

EPIC AND ROMANCE, W. P. Ker. Written by one of the foremost authorities on medieval literature, this is the standard survey of medieval epic and romance. It covers Teutonic epics, Icelandic sagas, Beowulf, French chansons de geste, the Roman de Troie, and many other important works of literature. It is an excellent account for a body of literature whose beauty and value has only recently come to be recognized. Index. xxiv + 398pp. 5⅜ x 8. T355 Paperbound **$2.00**

THE POPULAR BALLAD, F. B. Gummere. Most useful factual introduction; fund of descriptive material; quotes, cites over 260 ballads. Examines, from folkloristic view, structure; choral, ritual elements; meter, diction, fusion; effects of tradition, editors; almost every other aspect of border, riddle, kinship, sea, ribald, supernatural, etc., ballads. Bibliography. 2 indexes. 374pp. 5⅜ x 8. T548 Paperbound **$1.85**

MASTERS OF THE DRAMA, John Gassner. The most comprehensive history of the drama in print, covering drama in every important tradition from the Greeks to the Near East, China, Japan, Medieval Europe, England, Russia, Italy, Spain, Germany, and dozens of other drama producing nations. This unsurpassed reading and reference work encompasses more than 800 dramatists and over 2000 plays, with biographical material, plot summaries, theatre history, etc. "Has no competitors in its field," THEATRE ARTS. "Best of its kind in English," NEW REPUBLIC. Exhaustive 35 page bibliography. 77 photographs and drawings. Deluxe edition with reinforced cloth binding, headbands, stained top. xxii + 890pp. 5⅜ x 8. T100 Clothbound **$6.95**

THE DEVELOPMENT OF DRAMATIC ART, D. C. Stuart. The basic work on the growth of Western drama from primitive beginnings to Eugene O'Neill, covering over 2500 years. Not a mere listing or survey, but a thorough analysis of changes, origins of style, and influences in each period; dramatic conventions, social pressures, choice of material, plot devices, stock situations, etc.; secular and religious works of all nations and epochs. "Generous and thoroughly documented researches," Outlook. "Solid studies of influences and playwrights and periods," London Times. Index. Bibliography. xi + 679pp. 5⅜ x 8. T693 Paperbound **$2.75**

A SOURCE BOOK IN THEATRICAL HISTORY (SOURCES OF THEATRICAL HISTORY), A. M. Nagler. Over 2000 years of actors, directors, designers, critics, and spectators speak for themselves in this potpourri of writings selected from the great and formative periods of western drama. On-the-spot descriptions of masks, costumes, makeup, rehearsals, special effects, acting methods, backstage squabbles, theatres, etc. Contemporary glimpses of Molière rehearsing his company, an exhortation to a Roman audience to buy refreshments and keep quiet, Goethe's rules for actors, Belasco telling of $6500 he spent building a river, Restoration actors being told to avoid "lewd, obscene, or indecent postures," and much more. Each selection has an introduction by Prof. Nagler. This extraordinary, lively collection is ideal as a source of otherwise difficult to obtain material, as well as a fine book for browsing. Over 80 illustrations. 10 diagrams. xxiii + 611pp. 5⅜ x 8. T515 Paperbound **$3.00**

WORLD DRAMA, B. H. Clark. The dramatic creativity of a score of ages and eras — all in two handy compact volumes. Over 1/3 of this material is unavailable in any other current edition! 46 plays from Ancient Greece, Rome, Medieval Europe, France, Germany, Italy, England, Russia, Scandinavia, India, China, Japan, etc. — including classic authors like Aeschylus, Sophocles, Euripides, Aristophanes, Plautus, Marlowe, Jonson, Farquhar, Goldsmith, Cervantes, Molière, Dumas, Goethe, Schiller, Ibsen, and many others. This creative collection avoids hackneyed material and includes only completely first-rate works which are relatively little known or difficult to obtain. "The most comprehensive collection of important plays from all literature available in English," SAT. REV. OF LITERATURE. Introduction. Reading lists. 2 volumes. 1364pp. 5⅜ x 8. Vol. 1, T57 Paperbound **$2.25**
Vol. 2, T59 Paperbound **$2.50**

MASTERPIECES OF THE RUSSIAN DRAMA, edited with introduction by G. R. Noyes. This only comprehensive anthology of Russian drama ever published in English offers complete texts, in 1st-rate modern translations, of 12 plays covering 200 years. Vol. 1: "The Young Hopeful," Fonvisin; "Wit Works Woe," Griboyedov; "The Inspector General," Gogol; "A Month in the Country," Turgenev; "The Poor Bride," Ostrovsky; "A Bitter Fate," Pisemsky. Vol. 2: "The Death of Ivan the Terrible," Alexey Tolstoy "The Power of Darkness," Lev Tolstoy; "The Lower Depths," Gorky; "The Cherry Orchard," Chekhov; "Professor Storitsyn," Andreyev; "Mystery Bouffe," Mayakovsky. Bibliography. Total of 902pp. 5⅜ x 8.
Vol. 1 T647 Paperbound **$2.00**
Vol. 2 T648 Paperbound **$2.00**

EUGENE O'NEILL: THE MAN AND HIS PLAYS, B. H. Clark. Introduction to O'Neill's life and work. Clark analyzes each play from the early THE WEB to the recently produced MOON FOR THE MISBEGOTTEN and THE ICEMAN COMETH revealing the environmental and dramatic influences necessary for a complete understanding of these important works. Bibliography. Appendices. Index. ix + 182pp. 5⅜ x 8. T379 Paperbound **$1.35**

THE HEART OF THOREAU'S JOURNALS, edited by O. Shepard. The best general selection from Thoreau's voluminous (and rare) journals. This intimate record of thoughts and observations reveals the full Thoreau and his intellectual development more accurately than any of his published works: self-conflict between the scientific observer and the poet, reflections on transcendental philosophy, involvement in the tragedies of neighbors and national causes, etc. New preface, notes, introductions. xii + 228pp. 5⅜ x 8. T741 Paperbound **$1.50**

H. D. THOREAU: A WRITER'S JOURNAL, edited by L. Stapleton. A unique new selection from the Journals concentrating on Thoreau's growth as a conscious literary artist, the ideals and purposes of his art. Most of the material has never before appeared outside of the complete 14-volume edition. Contains vital insights on Thoreau's projected book on Concord, thoughts on the nature of men and government, indignation with slavery, sources of inspiration, goals in life. Index. xxxiii + 234pp. 5⅜ x 8. T678 Paperbound **$1.65**

THE HEART OF EMERSON'S JOURNALS, edited by **Bliss Perry.** Best of these revealing Journals, originally 10 volumes, presented in a one volume edition. Talks with Channing, Hawthorne, Thoreau, and Bronson Alcott; impressions of Webster, Everett, John Brown, and Lincoln; records of moments of sudden understanding, vision, and solitary ecstasy. "The essays do not reveal the power of Emerson's mind . . . as do these hasty and informal writings," N.Y. Times. Preface by Bliss Perry. Index. xiii + 357pp. 5⅜ x 8. T477 Paperbound **$1.85**

FOUNDERS OF THE MIDDLE AGES, E. K. Rand. This is the best non-technical discussion of the transformation of Latin pagan culture into medieval civilization. Covering such figures as Tertullian, Gregory, Jerome, Boethius, Augustine, the Neoplatonists, and many other literary men, educators, classicists, and humanists, this book is a storehouse of information presented clearly and simply for the intelligent non-specialist. "Thoughtful, beautifully written," AMERICAN HISTORICAL REVIEW. "Extraordinarily accurate," Richard McKeon, THE NATION. ix + 365pp. 5⅜ x 8. T369 Paperbound **$2.00**

PLAY-MAKING: A MANUAL OF CRAFTSMANSHIP, William Archer. With an extensive, new introduction by John Gassner, Yale Univ. The permanently essential requirements of solid play construction are set down in clear, practical language: theme, exposition, foreshadowing, tension, obligatory scene, peripety, dialogue, character, psychology, other topics. This book has been one of the most influential elements in the modern theatre, and almost everything said on the subject since is contained explicitly or implicitly within its covers. Bibliography. Index. xlii + 277pp. 5⅜ x 8. T651 Paperbound **$1.75**

HAMBURG DRAMATURGY, G. E. Lessing. One of the most brilliant of German playwrights of the eighteenth-century age of criticism analyzes the complex of theory and tradition that constitutes the world of theater. These 104 essays on aesthetic theory helped demolish the regime of French classicism, opening the door to psychological and social realism, romanticism. Subjects include the original functions of tragedy; drama as the rational world; the meaning of pity and fear, pity and fear as means for purgation and other Aristotelian concepts; genius and creative force; interdependence of poet's language and actor's interpretation; truth and authenticity; etc. A basic and enlightening study for anyone interested in aesthetics and ideas, from the philosopher to the theatergoer. Introduction by Prof. Victor Lange. xxii + 265pp. 4½ x 6⅜. T32 Paperbound **$1.45**

New Books

101 PATCHWORK PATTERNS, Ruby Short McKim. With no more ability than the fundamentals of ordinary sewing, you will learn to make over 100 beautiful quilts: flowers, rainbows, Irish chains, fish and bird designs, leaf designs, unusual geometric patterns, many others. Cutting designs carefully diagrammed and described, suggestions for materials, yardage estimates, step-by-step instructions, plus entertaining stories of origins of quilt names, other folklore. Revised 1962. 101 full-sized patterns. 140 illustrations. Index. 128pp. 7⅞ x 10¾.
T773 Paperbound **$1.85**

ESSENTIAL GRAMMAR SERIES
By concentrating on the essential core of material that constitutes the semantically most important forms and areas of a language and by stressing explanation (often bringing parallel English forms into the discussion) rather than rote memory, this new series of grammar books is among the handiest language aids ever devised. Designed by linguists and teachers for adults with limited learning objectives and learning time, these books omit nothing important, yet they teach more usable language material and do it more quickly and permanently than any other self-study material. Clear and rigidly economical, they concentrate upon immediately usable language material, logically organized so that related material is always presented together. Any reader of typical capability can use them to refresh his grasp of language, to supplement self-study language records or conventional grammars used in schools, or to begin language study on his own. Now available:

ESSENTIAL GERMAN GRAMMAR, Dr. Guy Stern & E. F. Bleiler. Index. Glossary of terms. 128pp. 5⅜ x 8.
T422 Paperbound **$1.00**

ESSENTIAL FRENCH GRAMMAR, Dr. Seymour Resnick. Index. Cognate list. Glossary. 159pp. 5⅜ x 8.
T419 Paperbound **$1.00**

ESSENTIAL ITALIAN GRAMMAR, Dr. Olga Ragusa. Index. Glossary. 111pp. 5⅜ x 8.
T779 Paperbound **$1.00**

ESSENTIAL SPANISH GRAMMAR, Dr. Seymour Resnick. Index. 50-page cognate list. Glossary. 138pp. 5⅜ x 8.
T780 Paperbound **$1.00**

PHILOSOPHIES OF MUSIC HISTORY: A Study of General Histories of Music, 1600-1960, Warren D. Allen. Unquestionably one of the most significant documents yet to appear in musicology, this thorough survey covers the entire field of historical research in music. An influential masterpiece of scholarship, it includes early music histories; theories on the ethos of music; lexicons, dictionaries and encyclopedias of music; musical historiography through the centuries; philosophies of music history; scores of related topics. Copiously documented. New preface brings work up to 1960. Index. 317-item bibliography. 9 illustrations; 3 full-page plates. 5⅜ x 8½. xxxiv + 382pp.
T282 Paperbound **$2.00**

MR. DOOLEY ON IVRYTHING AND IVRYBODY, Finley Peter Dunne. The largest collection in print of hilarious utterances by the irrepressible Irishman of Archey Street, one of the most vital characters in American fiction. Gathered from the half dozen books that appeared during the height of Mr. Dooley's popularity, these 102 pieces are all unaltered and uncut, and they are all remarkably fresh and pertinent even today. Selected and edited by Robert Hutchinson. 5⅜ x 8½. xii + 244p.
T626 Paperbound **$1.00**

TREATISE ON PHYSIOLOGICAL OPTICS, Hermann von Helmholtz. Despite new investigations, this important work will probably remain preeminent. Contains everything known about physiological optics up to 1925, covering scores of topics under the general headings of dioptrics of the eye, sensations of vision, and perecptions of vision. Von Helmholtz's voluminous data are all included, as are extensive supplementary matter incorporated into the third German edition, new material prepared for 1925 English edition, and copious textual annotations by J. P. C. Southall. The most exhaustive treatise ever prepared on the subject, it has behind it a list of contributors that will never again be duplicated. Translated and edited by J. P. C. Southall. Bibliography. Indexes. 312 illustrations. 3 volumes bound as 2. Total of 1749pp. 5⅜ x 8.
S15-16 Two volume set, Clothbound **$15.00**

THE ARTISTIC ANATOMY OF TREES, Rex Vicat Cole. Even the novice with but an elementary knowledge of drawing and none of the structure of trees can learn to draw, paint trees from this systematic, lucid instruction book. Copiously illustrated with the author's own sketches, diagrams, and 50 paintings from the early Renaissance to today, it covers composition; structure of twigs, boughs, buds, branch systems; outline forms of major species; how leaf is set on twig; flowers and fruit and their arrangement; etc. 500 illustrations. Bibliography. Indexes. 347pp. 5⅜ x 8.
T1016 Clothbound **$4.50**

CATALOGUE OF DOVER BOOKS